THE ORIGINS OF SCIENCE

MOMENTS OF

EDITED BY

George Schwartz

AND

Philip W. Bishop

WITH A FOREWORD BY

Linus Pauling

DISCOVERY

THE

Origins

OF

Science

BASIC BOOKS, INC., NEW YORK

ACKNOWLEDGMENTS

The editors wish to thank the following publishers, individuals, and organizations for permission to use materials from the publications indicated:

Bulletin of The Johns Hopkins Hospital: (from Vol. 39, 1926), A. R. Rich, "The Place of R. J. H. Dutrochet in the Development of Cell Theory."

Cambridge University Press: Sir James Jeans, *The New Background of Science,* 1934.

Columbia University Press: S. W. Lambert, *Proceedings of the Charaka Club,* Vol. 3, 1935.

E. P. Dutton & Co., Inc.: William Harvey, *Anatomical Disquisition On the Motion of the Heart and Blood,* 1906.

Ross G. Harrison and the Society for Experimental Biology and Medicine: "Observations on the Living Developing Nerve Fiber," *Proceedings of the Society for Experimental Biology and Medicine,* Vol. 4, 1907.

Harvard University Press: M. R. Cohen and I. Drabkin, *Source Book in Greek Science,* 1948; H. M. Leicester and H. S. Klickstein, *Source Book in Chemistry,* 1952; W. F. Magie, *Source Book in Physics,* 1935; H. Shapley and H. E. Howarth, *Source Book in Astronomy,* 1929.

Macmillan and Company Ltd. of London: J. B. Lamarck, *Zoological Philosophy,* St. Martin's Press Incorporated, 1912.

National Tuberculosis Association: Robert Koch, *The Etiology of Tuberculosis* (Dr. and Mrs. Max Pinner, trans.), 1932.

Open Court Publishing Company: Hugo De-Vries, *The Mutation Theory,* Vol. I, 1909.

Philosophical Library, Inc.: Max Planck, *Scientific Autobiography and Other Papers,* 1949.

Ray Society: A. Hort, *Linnaeus, Critica Botanica,* 1938.

The Royal Horticultural Society of London: Gregor Mendel, *Experiments in Plant-Hybridization.*

The Royal Society of Edinburgh: Amedeo Avogadro, "Essay on a Manner of Determining the Relative Masses of the Elementary Molecules of Bodies, and the Properties in Which They Enter into These Compounds," *Alembic Club Reprint,* No. 4; Joseph Gay-Lussac, "Memoir on the Combination of Gaseous Substances with Each Other," *Alembic Club Reprint,* No. 4.

The Royal Society of Medicine: B. Farrington, "Translation of Preface to 'De Humani Corporis Fabrica' of A. Vesalius," *Proceedings of the Royal Society of Medicine,* July 1932; James Young, Letter II, "Malpighi, About the Lungs," *Proceedings of the Royal Society of Medicine,* October 1929.

Simon and Schuster, Inc.: J. Robert Oppenheimer, *The Open Mind* (copyright ©, 1955, by J. Robert Oppenheimer).

University of Chicago Press: *Selected Readings in Natural Science I.*

FOREWORD

By Linus Pauling

The nature of the world of today has been greatly changed during recent centuries as a result of scientific discoveries. Every aspect of our lives—the food we eat, the clothes we wear, our methods of communication and transportation, the ways of waging war, the conduct of relations between nations—each of these has been revolutionized by the discoveries made by scientists. Even our philosophical attitude toward the world as a whole has been changed, in ways of fundamental significance to the understanding of the nature of man in relation to his environment. Hence everyone who lives in the world needs to have some understanding of the nature and effects of science.

The creative scientist lives in order to enrich our world by increasing our understanding of it. Many scientific discoveries, perhaps most of the significant ones, represent feats of imagination, insight, and originality closely similar to those involved in creative work in such fields as art and music. I recently read a statement, made by a worker in the humanities, that "Clearly the humanities deal with the creative and imaginative aspects of man's personality." I myself, as a scientist, might, because of my familiarity with the moments of discovery in science, be tempted to say that it is science that deals with the creative and imaginative aspects of man's personality, but of course this statement, like the preceding one, is too restrictive—there are many ways in which the creative and imaginative aspects of man's personality find expression.

It is for the moments of discovery that a creative scientist lives. When the idea of the theory of relativity appeared in Einstein's mind, the discovery was made—he had then only to work out the details of the theory. Another great moment of discovery came recently, when the physicists Lee and Yang had the idea, and entertained it seriously, that the world might in fact distinguish between right-handedness and left-handedness in an absolute way, which physicists had thought impossible before—and that the tiny constituents of the world called neutrinos could have the properties of right-handed propellers, with antineutrinos having the properties of left-handed propellers. Within a few months a dozen experiments had been carried out attesting to the correctness of this brilliant inspiration.

I do not know how Einstein felt when the idea of the theory of relativity came to him, or how Lee and Yang felt when they thought about the possibility of nonconservation of parity; but I remember very clearly some occasions when I have seen a new way of looking at a part of the world. One evening, early in 1945, I was having dinner in New York with a small group of men associated with the medical schools of the country. We were members of a Medical Advisory Committee appointed by Dr. Vannevar Bush to help him prepare replies to a series of questions posed in a letter sent to him by President Roosevelt. That evening one of the members of the committee, Dr. William B. Castle, of the Harvard University School of Medicine, began, in the course of the dinner conversation, to talk about the disease sickle cell anemia. This seemed to be a disease of the red corpuscles of the blood, which were twisted out of their normal shape in the blood of the patient. The disease seemed to involve a pathological state of the red corpuscle, but the red corpuscle is so large compared with molecules, and it contains so many hundreds of kinds of molecules, that there seemed to me to be little possibility that an understanding of the disease could be obtained in terms of molecules. However, when Dr. Castle said that the red cells of the blood are twisted out of shape in the venous blood of the patient and resume their normal shape when the blood passes through the lungs and enters the arterial circulation, the idea burst upon me that the molecules of hemoglobin in the red cells might be responsible for the disease—that the disease might be a molecular disease involving an abnormal sort of hemoglobin, manufactured by the patients because of their possession of abnormal genes in places of the normal genes that control the manufacture of normal hemoglobin molecules. This idea, the idea of molecular disease, seemed to me to be such a sound one that I had no doubt that it would ultimately be found to be correct.

I wish that it were possible for me to describe the feeling of happiness that came along with the idea. I think that creative activity in science and in other activities representing the expression of man's personality constitutes one of the principal sources of happiness. Moreover, everyone can share in this happiness by developing an understanding and appreciation of the new discoveries about the nature of the world that are made by scientists every year.

Moments of Discovery makes it possible for modern man to learn about how the modern world has developed, to understand his relation to it, to make predictions about the future. Since no one now can consider himself to be cultivated unless he has some knowledge of science, I hope that many people will read this fine book.

Pasadena, Calif.   Linus Pauling
July 7, 1958

PREFACE

The creative years of a scientist's life are but a moment in the span of history and, as we now enjoy the fruits of twenty-five hundred years of reflection and research, his patient endeavor toward discovery appears as an instantaneous experience. Our title, then, contains a measure of irony. We have not assembled a collection of the favorite legends about sudden revelations of a new truth in science. "Eureka" is not to be found in our vocabulary; for we have tried to show, from his own writings, how the scientist has moved, with infinite patience, one step at a time, in pursuit of his goal; and how the work of many scientists has slowly evolved into a pattern and, later, into a discipline.

Now that science is taken for granted and research is a necessary function of every business budget, it is desirable to pause and reflect upon the origins of our knowledge. No better material exists than the writings of those who laid the foundations of science. Personal preferences have, naturally, influenced the selections, but the experience of twenty years of teaching is not a wholly useless guide to the needs of those whose interest in man's search for understanding of the universe needs to be awakened. Some readers will regret the omissions; but if adequate samples of their writings were to be given of the eighty-three scientists chosen, discrimination was inevitable. Our hope is that the choices will be stimulating enough to encourage exploration of other anthologies or of the files of the first scientific bodies. The professional historian of science knows his way among these writings already and will not need our help.

Our debt to the editors of other anthologies, from which

we have drawn materials not otherwise available, is immense, as has been acknowledged in the text.

We are especially grateful also to Mr. Bern Dibner and Mrs. Adele Matthysse of the Burndy Library, Norwalk, Connecticut, for assistance in gathering the illustrations used and in checking many sources. The Burndy Library is one of the country's finest collections of original works in the history of science, and Mr. Dibner has been most generous in making its facilities available to us. The librarians of the New York Academy of Medicine, the Smithsonian Institution, the New York Public Library, the libraries of New York University, Forest Hills High School, as well as the Brooklyn and Queens Public Libraries have been generous with help, and we wish to acknowledge our gratitude to all of them.

We wish to express our thanks also to the translators, editors, and publishers who have permitted us to use materials for which they hold the copyright. All of these have been acknowledged fully elsewhere in these volumes.

Finally, we cannot permit to go unmentioned the enormous help given by Mrs. Hannah Schwartz in collecting material, typing manuscript, proofreading, and generally in seeing this work to press.

GEORGE SCHWARTZ
PHILIP W. BISHOP

CONTENTS

VOLUME ONE

The Origins of Science

I

The Nature of Science and Discovery

II
Technology Before Science

III

The Beginnings of the Scientific Approach

IV

The Bridge

V

The Scientific Revolution

THE BURNING QUESTION

The Origins

of

Science

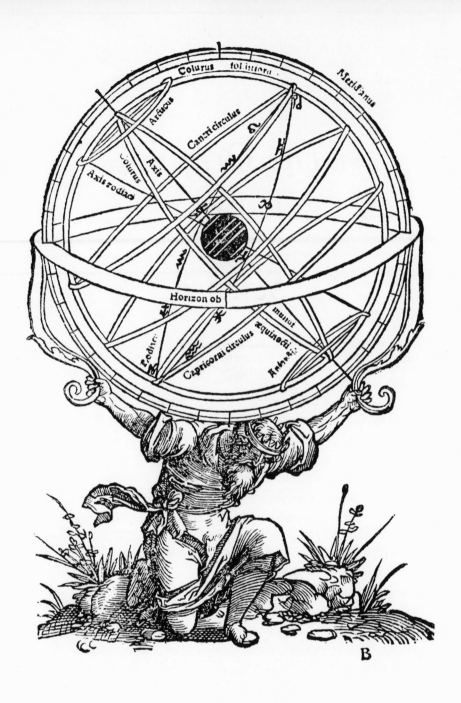

From Johannes Schoener's *Opusculum Geographicum*, 1533. (Courtesy of the Burndy Library.)

THE ORIGINS OF SCIENCE

Man's discoveries about himself and the world around him, put into an orderly form, have created that vast structure of knowledge we now call "science." This search for explanations began with his first observation of the "movement" of the sun or with his question, when he first penetrated the forest behind his cave, "Why do the leaves die before the snow comes?" And, since pride came no later than the ability to speak, no sooner were the questions phrased than controversy about the explanations began. For it is of the very nature of the scientific mind to question accepted patterns of knowledge, to suggest new explanations, and to defy those who claim to know better. The readings that make up this book have been chosen because each recalls something of the search for truth since the written record began. They commemorate some of the great discoverers, those whose observations proved so much better than their fellows' that the influence of their thought survives to form a part of our culture. As the Biblical writings or the plays of Shakespeare still give life to our language, so the discoveries of Hippocrates and Newton take their place among the influences on an Einstein or a Bohr.

We take science for granted today. Scarcely anything we do or anything we use to make life easy and comfortable is unaffected by science. Scientific research is looked upon now as syn-

onymous with progress; and without progress the elaborate structure of modern life will collapse. Our standard of living depends
on science to find new ways of using the resources we have and to
find new products among the old raw materials. Science—applied science—may even decide the political future of man.

All this is far removed from the picture of the early scientist,
perhaps a lonely man, examining the apparent movement of the
stars and trying to find a systematic relationship among them.
The spread of education and of the means of communication in
the last hundred years has made science a sidewalk activity. The
youngest student can look over the shoulder of the scientist while
he works, as he would supervise the artist at his easel on the dock
of an old fishing port, to observe the progress of the experiments
and to criticize the equations. But it is better that the student-
critic of the painter learn something of the story of art before he
presume to comment on the artist's interpretation of the scene
before him; to understand the purpose of art and its methods, he
should know something of Michelangelo and of Picasso. So, he
who wishes to talk about science, read about science and, especially, work in science, should examine the sources of modern
knowledge and appreciate the long history of man's exploration
of the unknown world.

Something is known of the earliest explorations from the
tablets left by the Babylonians. These records go back as far as
three thousand years before the Christian era, as do Chinese
records. Those of Egypt are generally of a later date. The ancient documents—clay tablets and papyri—show that ancient
man observed the regularity of the supposed movements of the
sun and the planets and connected them with the rhythm of
seed time and harvest. From these observations calendars were
evolved and such phenomena as eclipses were predicted.

In the hands of specialists, the science of prediction was, in
time, debased into the art of astrology, in which the movements
of the stars were alleged to foretell change in the affairs of men,
if, indeed, they did not directly influence them. Combined with
the rituals and mysteries of the temples, astrology brought science

down to the level of the common man. It was perhaps in this form that the early knowledge of the stars was transmitted to later generations and to other peoples.

These records show, too, how the art of counting was developed. The great pyramids of Egypt are the living testimony to the skill of the early priests who evolved the rules of measurement and found ways to use the plumb-line, to construct right angles, and to shape stone with a mason's square. Ahmes, "the moonborn," recorded, 3500 years ago, how to calculate the area of a circle. At sea, the Phoenicians, who sailed the Mediterranean and even the Atlantic when they sought the tin of Cornwall, observed the connection between the stars and their problem of setting a course and made rules which guided future mariners and helped the first map-makers.

Direct knowledge of these and similar discoveries by the ancients has come to us only in recent years as the excavations of the archeologists have found treasures hidden in the sands of centuries; but the influence of the earlier cultures came indirectly through the writings of the Greeks, the first people in Europe to produce an organized literature of science. Among the selections that make up this book, the Greek writings are the earliest; and they are chosen as typical of the writings which influenced the growth of knowledge in the rest of Europe after the decline of Greece's own civilization. The first of the writers chosen, Hippocrates, was of the Ionian Colony, which seems to have led the mother country in scientific developments, perhaps because it was in closer contact, geographically, with the older civilizations. Hippocrates was a pioneer in the observation of the ills of the human body. Others of his period put the study of nature generally on a systematic basis. In Ionia deductive geometry was first developed from the ground rules of measurement which had been evolved in Egypt; this "science of reason," as it has been called, was to provide countless generations of students, even until today, with an intellectual exercise which, if it had little to do with experimental science, certainly provided experience in reasoning and logic. In the hands of Descartes and Newton and others, as we shall see, it was translated from an abstraction into a useful tool of science in the form of coordinate geometry and the differential calculus.

The Greeks preferred, on the whole, to establish a theory—as, for instance, that all things are made of four "elements"; fire, air, water, and earth—and then to fit the facts to the theory. Although Hippocrates showed the value of observation and experiment, much of Greek science long depended on an approach typified by such propositions as: God is good; the sphere is the most perfect of forms; therefore, the universe must be spherical. Plato preferred this approach and despised experiment. Aristotle (384–322 B.C.), a student in Plato's Academy in Athens, brought together so great a collection of knowledge in his works that they survived to become, fifteen hundred years later, as we shall see, the basis of learning in the Middle Ages. In biology, embryology, and physiology, Aristotle added to knowledge by collecting facts including those to be found in dissecting—perhaps even vivisecting—animals. His authority in these fields gave him such influence that, in subjects in which he was less competent, such as physics, his writings held up progress when they were later rediscovered.

The climax of Greek advances in science come with Archimedes, 287-212 B.C., whose law of the lever will be described in Part III, and with the growth in importance of Alexandria, founded in Egypt by Alexander the Great in 332 B.C. There, a great research library, containing, it is said, some 400,000 manuscripts in literature, mathematics, astronomy, and medicine, later to be destroyed by Christians and Muslims, attracted such scholars as Euclid, Hipparchus, and Ptolemy. The *Almagest* of Ptolemy, published between A.D. 127 and 151, became a standard text in astronomy until Copernicus in 1543 upset the basic assumption which Ptolemy took over from Hipparchus, that the earth was the center of the universe.

The next great civilization, that of the Romans, which spread all over Europe, has only one representative in the selections below—Pliny the Elder (23-79). The reason for this is to be found in the preoccupation of the Romans in what we would now call applied science. As farmers, architects, and engineers, the Romans used Greek knowledge and developed the practical arts; and from Rome to the borders of Scotland roads, walls, aqueducts, and stadiums remain as monuments to their skill. Some, like Lucretius and Pliny the Elder, revived Greek learning or made encyclopedic compilations of the knowledge of the period. A Greek among them, Galen (*c.* 129-200), developed theories of bodily functions which were to dominate physiology for fifteen hundred years. In the main, however, Romans recorded the facts of their widespread observation but did little to advance theoretical science.

With the decline of the Roman Empire, which culminated around the 4th century after the Christian era, the advance of science was transferred into other hands. Europe entered a period of a thousand years during which the ancient classics lay unknown to the West. The Christian religion had, during its earliest years, inherited the traditions of Plato and Aristotle and these survived to maintain some sort of theological link, in Christian Europe, between the old and the new learning; but it was the Arabs and their colonists who, eastward from Constantinople and Alexandria, the last remaining outposts of Western knowledge, carried on the work of the Greeks, making new discoveries in chemistry and astronomy, in physics and mathematics. Omar Khayyam, best known for his *Rubaiyat* ("A Book of Verses underneath the Bow, a Jug of Wine, a Loaf of Bread —and Thou . . .") made important contributions to algebra.

Knowledge of the Arabic culture filtered back into Europe, largely through Spain, by the hands of the Sephardic Jews, and toward the end of the eleventh century there came a revival in that kind of questioning which leads, eventually, to new scientific advance. Averroes (1126-1198), a Spanish Muslim, published a commentary on Aristotle which had considerable influence in, for example, the Universities of Paris (founded *c.* 1170) and Oxford (*c.* 1168). His ideas of religion, though regarded as subversive by the Christian Schoolmen, stimulated a new examination of the relations between religion and philosophy. This led, in turn, to a revival of interest in the nature of the universe itself. Through the Arabic versions of Greek texts, translated into Latin during the twelfth and thirteenth centuries, scholars became familiar with the early philosophers and scientists, and especially with the works of Aristotle. Since Aristotle's teachings, helped by such commentators as Averroes, led to conflicts with the doctrines of the Church, it is not surprising that there ensued long and tortuous debates—for example, over such matters as the moment of time at which the soul enters the human embryo. Thomas Aquinas (*c.* 1225-1274), in his *Summa Theologiae* and other works, provided a reconciliation of Aristotelian philosophy with the Christian teachings and so began the influence of the Schoolmen.

Scholasticism held, in effect, that the mysteries of human existence and of our relationship with God could be perceived and examined by means of the concepts of natural truths which Plato and Aristotle explained even if they could not be proved by reason. Human reason could, then, give a *description* of the universe, but only the authority of the Catholic Church could provide the final answer. This kind of rationalism was not in sympathy with experiments which would lead to the growth of science, and the Renaissance, which is usually said to have begun around 1450, represents the reaction to this restriction on man's natural inquisitiveness.

Roger Bacon (*c.* 1214-1294), who is shown below as one of the first to proclaim the importance of experiment, was among the earliest to revolt against the scholastic restraints on the activity of the human mind. Such other scholars as Duns Scotus (*c.* 1266-1308) and Nicholas of Cusa (1401-1464) continued the opposition to scholasticism, the one arguing in favor of the idea of free-will, the other working in mathematics and physical science and, in effect, preparing the way for Copernicus by perceiving the error of Ptolemy.

The Middle Ages were not wholly lacking in contributions to scientific knowledge. In medicine, for example, some progress was made. Roger Bacon promoted the idea of the sphericity of the earth. Alchemy, by which men hoped to change the baser metals into gold, kept alive, at least, the study of chemistry. But it was not until the Renaissance that the horizons of scholars were lifted toward real discovery.

Two factors seem to have stimulated the change. The capture of Constantinople by the Turks in 1453 led to the migration of scholars westward with new manuscripts. Introduction to these encouraged the search for other collections hidden in monasteries for centuries. Moreover, the world suddenly became a larger place as Columbus discovered the New World (1492), Sebastian Cabot discovered Salvador in 1497, Vasco da Gama found the sea route to India (1497), and Magellan sailed around the world (1519).

The spirit of the times began to change. Science entered a new period of development in which its observations would no longer be limited to mere support of the doctrines of the Church. The revolt against the ecclesiastical tradition, led by such men as Martin Luther (1483-1546) and encouraged, for very different motives, by Henry VIII of England (1491-1547), seems to have influenced those men who, otherwise content with their religious environment, began to question the authority of the ancient Greeks. Traditional theory was set against the facts of their observation, and new explanations began to appear, at times tolerated by the Church and at others regarded as defiance of its authority.

In astronomy, Copernicus (1473-1543) revived controversy about the relation of the planets to one another and stimulated such men as Tycho Brahe (1546-1601) and Kepler (1571-1630). In mechanics, Galileo (1564-1642) found ways not only to establish some fundamental principles in physical science, as we shall see, but also, by writing in Italian instead of Latin and publishing his works, to bring the purpose of science before a much larger public. In effect, this was finally to destroy the hold of the Schoolmen on men's minds. His invention of the telescope revealed, for the first time, the content of the skies and took astronomy out of the realm of mathematical speculation into the unlimited world of observational science.

Throughout the whole of Europe this rebirth of curiosity, this spirit of discovery, emerged and set in motion with accumulating force that movement we call the Renaissance. Its most spectacular figure was Leonardo da Vinci (1452-1519), a man who is typical of the new age and whose birth date is taken as its beginning. Since he did not publish, during his lifetime, any of his voluminous "Notes," some of which remained hidden for centuries after his death, the impact of his great intellect came through his personal contacts and through his art. We can imagine, now that we can study his anatomical drawings, his projects in engineering, architecture, hydraulics, and optics, the kind of discussions that went on in his circles at Florence, Milan, and Rome. When one stands beside the great "Naviglio" (canal) connecting Milan with the River Ticino and hears one's Italian friend say proudly, "That was planned by Leonardo," one realizes the tremendous force he must have been at a time when the world was emerging from a long millenium of quiescence or mere talk. Leonardo set the pattern for the "new learning" and by example, if not by writing, forced men to look themselves for the facts of the world around them.

The revival in habits of observation, begun in astronomy and mechanics, spread rapidly to other areas of science (except, perhaps chemistry) and so began what we now call the Scientific Revolution, which reached its climax in the seventeenth century and especially in the work of Newton (1642-1727) on optics, on the movements of the planets, and on why bodies fall toward the earth. Newton's speculations led him to a synthesis of Renaissance thought and experiment which was to bring together in one place the discoveries of Galileo and others and to open the doors to a new age of reason.

At the same time, we observe a shift in leadership from the Mediterranean to the further north. The founding of scientific societies in London in 1662 and in Paris in 1666 merely recorded the fact that scientific discoveries were becoming known to the increasingly powerful groups who had been enriched by the expansion of foreign trade. Interest in science spread out from the universities among the middle class—the businessmen and the bourgeoisie. Science became useful. Indeed, with the opening of the eighteenth century, it is possible to see the beginnings of the Industrial Revolution; for as the needs of men in navigation and trade grew, the discoveries of science were increasingly put to the practical test; new ways had to be found to increase production, to make voyages overseas safer for ships and crews. Knowledge of the world was no longer the closely held secret of a few scientific philosophers.

Only in chemistry was there a serious lag in development. The whole field of inorganic chemistry was unknown until the theorists overcame a major impediment to progress. It had long been thought that when a substance burned, something (afterward called "phlogiston") was released, reducing the original body to its elementary ingredients. What was, in fact, a *property* of combustion was regarded as an actual *substance*. Combined with this was an ignorance of the properties of air and gases. Joseph Black (1728-1799), Henry Cavendish (1731-1810), and especially Antoine Laurent Lavoisier (1743-1794) were to complete the revolutions in chemistry when they observed *la principe oxygine* and discovered the gas oxygen. Combustion, they found, instead of reducing the weight of the original body, actually increases it by the combination of the substance with oxygen. Thus was opened up the new field of inorganic chemistry. The fundamental equipment was now complete for the development of modern science.

We shall see, in the first of these volumes, how the scientist shook himself free from the limitations imposed on him by medieval interpretations of Greek discoveries, and how he developed habits of observation and allowed facts to overcome dogmatic assertions about the workings of nature. We shall see, in their original form, samples of the reports of their scientific work, some of them representing, so to speak, the first drafts of the plan of modern science and others, actual parts of its foundations.

The second volume traces the progress of physics and chemistry, from the eighteenth century on, in selections from some of the important participants. This choice is a mere taste of a vast and ever-growing literature. A few of the momentous discoveries which have advanced the frontiers of science even beyond the limit of the earth's atmosphere are recorded; we witness some of the fundamental advances which have taken chemistry from mere analysis to synthesis, making possible the creation of new compounds and new products.

We have not attempted to do more than describe the theoretical work behind these accomplishments of applied science. The whole vast range of applied science in chemical engineering or in electricity has not been mentioned, for a good reason. The technology which has emerged to absorb so much of man's thinking and work is a story in itself. It began almost in ignorance of what the scientist was doing. In the latter days of the eighteenth century, practical men began evolving solutions of everyday problems in transportation and production with no scientific basis for their work. Solutions to such difficult problems as the construction of gear wheels were evolved by men ignorant of mathematics or of the nature of metallic substances. Steel took the place of iron by the method of trial and error at the hands of men who knew nothing of Galileo's thermometer and who relied on the brightness of a flame to tell them when the metallurgical changes were taking place.

This independent development of technology was, by the mid-nineteenth century, to force new problems on the scientist. He became increasingly, and all too often, a servant of industry, preoccupied by the immediate problems of industrial research. He left his study to enter an office in a plant. The opportunities for the achievement of broader explanations of natural phenomena increased as more and more data were observed; yet the number of men who could study the forest, as well as the trees in it, did not increase in the same proportion. Specialization might have retarded the great generalizations if the means of communication had not multiplied and brought more and more data to the small company of great discoverers. It is the latter, then, who are represented here—men who have, in effect, carried on the tradition of Leonardo, Galileo, and Newton, refusing to allow their great intellects to be confused by the daily needs of industrial progress and concentrating on pure science, attempting to explain only the fundamentals.

More attention has been given in the second volume to the developments in the study of life itself in the sciences of biology and medicine. We shall see how the theory of cells emerged from the earlier observations of Vesalius (1514-1564) and of Hooke (1635-1703), and how, beginning with Harvey's observation of the workings of the heart, reported in 1628, the science of physiology became established. Some of the landmarks in the search for an answer to the question "Where did man come from? Why does he act that way?" are seen as the ideas of Darwin and Mendel on evolution and heredity appeared. Finally, we observe some of the great discoveries which gave man the power, in large measure, to control disease and reduce pain.

In our day, when every newspaper has its science column and we take a man-made satellite almost in our stride, it is necessary to approach these writings with more than casual attention. When we visit some monument of the past, be it George Washington's home at Mount Vernon or the basilica of St. Peter in Rome, we try to recapture the spirit of the men who built and decorated it and made it their home. These writings are in a very real sense a monument to the discoverers who, with difficulty and often at the risk of their position in the society of their day, expanded the frontiers of knowledge. They showed how to use the work of others and how to assemble material in a systematic way. Their mistakes promoted controversy, out of which the "truth" gradually emerged. Though there was no clear path of progress before them, they succeeded in maintaining a course through the entangling mud of ignorance and the confusing by-paths of fact. Though their work is long since done, their example remains to guide the modern student, especially in that art of reflection without which no synthesis was ever made.

I

*The Nature
of Science
and Discovery*

I

*"Science is an organic system of activities;
and the pattern of its development is also organic."*
—Max Black

THE NATURE OF SCIENCE
AND DISCOVERY

From time to time the scientist turns from his telescope and computers, lays aside his microscopes and slide-rules, pauses in his pursuit of knowledge, and takes time to consider two questions: *Why* is he thus engaged? *How,* in fact, is he dealing with the problems he undertakes to solve?

Constant preoccupation with the study of the universe or with the investigation of the small problems of life can lead to a loss of direction, and most great men have found it essential to pause, to reflect, and to re-examine their methods and purposes. Sometimes the scientist has found himself in violent conflict with the methods of his contemporaries, and he is forced to restate his position so that his doubts and objections may be confirmed and his own course verified.

The readings that follow are selected from a great literature of reappraisal and reaffirmation of man's belief in himself. They show something of the cultural heritage of the modern scientist, a part of that intellectual discipline which governs, consciously or unconsciously, his attitude to investigation; but they also present the conclusions of science's great men in words which the layman can understand. They take science out of the laboratory and show something of its ideals and methods to those who

15

might otherwise be excluded. It is a healthy thing that scientists occasionally descend from the heights to the level of the layman; for not only do they attract sympathy to their work (and, indeed, encourage recruits to the field) but, risking, as they do, the criticism of their colleagues, they help to keep science in touch with the needs of life.

These selections are by no means comprehensive; but enough is shown of the development of scientific method to reveal the gradually evolving discipline. Sarton asserts: "The acquisition and systematization of positive knowledge is the only human activity which is truly cumulative and progressive." That the organization of man's mind to the service of science has also developed progressively and, in a sense, cumulatively is suggested by the passages that follow. All represent the thoughts of men endowed with unusual intellectual powers, expressed in the terms of their own environment. The progress which we can discern in the development of method is no reason to attribute to one a greater capacity than other. There is no measure of the difference between the genius of Hippocrates and Einstein; the latter would have been, no doubt, the first to disclaim any superiority over his predecessors. Their thoughts are to be judged against the background of their times.

The task of Hippocrates and Roger Bacon, at opposite ends of what may be called the period of Greek influence, was to overcome the power of religious dogmatism—not so much to show the separate domains of moral truth and scientific truth, as does Poincaré, but to eliminate that kind of deductive reasoning which establishes a "truth" as an axiom and then tries to fit the facts to the dogma. Francis Bacon goes further into the virtues of experimentation as replacing the specious logic of the Fathers of the Church in the discovery of the truth. Descartes shows how a general law should be developed step by step from the observed and verified data through "long chains of simple and easy reasoning." Newton points out that it is enough for man to establish a general law from the observed facts; to introduce hypotheses as to fundamental causes may lead to confusion and error.

The problem that is implicit in the essays up to and including Newton's concerns the appropriateness of the deductive and inductive method of reasoning about facts. Those who reasoned deductively—from a universal law to the individual phenomenon—were not always churchmen anxious to protect the basic dogmas of religion. With inadequate opportunities for observation, the deductive method was the only one available to the early scientist. A general law, derived from an imaginative conception of the universe, might assist in the interpretation of the few observations that were practicable. Moreover, by the time of Roger Bacon, the collection of facts became increasingly possible, especially through the interchange of scholars which accompanied the establishment of such religious orders as the Franciscans and the Dominicans. With Francis Bacon, the idea of evolving a natural law from the facts—the method of induction —was a natural accompaniment of the growing revolt against scholasticism. The reconciliation of the two extremes was the task of later scientists; it was not accomplished, fully, by the time of Newton, if his own attack on "hypotheses" is any guide.

The leap in time to Bernard, in our selections, takes us down to modern times. The scientific method had freed itself from the old controversies between the respective values of the deductive and inductive methods. Selection of data, trial hypotheses, and testing of results by experiment have permitted the pronouncement of more and more fundamental laws. Yet the extension of science at the hands of the atomic physicists and with the help of these new laws into new and ever more bewildering fields still leaves a modern scientist humble enough to say that he aims not at the ultimate but at the proximate.

Science, is after all, a function of man's questioning mind— or, as Descartes would put it, of his doubting mind. It is the great questions that produce the great thinkers. These readings are concerned with the thoughts of some only of the intellectual giants of our history, but they should not obscure the ever-growing army of smaller men (among whom may, indeed, be a hidden great one) whose work for the proximate goal is all too often forgotten as part of the organism that we call science.

*"No one disease is either more divine or more
human than another . . . but all are alike divine, for each has
its own nature, and each disease has a natural cause
and without a natural cause none arise."*

Hippocrates

c. 460—c. 375 B.C.

A SCIENTIFIC APPROACH TO THE STUDY
AND TREATMENT OF DISEASE
IS INTRODUCED

Greek natural philosophy arose from attempts to find an explanation for the events that affect man's daily life. In time, the philosophers or, better, the priests constructed a mythology in which the controls over man's destiny were assigned to various gods. The several "mysteries" in which the favor of the gods was sought and their anger propitiated were of a kind which allowed much scope for the imagination. Some men, like Socrates, suffered because it was alleged that they had been disrespectful of the gods; but, on the whole, intellectual inquiry was not discouraged. The settlers on the shores of Ionia, across the Aegean Sea from Athens, were especially curious about natural phenomena, probably because they had come into closer contact with the discoveries of Babylonia and Egypt. To them, the supernatural explanation was unsatisfactory. The causes of natural events had to be discovered among the facts of nature themselves.

Hippocrates and his school were among the first to compete with the priests in finding explanation of man's sicknesses. Until this time, disease had been explained as the consequence

18

of the anger of the gods toward men; remedies took the form of offerings, or of spells and incantations. But such intelligent men as the Greeks could not fail to find that, in the treatment of the wounds of war or in dealing with dislocations suffered by the gymnasts, it was possible to evolve a regular procedure. Why, then, should not disease itself be treated as a natural thing? As the Ionians began to record their observations of symptoms and the effects of their experimental remedies, the power of the gods lost ground. The Hippocratic writings are among the first records we have that show this development of a scientific approach to the treatment of disease. Whether or not the writings reproduced here are the works of Hippocrates himself is not important; that they are the work of the School on the Island of Cos and were written during the fifth and fourth centuries before the Christian era is well authenticated.

The writings attacked the speculations of the philosophers and taught that only by patient observation of the symptoms of disease and of the results of treatment of specific cases could the physician acquire that skill by which the sickness could be cured. The results of both observation and treatment were recorded for the instruction of those admitted to the profession. Continuity of learning was assured by the organization of physicians into a disciplined profession, expressing its corporate morale in the Hippocratic oath, which defined the relationship to be maintained between physician and patient and set standards of practice. The first steps had been taken to fight against that exploitation of man's natural fears which we now call quackery—a fight not wholly won, even today.

The effect of the rediscovery of the Hippocratic writings in the Middle Ages was so powerful as to retard new experiments and discovery, but their essential merit is not to be questioned; for the oath and some of the Hippocratic procedures still have their value.

The extracts that follow, which are from the Translations by W. H. S. Jones and E. T. Withington for the Loeb Classical Library (1923-1931), show something of the quality of the scientific methods propounded by Hippocrates and will suggest

why they retained their power to guide physicians even into the
seventeenth century. "On the Sacred Disease" brings observation and experiment into conflict with superstition and magic.
"On Airs, Waters and Places" shows how study of the environment is significant to diagnosis. The "Prognostic" guides the
physician into the difficult area of forecasting the course of disease
from his interpretation of the symptoms.

ON THE SACRED DISEASE

5. But this disease [epilepsy] is in my opinion no more divine than
any other; it has the same nature as other diseases, and the cause that gives
rise to individual diseases. It is also curable, no less than other illnesses,
unless by long lapse of time it be so ingrained as to be more powerful than
the remedies that are applied. Its origin, like that of other diseases, lies in
heredity. For if a phlegmatic parent has a phlegmatic child, a bilious parent
a bilious child, a consumptive parent a consumptive child, and a splenetic
parent a splenetic child, there is nothing to prevent some of the children
suffering from this disease when one or the other parent suffered from it;
for the seed comes from every part of the body, healthy seed from the
healthy parts, diseased seed from the diseased parts. Another strong proof
that this disease is no more divine than any other is that it affects the
naturally phlegmatic, but does not attack the bilious. Yet, if it were more
divine than others, this disease ought to have attacked all equally, without
making any difference between bilious and phlegmatic.

21. This disease styled sacred comes from the same causes as others,
from the things that come to and go from the body, from cold, sun, and
from the changing restlessness of winds. These things are divine. So that
there is no need to put the disease in a special class and to consider it more
divine than the others; they are all divine and all human. Each has a nature
and power of its own; none is hopeless or incapable of treatment. Most
are cured by the same things as caused them. One thing is food for one
thing, and another for another, though occasionally it does it harm. So
the physician must know how, by distinguishing the seasons for individual

things, he may assign to one thing nutriment and growth, and to another diminution and harm. For in this disease as in all others it is necessary, not to increase the illness, but to wear it down by applying to each what is most hostile to it, not that to which it is accustomed. For what is customary gives vigour and increase; what is hostile causes weakness and decay. Whoever knows how to cause in men by regimen moist or dry, hot or cold, he can cure this disease also, if he distinguish the seasons for useful treatment, without having recourse to purifications and magic.

ON AIRS, WATERS, AND PLACES

1. Whoever wishes to pursue properly the science of medicine must proceed thus. First we ought to consider what effects each season of the year can produce; for the seasons are not at all alike, but differ widely both in themselves and at their changes. The next point is the hot winds and the cold, especially those that are universal, but also those that are peculiar to each particular region. He must also consider the properties of the waters; for as these differ in taste and in weight, so the property of each is far different from that of any other. Therefore, on arrival at a town with which he is unfamiliar, a physician should examine its position with respect to the winds and to the risings of the sun. For a northern, a southern, an eastern, and a western aspect has each its own individual property. He must consider with the greatest care both these things and how the natives are off for water, whether they use marshy, soft waters, or such as are hard and come from rocky heights, or brackish and harsh. The soil, too, whether bare and dry or wooded and watered, hollow and hot or high and cold. The mode of life also of the inhabitants that is pleasing to them, whether they are heavy drinkers, taking lunch, and inactive, or athletic, industrious, eating much and drinking little.

2. Using this evidence he must examine the several problems that arise. For if a physician know these things well, by preference all of them, but at any rate most, he will not, on arrival at a town with which he is unfamiliar, be ignorant of the local diseases, or of the nature of those that commonly prevail; so that he will not be at a loss in the treatment of diseases, or make blunders, as is likely to be the case if he have not this knowledge before he consider his several problems. As time and the year passes he will be able to tell what epidemic diseases will attack the city either in summer or in winter, as well as those peculiar to the individual

which are likely to occur through change in mode of life. For knowing the changes of the seasons, and the risings and settings of the stars, with the circumstances of each of these phenomena, he will know beforehand the nature of the year that is coming. Through these considerations and by learning the times beforehand, he will have full knowledge of each particular case, will succeed best in securing health, and will achieve the greatest triumphs in the practice of his art. If it be thought that all this belongs to meteorology, he will find out, on second thoughts, that the contribution of astronomy to medicine is not a very small one but a very great one indeed. For with the seasons men's diseases, like their digestive organs, suffer change.

3. I will now set forth clearly how each of the foregoing questions ought to be investigated, and the tests to be applied. A city that lies exposed to the hot winds—these are those between the winter rising of the sun and its winter setting—when subject to these and sheltered from the north winds, the waters here are plentiful and brackish, and must be near the surface, hot in summer and cold in winter. The heads of the inhabitants are moist and full of phlegm, and their digestive organs are frequently deranged from the phlegm that runs down into them from the head. Most of them have a rather flabby physique, and they are poor eaters and poor drinkers. For men with weak heads will be poor drinkers, as the after-effects are more distressing to them. The endemic diseases are these. In the first place, the women are unhealthy and subject to excessive fluxes. Then many are barren through disease and not by nature, while abortions are frequent. Children are liable to convulsions and asthma, and to what they think causes the disease of childhood, and to be a sacred disease. Men suffer from dysentery, diarrhoea, ague, chronic fevers in winter, many attacks of eczema, and from hemorrhoids. Cases of pleurisy, pneumonia, ardent fever, and of diseases considered acute rarely occur. These diseases cannot prevail where the bowels are loose. Inflammations of the eyes occur with running, but are not serious; they are of short duration, unless a general epidemic take place after a violent change. When they are more than fifty years old, they are paralyzed by catarrhs supervening from the brain, when the sun suddenly strikes their head or they are chilled. These are their endemic diseases, but besides, they are liable to any epidemic disease that prevails through the change of the seasons.

PROGNOSTIC

1. I hold that it is an excellent thing for a physician to practise forecasting. For if he discover and declare unaided by the side of his patients the present, the past and the future, and fill in the gaps in the account given by the sick, he will be the more believed to understand the cases, so that men will confidently entrust themselves to him for treatment. Furthermore, he will carry out the treatment best if he know beforehand from the present symptoms what will take place later. Now to restore every patient to health is impossible. To do so indeed would have been better ever than forecasting the future. But as a matter of fact men do die, some owing to the severity of the disease before they summon the physician, others expiring immediately after calling him in—living one day or a little longer—before the physician by his art can combat each disease. It is necessary, therefore, to learn the natures of such diseases, how much they exceed the strength of men's bodies, and to learn how to forecast them. For in this way you will justly win respect and be an able physician. For the longer time you plan to meet each emergency the greater your power to save those who have a chance of recovery, while you will be blameless if you learn and declare beforehand those who will die and those who will get better.

2. In acute diseases the physician must conduct his inquiries in the following way. First he must examine the face of the patient, and see whether it is like the faces of healthy people, and especially whether it is like its usual self. Such likeness will be the best sign, and the greatest unlikeness will be the most dangerous sign. The latter will be as follows. Nose sharp, eyes hollow, temples sunken, ears cold and contracted with their lobes turned outwards, the skin about the face hard and tense and parched, the colour of the face as a whole being yellow or black. If at the beginning of the disease the face be like this, and if it be not yet possible with the other symptoms to make a complete prognosis, you must go on to inquire whether the patient has been sleepless, whether his bowels have been very loose, and whether he suffers at all from hunger. And if anything of the kind be confessed you must consider the danger to be less. The crisis comes after a day and a night if through these causes the face has such an appearance. But should no such confession be made, and should a

recovery not take place within this period, know that it is a sign of death. If the disease be longer standing than three days when the face has these characteristics, go on to make the same inquiries as I ordered in the previous case, and also examine the other symptoms, both of the body generally and those of the eyes. For if they shun the light, or weep involuntarily, or are distorted, or if one becomes less than the other, if the whites be red or livid or have black veins in them, should rheum appear around the eyeballs, should they be restless or protuding, or very sunken, or if the complexion of the whole face be changed—all these symptoms must be considered bad, in fact fatal. You must also examine the partial appearance of the eyes in sleep. For if a part of the white appear when the lids are closed, should the cause not be diarrhoea or purging, or should the patient not be in the habit of so sleeping, it is an unfavourable, in fact a very deadly symptom. But if, along with one of the other symptoms, eyelid, lip or nose be bent or livid, you must know that death is close at hand. It is also a deadly sign when the lips are loose, hanging, cold and very white.

"Without experience nothing can be sufficiently known."

Roger Bacon

1214 – 1294 (?)

THE FUNDAMENTAL IMPORTANCE OF
EXPERIMENT IN SCIENCE IS PROCLAIMED

The Middle Ages followed a period of five or six hundred years during which Western learning was, in effect, in hiding from war and invasion. The custody of the lamp of discovery was transferred, for the time being, to the Arabs and the Persians. In Europe, natural knowledge took second place to the development of the theology of the Christian Church and, except perhaps in the art of medicine, there were few, if any, advances in scientific thought.

The founding of universities in Southern Italy, Paris, and Oxford, early in the thirteenth century, came just at the time when the full impact of Arab culture was being felt in Spain. Men like Averroes, who made known the work of the Arabs to the West and provided the first translations of Aristotle, revived in these centers of learning a new interest in discovery. Soon after Averroes' death, the complete works of Aristotle were rediscovered and translated into Latin. One of the scholars who undertook this work was Robert Grosseteste (*c.* 1168-1253), Bishop of Lincoln in England and Chancellor of Oxford University. He was a secular member of the Franciscan Order of Friars, founded in 1209, and an important intellectual influence in church and university circles throughout Europe. Among his pupils was Roger Bacon.

25

Bacon, who himself became a Franciscan, some say in his forties, was to become a scholar among the "Schoolmen." His studies of the ancient form of the Greek language, of which he compiled a grammar, showed him that the followers of St. Thomas Aquinas (*c.* 1225-1274) were spending more energy on adapting the writings of Plato and Aristotle to the teachings of the Church than in trying to understand the significance of their work. "Scholasticism," as the system of St. Thomas is called, was much concerned with the discussion of trivialities and subleties, so that the value of Aristotle's scientific observation was submerged in unproductive controversy.

Bacon's own scholarly interest in Aristotle, stimulated by the teachings of Grosseteste, himself an experimenter, was no doubt responsible for quickening his scientific interests. Bacon was a quarrelsome man, intolerant of the inadequacies of others, if not sometimes jealous of their successes. It is not surprising, then, that he was frequently in trouble with his religious superiors and that his influence was slighter on his contemporaries than on later generations.

Bacon was opposed to dogmatism. Although his own interest in experiment was theoretical rather than practical, he saw clearly the value of the experimental method as the only route to certainty. His knowledge of science and mathematics, from the Greek and Arabic sources to which Grosseteste, no doubt, introduced him, was extensive and gave him the material with which to suggest experiments, even if he conducted but few of his own.

Bacon's work on an encyclopedia of knowledge (*Compendium Philosophiae*) was abandoned in 1266 in favor of a more positive statement of his position. He prepared four works: the *Opus Majus* (from which the extracts below are taken, from the English translation by Robert Belle Burke, Philadelphia, 1928), the *Opus Minus,* the *Opus Tertium,* and *De Multiplicatione Specierum.* In these he presented his views on mathematics, astronomy, astrology, mechanics and optics, alchemy, geography, and medicine; attacked the contemporary interest in logic for logic's sake; developed his case in favor of experimental science;

and indulged in prophecies of a future in which man would circumnavigate the globe and fly in the air.

Many inventions have been ascribed to Bacon, but none can definitely be attributed to him. As a believer in the sphericity of the earth, he may, indeed, have inspired Columbus. His experiments with mirrors and lenses brought him to the threshold of the invention of the microscope and the telescope. It is perhaps not without significance that spectacles came into use shortly after his death. He was once credited with inventing gunpowder; this is unlikely, but his reference to a powder, the force of which would be increased if it were enclosed in an instrument of solid material, suggests that he foresaw the use of gunpowder as a propellant, to be used a century later in the form of firearms.

Bacon's attack on the "obstacles in grasping truth"—unworthy authority, custom, prejudice, and "concealment of our own ignorance accompanied by ostentatious display of our knowledge"—and his statement of the principles of experimental science were not much followed by the scholars of his time but had their influence in the sixteenth century and later, when his works were rediscovered and published.

CAUSES OF ERROR

Now there are four chief obstacles in grasping truth, which hinder every man, however learned, and scarcely allow any one to win a clear title to learning, namely, submission to faulty and unworthy authority, influence of custom, popular prejudice, and concealment of our own ignorance accompanied by an ostentatious display of our knowledge. Every man is entangled in these difficulties, every rank is beset. For people without distinction draw the same conclusion from three arguments, than which none could be worse, namely for this the authority of our predecessors is adduced, this is the custom, this is the common belief; hence correct. But an opposite conclusion and a far better one should be drawn from the premises, as I shall abundantly show by authority, experience and reason. Should, however, these three errors be refuted by the convincing force of reason, the fourth is always ready and on everyman's lips for the excuse of his own ignorance, and although he has no knowledge worthy of the name, he may yet shamelessly magnify it, so that at least to the wretched satisfaction of his own folly he suppresses and evades the truth. Moreover, from these deadly banes come all the evils of the human race; for the most useful, the greatest, and most beautiful lessons of knowledge, as well as the secrets of science and art, are unknown. But, still worse, men blinded in the fog of these four errors do not perceive their own ignorance, but with every precaution cloak and defend it so as not to find a remedy; and worst of all, although they are in the densest shadows of error, they think that they are in the full light of truth. For these reasons they reckon that truths most firmly established are at the extreme limits of falsehood, that our greatest blessings are of no moment, and our chief interests possess neither weight nor value. On the contrary, they proclaim what is most false, praise what is worst, extol what is most vile, blind to every gleam of wisdom and scorning what they can obtain with great ease. In the excess of their folly they expend their utmost efforts, consume much time, pour out large expenditures on matters of little or no use and of no merit in the judgment of a wise man. Hence it is necessary that the violence and banefulness of these four causes of all evils should be recognized in the beginning and rebuked and banished far from the consideration of science. For where these three bear sway, no reason influences, no right decides, no law binds, religion has no place, nature's mandate fails, the complexion of things is changed, their order is confounded, vice prevails, virtue is extinguished, falsehood reigns, truth is hissed off the scene. Therefore, nothing is more necessary of consideration than the positive condemnation of those four errors through the chosen arguments of wise men which shall prove irrefutable.

ON EXPERIMENTAL SCIENCE

Having laid down fundamental principles of the wisdom of the Latins so far as they are found in language, mathematics and optics, I now wish to unfold the principles of experimental science, since without experience nothing can be sufficiently known. For there are two modes of acquiring knowledge, namely, by reasoning and experience. Reasoning draws a conclusion and makes us grant the conclusion, but does not make the conclusion certain, nor does it remove doubt so that the mind may rest on the intuition of truth, unless the mind discovers it by the path of experience; since many have the arguments relating to what can be known, but because they lack experience they neglect the arguments, and neither avoid what is harmful nor follow what is good. For if a man who has never seen a fire should prove by adequate reasoning that fire burns and injures things and destroys them, his mind would not be satisfied thereby, nor would he avoid fire, until he placed his hand or some combustible substance in the fire, so that he might prove by experience that which reasoning taught. But when he has had actual experience of combustion his mind is made certain and rests in the full light of truth. Therefore reasoning does not suffice, but experience does.

*   *   *

He therefore who wishes to rejoice without doubt in regard to the truths underlying phenomena must know how to devote himself to experiment. For authors write many statements, and believe them through reasoning which they formulate without experience. Their reasoning is wholly false. For it is generally believed that the diamond cannot be broken except by goat's blood, and philosophers and theologians misuse this idea. But fracture by means of blood of this kind has never been verified, although the effort has been made and without that blood it can be broken easily. For I have seen this with my own eyes, and this is necessary, because gems cannot be carved except by fragments of this stone.

*   *   *

Moreover, it is generally believed that hot water freezes more quickly than cold water in vessels, and the argument in support of this is advanced that contrary is excited by contrary, just like enemies meeting each other. But it is certain that cold water freezes more quickly for any one who makes the experiment. . . . If hot water and cold are placed in two vessels, the cold will freeze more quickly. Therefore all things must be verified by experiment.

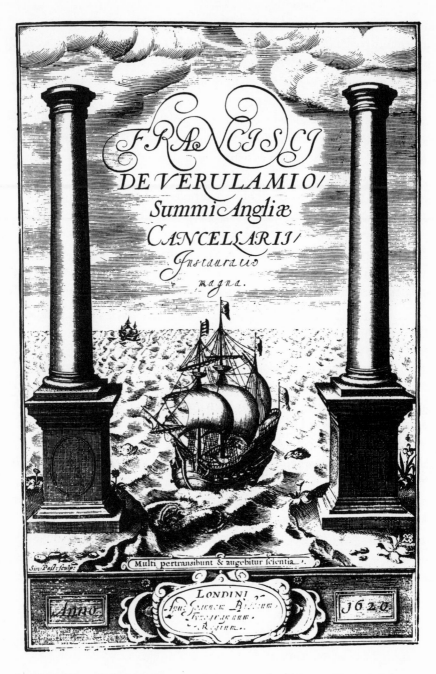

Frontispiece of Francis Bacon's *Instauratio Magna,* 1620. Bacon here pictures science as a ship venturing beyond The Pillars of Hercules, which represent the limits of the Old World. (Courtesy of the Burndy Library.)

*"The real and legitimate good of the sciences
is the endowment of human life with new inventions
and order."*

Francis Bacon

1561 — 1626

THE IMPORTANCE OF THE INDUCTIVE
METHOD IN SCIENCE IS DETAILED

Francis Bacon was born into a world in transition. He took
part in its political life as an ambitious lawyer and attained the
Lord Chancellorship, the highest legal office in England. In spite
of such preoccupations, he contrived to become an important
figure in English literature (some, indeed, now credit him with
the authorship of the plays of Shakespeare, his contemporary)
and in the history of scientific method.

Bacon's interest in scientific method was derived from the
intellectual activity of his time. He was certainly familiar with
the work of Gilbert (1544-1603), whose *De Magnete,* published in 1600, investigated the attraction between magnets and
founded, in effect, the science of electricity. He knew of the theories of Copernicus, Galileo, and Brahe. How much of their detailed experimental work was known to him is difficult to assess.
There is no doubt, however, about the effects on him of that
religious dogmatism which Roger Bacon had described as those
"specious meditations, speculations and theories of mankind
[which] are but a kind of insanity, only there is no one to stand
by and observe it." Perhaps this alone was sufficient to stimulate

Francis Bacon's well-trained legal mind to set up a system to oppose this obscurantism as well as "the present system of logic" which "is useless for the discovery of the sciences."

Bacon's pronouncements on scientific method were abstractions in the sense that he arrived at his conclusions without benefit of direct experience in the laboratory; his conclusions were the result of hard thinking, starting from the teachings of Aristotle, but taking its force from an obvious desire to present a program which would deal once and for all with the negativeness of the Schoolmen. The result was the *Novum Organum,* published in 1620 while he was still in the King's service. In this, he describes his method of "induction," by which a theory of the universe might be constructed. Man should observe all available facts, make every possible experiment and, having organized the results in a systematic way, observe the connection between the facts and derive a general law from his observations.

Critics of Bacon are quick to point out that to delay the conclusion until all possible observations have been made would hardly be practical, and that the use of preliminary hypotheses to be tested against the known facts or to be demonstrated by means of specially designed experiments vastly speeds up the development of a scientific theory. As Herbert Butterfield has pointed out in *The Origins of Modern Science,* however, it is not sufficient to judge Bacon according to the views of the present day. "We must know where each particular science stood at the time when he was writing, and exactly how he would play upon the margin of it."

Bacon's influence on the men who were already working in experimental science may have been small. We have no evidence, for example, that William Harvey interrupted his medical work and his studies of the blood to read Bacon's writings, even though the latter was one of his patients. The influence may well have been in the other direction, Bacon getting some of his ideas from his observations of Harvey's method. Yet Bacon expressed the spirit of the Renaissance and he captured in his writings something of the urge to discovery which was to transform the scholar, the mere reader of books, into an active investigator of the facts of life.

NOVUM ORGANUM

PREFACE

THEY WHO have presumed to dogmatize on nature, as on some well investigated subject, either from self-conceit or arrogance, and in the professorial style, have inflicted the greatest injury on philosophy and learning. For they have tended to stifle and interrupt inquiry exactly in proportion as they have prevailed in bringing others to their opinion; and their own activity has not counterbalanced the mischief they have occasioned by corrupting and destroying that of others. They again who have entered upon a contrary course, and asserted that nothing whatever can be known, whether they have fallen into this opinion from their hatred of the ancient sophists, or from the hesitation of their minds, or from an exurberance of learning, have certainly adduced reasons for it which are by no means contemptible. They have not, however, derived their opinion from true sources, and, hurried on by their zeal and some affectation, have certainly exceeded due moderation. But the more ancient Greeks (whose writings have perished), held a more prudent mean, between the arrogance of dogmatism, and the despair of scepticism; and though too frequently intermingling complaints and indignation at the difficulty of inquiry, and the obscurity of things, and champing, as it were, the bit, have still persisted in pressing their point, and pursuing their intercourse with nature; thinking, as it seems, that the better method was not to dispute upon the very point of the possibility of anything being known, but to put it to the test of experience. Yet they themselves, by only employing the power of the understanding, have not adopted a fixed rule, but have laid their whole stress upon intense meditation, and a continual exercise and perpetual agitation of the mind.

Our method, though difficult in its operation, is easily explained. It consists in determining the degrees of certainty, whilst we, as it were, restore the senses to their former rank, but generally reject that operation of the mind which follows close upon the senses, and open and establish a new and certain course for the mind from the first actual perceptions of the senses themselves. This, no doubt, was the view taken by those who have assigned so much to logic; showing clearly thereby that they sought some support for the mind, and suspected its natural and spontaneous mode of action. But this is now employed too late as a remedy, when all is clearly lost, and after the mind, by the daily habit and intercourse of life, has come prepossessed with corrupted doctrines, and filled with the vainest idols. The art of logic, therefore, being (as we have mentioned), too late a precaution, and in no way remedying the matters, has tended more to confirm errors, than to disclose truth. Our only remaining hope and salvation is to begin the whole labor of the mind again; not leaving it to itself, but directing it perpetually from the very first, and attaining our end as it were by mechanical aid. If men, for instance, had attempted mechanical labors with their hands alone, and without the power and aid of instruments, as they have not hesitated to carry on the labors of their understanding with the unaided efforts of their mind, they would have been able to move and overcome but little, though they had exerted their utmost and united powers. And just to pause awhile on this comparison, and look into it as a mirror; let us ask, if any obelisk of a remarkable size were perchance required to be moved, for the purpose of gracing a triumph or any similar pageant, and men were to attempt it with their bare hands, would not any sober spectator avow it to be an act of the greatest madness? And if they should increase the number of workmen, and imagine that they could thus succeed, would he not think so still more? But if they chose to make a selection, and to remove the weak, and only employ the strong and vigorous, thinking by this means, at any rate, to achieve their object, would he not say that they were more fondly deranged? Nay, if not content with this, they were to determine on consulting the athletic art, and were to give orders for all to appear with their hands, arms, and muscles regularly oiled and prepared, would he not exclaim that they were taking pains to rave by method and design? Yet men are hurried on with the same senseless energy and useless combination in intellectual matters, as long as they expect great results either from the number and agreement, or the excellence and acuteness of their wits; or even strengthen their minds with logic, which may be considered as an athletic preparation, but yet do not desist (if we rightly consider the matter) from applying their own understandings merely with all this zeal and effort. Whilst nothing is more clear, than that in every great work executed by the hand of man without machines or implements, it is impossible for the strength of individuals to be increased, or that of the multitude to combine.

Having premised so much, we lay down two points on which we would admonish mankind, lest they should fail to see or to observe them. The first of these is, that it is our good fortune (as we consider it), for the sake of extinguishing and removing contradiction and irritation of mind, to leave the honor and reverence due to the ancients untouched and undiminished, so that we can perform our intended work, and yet enjoy the benefit of our respectful moderation. For if we should profess to offer something better than the ancients, and yet should pursue the same course as they have done, we could never, by any artifice, contrive to avoid the imputation of having engaged in a contest or rivalry as to our respective wits, excellencies, or talents; which, though neither inadmissible or new (for why should we not blame and point out anything that is imperfectly discovered or laid down by them, of our own right, a right common to all), yet however just and allowable, would perhaps be scarcely an equal match, on account of the disproportion of our strength. But since our present plan leads up to open an entirely different course to the understanding, and one unattempted and unknown to them; the case is altered. There is an end to party zeal, and we only take upon ourselves the character of a guide, which requires a moderate share of authority and good fortune, rather than talents and excellence. The first admonition relates to persons, the next to things.

We make no attempt to disturb the system of philosophy that now prevails, or any other which may or will exist, either more correct or more complete. For we deny not that the received system of philosophy, and others of a similar nature, encourage discussion, embellish harangues, are employed, and are of service in the duties of the professor, and the affairs of civil life. Nay, we openly express and declare that the philosophy we offer will not be very useful in such respects. It is not obvious, nor to be understood in a cursory view, nor does it flatter the mind in its preconceived notions, nor will it descend to the level of the generality of mankind unless by its advantages and effects.

Let there exist, then (and may it be of advantage to both), two sources, and two distributions of learning, and in like manner two tribes, and as it were kindred families of contemplators or philosophers, without any hostility or alienation between them; but rather allied and united by mutual assistance. Let there be, in short, one method of cultivating the sciences, and another of discovering them. And as for those who prefer and more readily receive the former, on account of their haste or from motives arising from their ordinary life, or because they are unable from weakness of mind to comprehend and embrace the other (which must necessarily be the case with by far the greater number), let us wish that they may prosper as they desire in their undertaking, and attain what they pursue. But if any individual desire, and is anxious not merely to adhere to, and make use of present discoveries, but to penetrate still further, and not to overcome his adversaries in disputes, but nature by labor, not in short to give elegant and specious opinions, but to know to a certainty and demonstration, let him, as a true son of science (if such be his wish), join with us; that when he has left the antechambers of nature trodden by the multitude, an entrance may at last be discovered to her inner apartments. And in order to be better understood, and to render our meaning more familiar by assigning determinate names, we have accustomed ourselves to call the one method the anticipation of the mind, and the other the interpretation of nature.

We have still one request left. We have at least reflected and taken pains, in order to render our propositions not only true, but of easy and familiar access to men's minds, however wonderfully prepossessed and limited. Yet it is but just that we should obtain this favor from mankind (especially in so great a restoration of learning and the sciences), that whosoever may be desirous of forming any determination upon an opinion of this our work either from his own perceptions, or the crowd of authorities, or the forms of demonstrations, he will not expect to be able to do so in a cursory manner, and whilst attending to other matters; but in order to have a thorough knowledge of the subject, will himself, by degrees, attempt the course which we describe and maintain; will be accustomed to the subtility of things which is manifested by experience; and will correct the depraved and deeply-rooted habits of his mind by a seasonable, and, as it were, just hesitation: and then, finally (if he will), use his judgment when he has begun to be master of himself.

APHORISMS

ON THE INTERPRETATION OF NATURE
AND THE EMPIRE OF MAN

MAN, as the minister and interpreter of nature, does and understands as much as his observations on the order of nature, either with regard to things or the mind, permit him, and neither knows nor is capable of more.

2. The unassisted hand and the understanding left to itself possess but little power. Effects are produced by the means of instruments and helps, which the understanding requires no less than the hand; and as instruments either promote or regulate the motion of the hand, so those that are applied to the mind prompt or protect the understanding.

3. Knowledge and human power are synonymous, since the ignorance of the cause frustrates the effect; for nature is only subdued by submission, and that which in contemplative philosophy corresponds with the cause in practical science becomes the rule.

4. Man whilst operating can only apply or withdraw natural bodies; nature internally performs the rest.

5. Those who become practically versed in nature are, the mechanic, the mathematician, the physician, the alchemist, and the magician, but all (as matters now stand) with faint efforts and meagre success.

6. It would be madness and inconsistency to suppose that things which have never yet been performed can be performed without employing some hitherto untried means.

7. The creations of the mind and hand appear very numerous, if we judge by books and manufactures; but all that variety consists of an excessive refinement, and of deductions from a few well-known matters— not of a number of axioms.

8. Even the effects already discovered are due to chance and experiment, rather than to the sciences; for our present sciences are nothing more than peculiar arrangements of matters already discovered, and not methods for discovery or plans for new operations.

9. The sole cause and root of almost every defect in the sciences is this, that while we falsely admire and extol the powers of the human mind, we do not search for its real helps.

10. The subtility of nature is far beyond that of sense or of the

understanding; so that the specious meditations, speculations, and theories of mankind are but a kind of insanity, only there is no one to stand by and observe it.

11. As the present sciences are useless for the discovery of effects, so the present system of logic is useless for the discovery of the sciences.

12. The present system of logic rather assists in confirming and rendering inveterate the errors founded on vulgar notions than in searching after truth, and is therefore more hurtful than useful.

13. The syllogism is not applied to the principles of the sciences, and is of no avail in intermediate axioms, as being very unequal to the subtility of nature. It forces assent, therefore, and not things.

14. The syllogism consists of propositions, propositions of words; words are the signs of notions. If, therefore, the notions (which form the basis of the whole) be confused and carelessly abstracted from things, there is no solidity in the superstructure. Our only hope, then, is in genuine induction.

15. We have no sound notions either in logic or physics; substance, quality, actions, passion, and existence are not clear notions; much less weight, levity, density, tenuity, moisture, dryness, generation, corruption, attraction, repulsion, element, matter, form, and the like. They are all fantastical and ill-defined.

16. The notions of less abstract natures, as man, dog, dove, and the immediate perceptions of sense, as heat, cold, white, black, do not deceive us materially, yet even these are sometimes confused by the mutability of matter and the intermixture of things. All the rest which men have hitherto employed are errors, and improperly abstracted and deduced from things.

17. There is the same degree of licentiousness and error in forming axioms as in abstracting notions, and that in the first principles, which depend on common induction; still more is this the case in axioms and inferior propositions derived from syllogisms.

18. The present discoveries in science are such as lie immediately beneath the surface of common notions. It is necessary, however, to penetrate the more secret and remote parts of nature, in order to abstract both notions and axioms from things by a more certain and guarded method.

19. There are and can exist but two ways of investigating and discovering truth. The one hurries on rapidly from the senses and particulars to the most general axioms, and from them, as principles and their sup-

posed indisputable truth, derives and discovers the intermediate axioms. This is the way now in use. The other constructs its axioms from the senses and particulars, by ascending continually and gradually, till it finally arrives at the most general axioms, which is the true but unattempted way.

20. The understanding when left to itself proceeds by the same way as that which it would have adopted under the guidance of logic, namely, the first; for the mind is fond of starting off to generalities, that it may avoid labor, and after dwelling a little on a subject is fatigued by experiment. But those evils are augmented by logic, for the sake of the ostentation of dispute.

21. The understanding, when left to itself in a man of a steady, patient, and reflecting disposition (especially when unimpeded by received doctrines), makes some attempt in the right way, but with little effect, since the understanding, undirected and unassisted, is unequal to and unfit for the task of vanquishing the obscurity of things.

22. Each of these two ways begins from the senses and particulars, and ends in the greatest generalities. But they are immeasurably different; for the one merely touches cursorily the limits of experiment and particulars, whilst the other runs duly and regularly through them—the one from the very outset lays down some abstract and useless generalities, the other gradually rises to those principles which are really the most common in nature.

23. There is no small difference between the idols of the human mind and the ideas of the Divine mind—that is to say, between certain idle dogmas and the real stamp and impression of created objects, as they are found in nature.

24. Axioms determined upon in argument can never assist in the discovery of new effects; for the subtility of nature is vastly superior to that of argument. But axioms properly and regularly abstracted from particulars easily point out and define new particulars, and therefore impart activity to the sciences.

25. The axioms now in use are derived from a scanty handful, as it were, of experience, and a few particulars of frequent occurrence, whence they are of much the same dimensions or extent as their origin. And if any neglected or unknown instance occurs, the axiom is saved by some frivolous distinction, when it would be more consistent with truth to amend it.

26. We are wont, for the sake of distinction, to call that human reasoning which we apply to nature the anticipation of nature (as being rash and premature), and that which is properly deduced from things the interpretation of nature.

27. Anticipations are sufficiently powerful in producing unanimity, for if men were all to become even uniformly mad, they might agree tolerably well with each other.

28. Anticipations, again, will be assented to much more readily than interpretations, because being deduced from a few instances, and these principally of familiar occurrence, they immediately hit the understanding and satisfy the imagination; whilst on the contrary interpretations, being deduced from various subjects, and these widely dispersed, cannot suddenly strike the understanding, so that in common estimation they must appear difficult and discordant, and almost like the mysteries of faith.

29. In sciences founded on opinions and dogmas, it is right to make use of anticipations and logic if you wish to force assent rather than things.

30. If all the capacities of all ages should unite and combine and transmit their labors, no great progress will be made in learning by anticipations, because the radical errors, and those which occur in the first process of the mind, are not cured by the excellence of subsequent means and remedies.

31. It is in vain to expect any great progress in the sciences by the superinducing or engrafting new matters upon old. An instauration must be made from the very foundations, if we do not wish to revolve forever in a circle, making only some slight and contemptible progress.

32. The ancient authors and all others are left in undisputed possession of their honors; for we enter into no comparison of capacity or talent, but of method, and assume the part of a guide rather than of a critic.

33. To speak plainly, no correct judgment can be formed either of our method or its discoveries by those anticipations which are now in common use; for it is not to be required of us to submit ourselves to the judgment of the very method we ourselves arraign.

34. Nor is it an easy matter to deliver and explain our sentiments; for those things which are in themselves new can yet be only understood from some analogy to what is old.

35. Alexander Borgia said of the expedition of the French into Italy that they came with chalk in their hands to mark up their lodgings, and

not with weapons to force their passage. Even so do we wish our philosophy to make its way quietly into those minds that are fit for it, and of good capacity; for we have no need of contention where we differ in first principles, and in our very notions, and even in our forms of demonstration.

36. We have but one simple method of delivering our sentiments, namely, we must bring men to particulars and their regular series and order, and they must for a while renounce their notions, and begin to form an acquaintance with things.

37. Our method and that of the sceptics agree in some respects at first setting out, but differ most widely, and are completely opposed to each other in their conclusion; for they roundly assert that nothing can be known; we, that but a small part of nature can be known, by the present method; their next step, however, is to destroy the authority of the senses and understanding, whilst we invent and supply them with assistance.

38. The idols and false notions which have already preoccupied the human understanding, and are deeply rooted in it, not only so beset men's minds that they become difficult of access, but even when access is obtained will again meet and trouble us in the instauration of the sciences, unless mankind when forewarned guard themselves with all possible care against them.

39. Four species of idols beset the human mind, to which (for distinction's sake) we have assigned names, calling the first Idols of the Tribe, the second Idols of the Den, the third Idols of the Market, the fourth Idols of the Theatre.

40. The formation of notions and axioms on the foundation of true induction is the only fitting remedy by which we can ward off and expel these idols. It is, however, of great service to point them out; for the doctrine of idols bears the same relation to the interpretation of nature as that of the confutation of sophisms does to common logic.

41. The idols of the tribe are inherent in human nature and the very tribe or race of man; for man's sense is falsely asserted to be the standard of things; on the contrary, all the perceptions both of the senses and the mind bear reference to man and not to the universe, and the human mind resembles those uneven mirrors which impart their own properties to different objects, from which rays are emitted and distort and disfigure them.

42. The idols of the den are those of each individual; for everybody (in addition to the errors common to the race of man) has his own indi-

vidual den or cavern, which intercepts and corrupts the light of nature, either from his own peculiar and singular disposition, or from his education and intercourse with others, or from his reading, and the authority acquired by those whom he reverences and admires, or from the different impressions produced on the mind, as it happens to be preoccupied and predisposed, or equable and tranquil, and the like; so that the spirit of man (according to its several dispositions), is variable, confused, and, as it were, actuated by chance; and Heraclitus said well that men search for knowledge in lesser worlds, and not in the greater or common world.

43. There are also idols formed by the reciprocal intercourse and society of man with man, which we call idols of the market, from the commerce and association of men with each other; for men converse by means of language, but words are formed at the will of the generality, and there arises from a bad and unapt formation of words a wonderful obstruction to the mind. Nor can the definitions and explanations with which learned men are wont to guard and protect themselves in some instances afford a complete remedy—words still manifestly force the understanding, throw everything into confusion, and lead mankind into vain and innumerable controversies and fallacies.

44. Lastly, There are idols which have crept into men's minds from the various dogmas of peculiar systems of philosophy, and also from the perverted rules of demonstration, and these we denominate idols of the theatre: for we regard all the systems of philosophy hitherto received or imagined, as so many plays brought out and performed, creating fictitious and theatrical worlds. Nor do we speak only of the present systems, or of the philosophy and sects of the ancients, since numerous other plays of a similar nature can be still composed and made to agree with each other, the causes of the most opposite errors being generally the same. Nor, again, do we allude merely to general systems, but also to many elements and axioms of sciences which have become inveterate by tradition, implicit credence, and neglect. We must, however, discuss each species of idols more fully and distinctly in order to guard the human understanding against them.

"I think, therefore, I am."

René Descartes

1596 — 1650

THE ROLE OF DOUBT AND REASON IN
INTERPRETING THE UNIVERSE IS
EMPHASIZED, ALONG WITH A
DISCOURSE ON METHOD

Descartes's *Discourse on Method* is a vindication of man's
privilege to apply his mind "rightly." His basic assumption is
that all men start with an equal share of good sense; he claimed
no better mental equipment than most men; he had schooled
himself, in his search for truth, to question all that he had been
told or read and to look for his answers in the study of other
men and, most of all, of himself.

Unlike Francis Bacon, who, as we have seen, was a man of
affairs in touch with the practical side of life, Descartes was a
scholar. He was not "in a condition which compelled me to make
merchandise of science for the bettering of my fortune"; in other
words, he was free to pursue his interests in mathematics as he
pleased when he left his Jesuit school. So he began his career, as
would any gentleman of the time, continuing his reading and
writing in Paris.

Descartes's rejection of mere books occurred during a visit
to Germany when he was twenty-three or so; he abandoned his
Parisian comforts to join the army—the army of the Dutch. After
nine years of "the study of other men," he settled down in Holland, where he resumed his study of mathematics—and presum-

ably of himself; and his own books now began to appear. His work took three main directions; the separation of the fund of existing knowledge from the mass of interpretation attached to it by medieval scholarship; the development of a theory of the universe; and, in effect, the adaptation of mathematics to the service of the scientist.

Descartes's own theory of the universe depended largely on his distinction between matter and spirit, between man's soul and his body. This "dualism" has continued to influence philosophers even to the present time and has, indeed, permeated the thinking of many ordinary people. The approach was not of much help to Descartes in his attempts to explain the physical universe, for it led him to the conclusion that everything could be accounted for mathematically, with the final control in the hands of God as the ultimate First Cause.

In mathematics, however, Descartes left his mark. He found the way to combine algebra and geometry in the form we now call *analytical geometry,* a system which was independently discovered by another Frenchman, Fermat (1601-1665). In this, the relationships demonstrated by Euclidean geometry were expressed by algebraic formulas. With these, the scientist could make his calculations with facility (and, today, adapt them to the operations of electronic computers) and express the results in the geometric form. Newton was among the first to avail himself of Descartes's methods.

Descartes intended the *Discourse on Method* to be a preface to his major works on optics, the theory of matter, and geometry. It has survived as a major defense of philosophical doubt as the basis for clear reasoning. His insistence on the independence of the mind from matter permitted him to recognize the importance of *perception:* " . . . by its use my mind was becoming gradually habituated to clearer and more distinct conceptions of its objects." Hence, experiment is not an essential, except as permitting demonstration of the truth of what had been perceived.

In essence, Descartes's plea is for the use of reason under such control that "precipitancy and anticipation in judgment" can be avoided. Who can say, in these days of "crash" programs

to deal with this or that human problem, that Descartes's teachings are without revelance?

The extract is from the Everyman Edition of the *Discourse
on Method*.

DISCOURSE ON METHOD

GOOD sense is, of all things among men, the most equally distributed; for
every one thinks himself so abundantly provided with it, that those even
who are the most difficult to satisfy in everything else, do not usually desire
a larger measure of this quality than they already possess. And in this it is
not likely that all are mistaken: the conviction is rather to be held as testify-
ing that the power of judging aright and of distinguishing truth from error,
which is properly what is called good sense or reason, is by nature equal in
all men; and that the diversity of our opinions, consequently, does not arise
from some being endowed with a larger share of reason than others, but
solely from this, that we conduct our thoughts along different ways, and do
not fix our attention on the same objects. For to be possessed of a vigorous
mind is not enough; the prime requisite is rightly to apply it. The greatest
minds, as they are capable of the highest excellences, are open likewise to
the greatest aberrations; and those who travel very slowly may yet make
far greater progress, provided they keep always to the straight road, than
those who, while they run, forsake it.

For myself, I have never fancied my mind to be in any respect more
perfect than those of the generality; on the contrary, I have often wished
that I were equal to some others in promptitude of thought, or in clearness
and distinctness of imagination, or in fulness and readiness of memory.
And besides these, I know of no other qualities that contribute to the perfection of the mind; for as to the reason or sense, inasmuch as it is that
alone which constitutes us men, and distinguishes us from the brutes, I am
disposed to believe that it is to be found complete in each individual; and
on this point to adopt the common opinion of philosophers, who say that
the difference of greater and less holds only among the *accidents,* and not
among the *forms* or *natures* of *individuals* of the same *species*.

I will not hesitate, however, to avow my belief that it has been my singular good fortune to have very early in life fallen in with certain tracks which have conducted me to considerations and maxims, of which I have formed a method that gives me the means, as I think, of gradually augmenting my knowledge, and of raising it by little and little to the highest point which the mediocrity of my talents and the brief duration of my life will permit me to reach. For I have already reaped from it such fruits that, although I have been accustomed to think lowly enough of myself, and although when I look with the eye of a philosopher at the varied courses and pursuits of mankind at large, I find scarcely one which does not appear vain and useless, I nevertheless derive the highest satisfaction from the progress I conceived myself to have already made in the search after truth, and cannot help entertaining such expectations of the future as to believe that if, among the occupations of men as men, there is any one really excellent and important, it is that which I have chosen.

After all, it is possible I may be mistaken; and it is but a little copper and glass, perhaps, that I take for gold and diamonds. I know how very liable we are to delusion in what relates to ourselves, and also how much the judgments of our friends are to be suspected when given in our favour. But I shall endeavour in this discourse to describe the paths I have followed, and to delineate my life as in a picture, in order that each one may be able to judge of them for himself, and that in the general opinion entertained of them, as gathered from current report, I myself may have a new help towards instruction to be added to those I have been in the habit of employing.

My present design, then, is not to teach the method which each ought to follow for the right conduct of his reason, but solely to describe the way in which I have endeavoured to conduct my own. They who set themselves to give precepts must of course regard themselves as possessed of greater skill than those to whom they prescribe; and if they err in the slightest particular, they subject themselves to censure. But as this tract is put forth merely as a history, or, if you will, as a tale, in which, amid some examples worthy of imitation, there will be found, perhaps, as many more which it were advisable not to follow, I hope it will prove useful to some without being hurtful to any, and that my openness will find some favour with all.

From my childhood, I have been familiar with letters; and as I was given to believe that by their help a clear and certain knowledge of all that is useful in life might be acquired, I was ardently desirous of instruction. But as soon as I had finished the entire course of study, at the close of which it is customary to be admitted into the order of the learned, I completely changed my opinion. For I found myself involved in so many doubts and errors, that I was convinced I had advanced no farther in all my attempts at learning, than the discovery at every turn of my own ignorance. And yet I was studying in one of the most celebrated schools in Europe, in which I thought there must be learned men, if such were anywhere to be found. I had been taught all that others learned there; and not contented with the sciences actually taught us, I had, in addition, read all the books that had fallen into my hands, treating of such branches as are esteemed the most curious and rare. I knew the judgment which others had formed of me; and I did not find that I was considered inferior to my fellows, although there were among them some who were already marked out to fill the places of our instructors. And, in fine, our age appeared to me as flourishing, and as fertile in powerful minds as any preceding one. I was thus led to take the liberty of judging of all other men by myself, and of concluding that there was no science in existence that was of such a nature as I had previously been given to believe.

I still continued, however, to hold in esteem the studies of the schools. I was aware that the languages taught in them are necessary to the understanding of the writings of the ancients; that the grace of fable stirs the mind; that the memorable deeds of history elevate it; and, if read with discretion, aid in forming the judgment; that the perusal of all excellent books is, as it were, to interview with the noblest men of past ages, who have written them, and even a studied interview, in which are discovered to us only their choicest thoughts; that eloquence has incomparable force and beauty; that poesy has its ravishing graces and delights; that in the mathematics there are many refined discoveries eminently suited to gratify the inquisitive, as well as further all the arts and lessen the labour of man; that numerous highly useful precepts and exhortations to virtue are contained in treatises on morals; that theology points out the path to heaven; that philosophy affords the means of discoursing with an appearance of truth on all matters, and commands the admiration of the more simple; that jurisprudence, medicine, and the other sciences, secure for their cultivators honours and riches; and, in fine, that it is useful to bestow some attention upon all, even upon those abounding the most in superstition and error, that we may be in a position to determine their real value, and guard against being deceived.

*   *   *

I was especially delighted with the mathematics, on account of the certitude and evidence of their reasonings; but I had not as yet a precise knowledge of their true use; and thinking that they but contributed to the advancement of the mechanical arts, I was astonished that foundations, so strong and solid, should have had no loftier superstructure reared on them. On the other hand, I compared the disquisitions of the ancient moralists to very towering and magnificent palaces with no better foundation than sand and mud: they laud the virtues very highly, and exhibit them as estimable far above anything on earth; but they give us no adequate criterion of virtue, and frequently that which they designate with so fine a name is but apathy, or pride, or despair, or parricide.

I revered our theology, and aspired as much as any one to reach heaven: but being given assuredly to understand that the way is not less open to the most ignorant than to the most learned, and that the revealed truths which lead to heaven are above our comprehension, I did not presume to subject them to the impotency of my reason; and I thought that in order competently to undertake their examination, there was need of some special help from heaven, and of being more than man.

Of philosophy I will say nothing, except that when I saw that it had been cultivated for many ages by the most distinguished men, and that yet there is not a single matter within its sphere which is not still in dispute, and nothing, therefore, which is above doubt, I did not presume to anticipate that my success would be greater in it than that of others; and further, when I considered the number of conflicting opinions touching a single matter that may be upheld by learned men, while there can be but one true, I reckoned as well-nigh false all that was only probable.

As to the other sciences, inasmuch as these borrow their principles from philosophy, I judged that no solid superstructures could be reared on foundations so infirm; and neither the honour nor the gain held out by them was sufficient to determine me to their cultivation: for I was not, thank Heaven, in a condition which compelled me to make merchandise of science for the bettering of my fortune; and though I might not profess to scorn glory as a cynic, I yet made very slight account of that honour which I hoped to acquire only through fictitious titles. And, in fine, of false sciences I thought I knew the worth sufficiently to escape being deceived by the professions of an alchemist, the predictions of an astrologer, the impostures of a magician, or by the artifices and boasting of any of those who profess to know things of which they are ignorant.

For these reasons, as soon as my age permitted me to pass from under the control of my instructors, I entirely abandoned the study of letters, and resolved no longer to seek any other science than the knowledge of myself, or of the great book of the world. I spent the remainder of my youth in travelling, in visiting courts and armies, in holding intercourse with men of different dispositions and ranks, in collecting varied experience, in proving myself in the different situations into which fortune threw me, and, above all, in making such reflection on the matter of my experience as to secure my improvement. For it occurred to me that I should find much more truth in the reasonings of each individual with reference to the affairs in which he is personally interested, and the issue of which must presently punish him if he has judged amiss, than in those conducted by a man of letters in his study, regarding speculative matters that are of no practical moment, and followed by no consequences to himself, farther, perhaps, than that they foster his vanity the better the more remote they are from common sense; requiring, as they must in this case, the exercise of greater ingenuity and art to render them probable. In addition, I had always a most earnest desire to know how to distinguish the true from the false, in order that I might be able clearly to discriminate the right path in life, and proceed in it with confidence.

It is true that, while busied only in considering the manners of other men, I found here, too, scarce any ground for settled conviction, and remarked hardly less contradiction among them than in the opinions of the philosophers. So that the greatest advantage I derived from the study consisted in this, that, observing many things which, however extravagant and ridiculous to our apprehension, are yet by common consent received and approved by other great nations, I learned to entertain too decided a belief in regard to nothing of the truth of which I had been persuaded merely by example and custom; and thus I gradually extricated myself from many errors powerful enough to darken our natural intelligence, and incapacitate us in great measure from listening to reason. But after I had been occupied several years in thus studying the book of the world, and in essaying to gather some experience, I at length resolved to make myself an object of study, and to employ all the powers of my mind in choosing the paths I ought to follow, an undertaking which was accompanied with greater success than it would have been had I never quitted my country or my books.

*   *   *

The majority of men is composed of two classes, for neither of which would this be at all a befitting resolution: in the *first* place, of those who with more than a due confidence in their own powers, are precipitate in their judgments and want the patience requisite for orderly and circumspect thinking; whence it happens, that if men of this class once take the liberty to doubt of their accustomed opinions, and quit the beaten highway, they will never be able to thread the byway that would lead them by a shorter course, and will lose themselves and continue to wander for life; in the *second* place, of those who, possessed of sufficient sense or modesty to determine that there are others who excel them in the power of discriminating between truth and error, and by whom they may be instructed, ought rather to content themselves with the opinions of such than trust for more correct to their own reason.

For my own part, I should doubtless have belonged to the latter class, had I received instruction from but one master, or had I never known the diversities of opinion that from time immemorial have prevailed among men of the greatest learning. But I had become aware, even so early as during my college life, that no opinion, however absurd and incredible, can be imagined, which has not been maintained by some one of the philosophers; and afterwards in the course of my travels I remarked that all those whose opinions are decidedly repugnant to ours are not on that account barbarians and savages, but on the contrary that many of these nations make an equally good, if not a better, use of their reason than we do. I took into account also the very different character which a person brought up from infancy in France or Germany exhibits, from that which, with the same mind originally, this individual would have possessed had he lived always among the Chinese or with savages, and the circumstance that in dress itself the fashion which pleased us ten years ago, and which may again, perhaps, be received into favour before ten years have gone, appears to us at this moment extravagant and ridiculous. I was thus led to infer that the ground of our opinions is far more custom and example than any certain knowledge. And, finally, although such be the ground of our opinions, I remarked that a plurality of suffrages is no guarantee of truth where it is at all of difficult discovery, as in such cases it is much more likely that it will be found by one than by many. I could, however, select from the crowd no one whose opinions seemed worthy of preference, and thus I found myself constrained, as it were, to use my own reason in the conduct of my life.

But like one walking alone and in the dark, I resolved to proceed so slowly and with such circumspection, that if I did not advance far, I would at least guard against falling. I did not even choose to dismiss summarily any of the opinions that had crept into my belief without having been introduced by reason, but first of all took sufficient time carefully to satisfy myself of the general nature of the task I was setting myself, and ascertain the true method by which to arrive at the knowledge of whatever lay within the compass of my powers.

Among the branches of philosophy, I had, at an earlier period, given some attention to logic, and among those of the mathematics to geometrical analysis and algebra,—three arts or sciences which ought, as I conceived, to contribute something to my design. But, on examination, I found that, as for logic, its syllogisms and the majority of its other precepts are of avail rather in the communication of what we already know, or even as the art of Lully, in speaking without judgment of things of which we are ignorant, than in the investigation of the unknown; and although this science contains indeed a number of correct and very excellent precepts, there are, nevertheless, so many others, and these either injurious or superfluous, mingled with the former, that it is almost as difficult to effect a severance of the true from the false as it is to extract a Diana or a Minerva from a rough block of marble. Then as to the analysis of the ancients and the algebra of the moderns, besides that they embrace only matters highly abstract, and, to appearance, of no use, the former is so exclusively restricted to the consideration of figures, that it can exercise the understanding only on condition of greatly fatiguing the imagination; and, in the latter, there is so complete a subjection to certain rules and formulas, that there results an art full of confusion and obscurity calculated to embarrass, instead of a science fitted to cultivate the mind. By these considerations I was induced to seek some other method which would comprise the advantages of the three and be exempt from their defects. And as a multitude of laws often only hampers justice, so that a state is best governed when, with few laws, these are rigidly administered;

in like manner, instead of the great number of precepts of which logic is composed, I believed that the four following would prove perfectly sufficient for me, provided I took the firm and unwavering resolution never in a single instance to fail in observing them.

The *first* was never to accept anything for true which I did not clearly know to be such; that is to say, carefully to avoid precipitancy and prejudice, and to comprise nothing more in my judgment than what was presented to my mind so clearly and distinctly as to exclude all ground of doubt.

The *second,* to divide each of the difficulties under examination into as many parts as possible, and as might be necessary for its adequate solution.

The *third,* to conduct my thoughts in such order that, by commencing with objects the simplest and easiest to know, I might ascend by little and little, and, as it were, step by step, to the knowledge of the more complex; assigning in thought a certain order even to those objects which in their own nature do not stand in a relation of antecedence and sequence.

And the *last,* in every case to make enumerations so complete, and reviews so general, that I might be assured that nothing was omitted.

The long chains of simple and easy reasonings by means of which geometers are accustomed to reach the conclusions of their most difficult demonstrations, had led me to imagine that all things, to the knowledge of which man is competent, are mutually connected in the same way, and that there is nothing so far removed from us as to be beyond our reach, or so hidden that we cannot discover it, provided only we abstain from accepting the false for the true, and always preserve in our thoughts the order necessary for the deduction of one truth from another. And I had little difficulty in determining the objects with which it was necessary to commence, for I was already persuaded that it must be with the simplest and easiest to know, and, considering that of all those who have hitherto sought truth in the sciences, the mathematicians alone have been able to find any demonstrations, that is, any certain and evident reasons, I did not doubt but that such must have been the rule of their investigations. I resolved to commence, therefore, with the examination of the simplest objects, not anticipating, however, from this any other advantage than that to be found in accustoming my mind to the love and nourishment of truth, and to a distaste for all such reasonings as were unsound. But I had no intention on that account of attempting to master all the particular sciences commonly denominated mathematics: but observing that, however different their objects, they all agree in considering only the various relations or proportions subsisting among those objects, I thought it best for my purpose to consider these proportions in the most general form possible, without referring them to any objects in particular, except such as would most facilitate the knowledge of them, and without by any means restricting them to these, that afterwards I might thus be the better able to apply them to every other class of objects to which they are legitimately applicable. Perceiving further, that in order to understand these relations I should sometimes have to consider them one by one, and sometimes only to bear them in mind, or embrace them in the aggregate, I thought that, in order the better to consider them individually, I should view them as subsisting between straight lines, than which I could find no objects more simple, or capable of being more distinctly represented to my imagination and senses; and on the other hand, that in order to retain them in the memory, or embrace an aggregate of many, I should express them by certain characters the briefest possible. In this way I believed that I could borrow all that was best both in geometrical analysis and in algebra, and correct all the defects of the one by help of the other.

And, in point of fact, the accurate observance of these few precepts gave me, I take the liberty of saying, such ease in unravelling all the questions embraced in these two sciences, that in the two or three months I devoted to their examination, not only did I reach solutions of questions I had formerly deemed exceedingly difficult, but even as regards questions of the solution of which I continued ignorant, I was enabled, as it appeared to me, to determine the means whereby, and the extent to which, a solution was possible; results attributable to the circumstance that I commenced with the simplest and most general truths, and that thus each truth discovered was a rule available in the discovery of subsequent ones. Nor in this perhaps shall I appear too vain, if it be considered that, as the truth on any particular point is one, whoever apprehends the truth, knows all that on that point can be known. The child, for example, who has been instructed in the elements of arithmetic, and has made a particular addition, according to rule, may be assured that he has found, with respect to the sum of the numbers before him, all that in this instance is within the reach of human genius. Now, in conclusion, the method which teaches adherence to the true order, and an exact enumeration of all the conditions of the thing sought includes all that gives certitude to the rules of arithmetic.

But the chief ground of my satisfaction with this method, was the assurance I had of thereby exercising my reason in all matters, if not with absolute perfection, at least with the greatest attainable by me: besides, I was conscious that by its use my mind was becoming gradually habituated to clearer and more distinct conceptions of its objects; and I hoped also, from not having restricted this method to any particular matter, to apply it to the difficulties of the other sciences, with not less success than to those of algebra. I should not, however, on this account have ventured at once on the examination of all the difficulties of the sciences which presented themselves to me, for this would have been contrary to the order prescribed in the method, but observing that the knowledge of such is dependent on principles borrowed from philosophy, in which I found nothing certain, I thought it necessary first of all to endeavour to establish its principles. And because I observed, besides, that an inquiry of this kind was of all others of the greatest moment, and one in which precipitancy and anticipation in judgment were most to be dreaded, I thought that I ought not to approach it till I had reached a more mature age (being at that time but twenty-three), and had first of all employed much of my time in preparation for the work, as well by eradicating from my mind all the erroneous opinions I had up to that moment accepted, as by amassing variety of experience to afford materials for my reasonings, and by continually exercising myself in my chosen method with a view to increased skill in its application.

* * *

In conclusion, I am unwilling here to say anything very specific of the progress which I expect to make for the future in the sciences, or to bind myself to the public by any promise which I am not certain of being able to fulfil; but this only will I say, that I have resolved to devote what time I may still have to live to no other occupation than that of endeavoring to acquire some knowledge of Nature, which shall be of such a kind as to enable us therefrom to deduce rules in medicine of greater certainty than those at present in use; and that my inclination is so much opposed to all other pursuits, especially to such as cannot be useful to some without being hurtful to others, that if, by any circumstances, I had been constrained to engage in such, I do not believe that I should have been able to succeed. Of this I here make a public declaration, though well aware that it cannot serve to procure for me any consideration in the world, which, however, I do not in the least affect; and I shall always hold myself more obliged to those through whose favour I am permitted to enjoy my retirement without interruption than to any who might offer me the highest earthly preferments.

*"Hypotheses, whether metaphysical or physical,
whether of occult qualities or mechanical, have no place
in experimental philosophy."*

Isaac Newton

1642 – 1727

RULES OF REASONING IN PHILOSOPHY
ARE PRESENTED AS A SIMPLE, CLEAR
APPROACH TO SCIENCE IN GENERAL

It is regrettable that the necessity for a plan in this book
prevents a digression here to discuss the significance of Newton's
"Rules of Reasoning in Philosophy" in the context of their
origin, for they represent less the achievement of one man than
the fruit of an extraordinary period. Less than one hundred years
separate the birth of Galileo from the time when, as a young
man of twenty-three, Newton developed the main structure of
his synthesis and reconciled the observations and the speculations
of his illustrious colleagues about the laws which control the
universe. In him, the Renaissance attained the full development
of its power over the mind of scientific man.

The immediate influence on Newton was, probably, that
of Descartes, because it was the latter's *Geometry* which provided
Newton with the basic tools for the mathematical work leading
to his "moment of discovery." Yet behind Descartes lay a gradually evolving explanation of the physical universe. If Newton
synthesized this knowledge in two short years while he was a
refugee from the Great Plague of 1665, it was because he had

been blessed with the sort of mind described by Descartes, one with an extraordinary ability to perceive the unity in his predecessors' observations and to pursue the evidence to a general conclusion supported by mathematical proofs.

Newton was fortunate, too, in that he avoided the trap which had long ago been set by the Schoolmen; he refused to confuse the issue by introducing metaphysics—that is, to theorize about the nature of being. Though he was, undoubtedly, a religious man, he took it as a fundamental assumption that the primary causes were in the hands of an all-powerful creator. His demonstration of the *effects* of gravity and his evolution of the laws of motion did not, therefore, lead him into inquiry into the *cause* of gravity. This would have forced him to make hypotheses about matters which could not be handled by experiment and observation.

We must beware of attributing to Newton an objection to that use of hypothesis which, as we shall see later, characterizes the modern scientific method. To make a supposition on the basis of observed facts and then to verify it by gathering further facts is good practice and economical of effort. This is, in a sense, the intuitive approach advocated by Descartes. It is a far cry from the method of the Schoolmen, who sought to prove their dogma, their unverified assumption, by twisting the facts to suit it.

Hence the value of Newton's "Rules of Reasoning." They were published in the *Principia Mathematica* in 1687, more than twenty years after the pattern of his physical laws had been established and at the peak of his scientific career. Like Descartes's *Discourse,* his Rules are the essence of his experience, although, unlike his mathematical mentor, he had been engaged in scientific experiment of a severely practical kind. Newton was not unique in having these qualifications, but he symbolizes and even dramatizes that triumph of communication which lay back of his own success. The first scientific journals appeared early in 1665, and Newton's period reflected the influence of the scientific societies which came into formal being around the time of his youth. The Royal Society of London for the Improving of Natural Knowledge, founded by Charles II in 1662, for example, provided that stimulus to Newton which a professional society today will furnish by exerting a pressure on its members to publish their ideas. Newton's Rules had, too, a direct influence on his neighbors, for who would not respect the advice of a man who could demonstrate his practical abilities as an efficient Master of the Royal Mint? Francis Bacon started his life as a government official; Newton wound up his career administering the currency, keeping his contact with science as a member of the Royal Society, of which he was president for more than twenty years.

We shall read more of Newton's contributions to science later on in this volume. In the meantime, his "Rules of Reasoning" give him an important place in our short history of the development of the methodology of science.

Of the readings that follow, the first is from *Sir Isaac Newton's Opticks,* fourth edition, published in 1730; the second from the Andrew Motte translation of Newton's *Principia Mathematica,* revised by Florian Cajori, reprinted by permission of the University of California Press.

OPTICKS

As in Mathematicks, so in Natural Philosophy, the Investigation of difficult Things by the Method of Analysis, ought ever to precede the Method of Composition. This Analysis consists in making Experiments and Observations, and in drawing general Conclusions from them by Induction, and admitting of no Objections against the Conclusions, but such as are taken from Experiments, or other certain Truths. For Hypotheses are not to be regarded in experimental Philosophy. And although the arguing from Experiments and Observations by Induction be no Demonstration of general Conclusions; yet it is the best way of arguing which the Nature of Things admits of, and may be looked upon as so much the stronger, by how much the Induction is more general. And if no Exception occur from Phænomena, the Conclusion may be pronounced generally. But if at any time afterwards any Exception shall occur from Experiments, it may then begin to be pronounced with such Exceptions as occur. By this way of Analysis we may proceed from Compounds to Ingredients, and from Motions to the Forces producing them; and in general, from Effects to their Causes, and from particular Causes to more general ones, till the Argument end in the most general. This is the Method of Analysis: And the Synthesis consists as assuming the Causes discover'd, and establish'd as Principles, and by them explaining the Phænomena proceeding from them, and proving the Explanations.

RULES OF REASONING IN PHILOSOPHY

RULE I

We are to admit no more causes of natural things than such as are both true and sufficient to explain their appearances.

To this purpose the philosophers say that Nature does nothing in vain, and more is in vain when less will serve; for Nature is pleased with simplicity, and affects not the pomp of superfluous causes.

RULE II

Therefore to the same natural effects we must, as far as possible, assign the same causes.

As to respiration in a man and in a beast; the descent of stones in *Europe* and in *America;* the light of our culinary fire and of the sun; the reflection of light in the earth, and in the planets.

RULE III

The qualities of bodies, which admit neither intensification nor remission of degrees, and which are found to belong to all bodies within the reach of our experiments, are to be esteemed the universal qualities of all bodies whatsoever.

For since the qualities of bodies are only known to us by experiments, we are to hold for universal all such as universally agree with experiments; and such as are not liable to diminution can never be quite taken away. We are certainly not to relinquish the evidence of experiments for the sake of dreams and vain fictions of our own devising; nor are we to recede from the analogy of Nature, which is wont to be simple, and always consonant to itself. We no other way know the extension of bodies than by our senses, nor do these reach it in all bodies; but because we perceive extension in all that are sensible, therefore we ascribe it universally to all others also. That abundance of bodies are hard, we learn by experience; and because the hardness of the whole arises from the hardness of the parts, we therefore justly infer the hardness of the undivided particles not only of the bodies we feel but of all others. That all bodies are impenetrable, we gather not from reason, but from sensation. The bodies which we handle we find impenetrable, and thence conclude impenetrability to be an universal property of all bodies whatsoever. That all bodies are movable, and endowed with certain powers (which we call the inertia) of persevering in their motion, or in their rest, we only infer from the like properties observed in the bodies which we have seen. The extension, hardness, impenetrability, mobility, and inertia of the whole, result from the extension, hardness, impenetrability, mobility, and inertia of the parts; and hence we conclude the least particles of all bodies to be also all extended, and hard and impenetrable, and movable, and endowed with their proper inertia. And this is the foundation of all philosophy. Moreover, that the divided but contiguous particles of bodies may be separated from one another, is a matter of observation; and, in the particles that remain undivided, our minds are able to distinguish yet lesser parts, as is mathematically demonstrated. But whether the parts so distinguished, and not yet divided, may, by the powers of Nature, be actually divided and separated from one another, we cannot certainly determine. Yet, had we the proof of but one experiment that any undivided particle, in breaking a hard and solid body, suffered a division, we might by virtue of this rule conclude that the undivided as well as the divided particles may be divided and actually separated to infinity.

Lastly, if it universally appears, by experiments and astronomical observations, that all bodies about the earth gravitate towards the earth, and that in proportion to the quantity of matter which they severally contain; that the moon likewise, according to the quantity of its matter, gravitates towards the earth; that, on the other hand, our sea gravitates towards the moon; and all the planets one towards another; and the comets in like manner towards the sun; we must, in consequence of this rule, universally allow that all bodies whatsoever are endowed with a principle of mutual gravitation. For the argument from the appearances concludes with more force for the universal gravitation of all bodies than for their impenetrability; of which, among those in the celestial regions, we have no experiments, nor any manner of observation. Not that I affirm gravity to be essential to bodies: by their *vis insita* I mean nothing but their inertia. This is immutable. Their gravity is diminished as they recede from the earth.

RULE IV

In experimental philosophy we are to look upon propositions inferred by general induction from phenomena as accurately or very nearly true, notwithstanding any contrary hypotheses that may be imagined, till such time as other phenomena occur, by which they may either be made more accurate, or liable to exceptions.

This rule we must follow, that the argument of induction may not be evaded by hypotheses.

*"Even mistaken hypotheses and theories are of use
in leading to discoveries. . . . It seems, indeed, a necessary
weakness of our mind to reach truth only across
a multitude of errors and obstacles."*

Claude Bernard

1813 – 1878

SOME GENERAL PRINCIPLES OF EXPERIMENTATION IN MEDICINE ARE SET FORTH

Nearly two hundred years separate Bernard's *Introduction to the Study of Experimental Medicine* from Newton's *Principia.* Newton's work was a landmark in the development of the physical sciences; it stimulated work in all directions in astronomy, mathematics, and other fields. One important field, however, showed no similar growth: the study of the human body and of the phenomena of life itself. Until a few years before Bernard's birth, indeed, people were still talking about "vital forces" which controlled the body's functions. Bernard was the first great exponent of the experimental method in physiology. Hence the significance of the *Introduction;* it was the report on method by a man who was as much a pioneer as Newton.

Later, in the second volume of this book we shall see a specimen of Bernard's scientific work. Our immediate concern is with his ideas on scientific method; but a glance at some of his major contributions to biological discovery will assist our appreciation of his discussion of the distinction between observation and experiment. Inspired by some studies of an American Army surgeon who had watched the digestive processes through a gun-shot wound in the stomach of a woodsman, Bernard made similar observations, using living animals. He was able to reach important conclusions as to the way in which the pancreatic juice converts fats into glycerine and starch into sugar. He thus proved experimentally the falsity of the old theory that, although plants synthesize or build up from the nutriment they absorb, man only analyzes or breaks down his food. Bernard's study of the liver led to his observation of "glycogen" or animal starch—the form in which the body stores its sugar. This was a tremendous advance toward the understanding of diabetes.

Bernard showed, also, how carbon monoxide combines with hemoglobin and renders it incapable of carrying oxygen. From these and other studies, he evolved his concept that the body is, to a large extent, built around and unified by the effort to maintain the constancy of the "internal environment." He also suggested the existence of internal secretions, the first step in establishing the science of endocrinology, the study of the ductless glands.

Bernard's discussion of the words "observation" and "experience" is, in itself, an excellent example of scientific thinking. He rejects a distinction between the two terms which depends on the degree of effort exerted by the researcher. The experimental method is always positive: "experience is always gained by virtue of precise reasoning based on an idea born of observation and controlled by experiment."

Under such a discipline, "mistaken hypotheses" have their place; for the perceptive mind is fallible, having "only the feeling of a necessary relation between things," and, naturally, without the controls and checks provided by experiment, it can fall into error. Yet something will always be gained fom the mistake. Comparisons and judgments are a necessary part of the experimental method; to derive theories from reasoning is a power reserved to man and experience is the tool by which he verifies them and so approaches nearer to the truth.

These passages from the translation by Greene offer an interesting comment on Newton's objection to "hypotheses." With a greater independence of science from tradition, the larger, scholastic hypotheses had been replaced by that "short-cut" tool of the scientist, the working hypothesis. It was no longer necessary to depend, for the useful generalization, on an unlimited number of experiments. Experiment could be used for verification as well as for observation.

OBSERVATION AND EXPERIMENT

Only within very narrow boundaries can man observe the phenomena which surround him; most of them naturally escape his senses, and mere observation is not enough. To extend his knowledge, he has had to increase the power of his organs by means of special appliances; at the same time he has equipped himself with various instruments enabling him to penetrate inside of bodies, to dissociate them and to study their hidden parts. A necessary order may thus be established among the different processes of investigation or research, whether simple or complex: the first apply to those objects easiest to examine, for which our senses suffice; the second bring within our observation, by various means, objects and phenomena which would otherwise remain unknown to us forever, because in their natural state they are beyond our range. Investigation, now simple, again equipped and perfected, is therefore destined to make us discover and note the more or less hidden phenomena which surround us.

But man does not limit himself to seeing; he thinks and insists on learning the meaning of the phenomena whose existence has been revealed to him by observation. So he reasons, compares facts, puts questions to them, and by the answers which he extracts, tests one by another. This sort of control, by means of reasoning and facts, is what constitutes experiment, properly speaking; and it is the only process that we have for teaching ourselves about the nature of things outside us.

In the philosophic sense, observation shows, and experiment teaches. This first distinction will serve as our starting point in examining the different definitions of observation and experiment devised by philosophers and physicians.

I. VARIOUS DEFINITIONS OF OBSERVATION AND EXPERIMENT

Men sometimes seem to confuse experiment with observation. Bacon appears to combine them when he says: "Observation and experiment for gathering material, induction and deduction for elaborating it: these are our only good intellectual tools."

Physicians and physiologists, like most men of science, distinguish observation from experiment, but do not entirely agree in defining the two terms.

Zimmermann expresses himself as follows: "An experiment differs from an observation in this, that knowledge gained through observation seems to appear of itself, while that which an experiment brings us in the fruit of an effort that we make, with the object of knowing whether something exists or does not exist."

This definition embodies a rather generally accepted opinion. According to this definition, observation would be noting objects or phenomena, as nature usually presents them, while experiment would be noting phenomena created or defined by the experimenter. We should set up a sort of contrast, in this way, between observers and experimenters: the first being passive in the appearance of phenomena; the second, on the other hand, taking a direct and active part in producing them. Cuvier expressed the same thought in saying: "The observer listens to nature; the experimenter questions and forces her to unveil herself."

At first sight, and considering things in a general way, this distinction between the experimenter's activity and the observer's passivity seems plain and easy to establish. But as soon as we come down to experimental practice we find that, in many instances, the separation is very hard to make, and that it sometimes even involves obscurity. This comes, it seems to me, from confusing the art of investigation, which seeks and establishes facts, with the art of reasoning, which works them up logically in the search for truth. Now in investigation there may be activity, at once of the mind and of the senses, whether in making observations or in making experiments.

Indeed, if we chose to admit that observation is characterized by this alone, that men of science note phenomena which nature produces spontaneously and without interference by them, still we could not conclude that the mind, like the hand, always remains inactive in observation; and we should be led to distinguish under this head two kinds of observations, some passive, others active. I assume, for instance, what often occurs,— that some endemic disease appears in a region and presents itself to a physician's observation. Here is a spontaneous or passive observation which the physician makes by chance and without being led to it by any preconceived idea. But after observing the first case, if the physician has an idea that the appearance of this disease may well be related to certain special meteorological or hygienic circumstances, he takes a journey to other regions where the same disease prevails, to see whether it develops under the same conditions. This second observation, made in view of a preconceived idea of the nature and cause of the disease, is what we must obviously call an induced or active observation. I should say as much of an astronomer who, in watching the sky, discovers a planet passing, by chance, before his telescope; in this case he makes a fortuitous or passive observation, i.e., without preconceived idea. But, if the astronomer, after noting the aberrations of a planet, goes on to make observations, to seek a reason for them, then I should say that he makes active observations, i.e., observations produced by a preconceived idea of the cause of the aberration. We might multiply instances of this kind *ad infinitum,* to prove that, in noting natural phenomena that present themselves, the mind is now passive, now active,—which means, in other words, that observations are made, now without a preconceived idea and by chance, and again with a preconceived idea, i.e., with intention to verify the accuracy of a mental conception.

On the other hand, if we concede, as we said above, that experiment is characterized by this alone, that men of science note phenomena which they have produced artificially and which would not naturally have presented themselves, even then we could not find that the experimenter's hand always actively interfered to bring about the appearance of these phenomena. In certain cases indeed we have seen accidents where nature acted for him; and here again, from the point of view of manual intervention, we shall be forced to distinguish between active experiments and passive experiments. Let me assume that a physiologist wishes to study digestion and to learn what happens in a living animal's stomach; he will divide the walls of the abdomen and stomach according to known operative rules and will establish what is called a gastric fistula. The physiologist

will certainly think that he has made an experiment, because he has interfered actively to make phenomena appear which did not present themselves naturally to his eyes. But now, let me ask, did Dr. W. Beaumont
make an experiment when he came across that young Canadian hunter
who had received a point-blank gun-shot in the left hypochondria, and
who had a wide fistula of the stomach in the scar, through which one could
look inside that organ? Dr. Beaumont took this man into his service and
was able to study the phenomena of gastric digestion *de visu* for several
years, as he shows in the interesting journal which he has given us on
this subject. In the first case, the physiologist acted on the preconceived
idea of studying digestive phenomena and made an active experiment. In
the second case, an accident produced a fistula of the stomach, and it
presented itself fortuitously to Dr. Beaumont. According to our definition,
he made a passive experiment. These examples therefore prove that, in
verifying the phenomena called experiments, the experimenter's manual
activity does not always come in, since it happens that the phenomena,
as we have seen, may present themselves as fortuitous or passive observations.

But certain physiologists and physicians characterize observation and
experiment somewhat differently. For them, observation consists in noting
everything normal and regular. It matters little whether the investigator
has produced the appearance of the phenomena himself or by another's
hands or by accident; he considers them without disturbing them in their
natural state and so makes an observation. Thus, according to these authors,
observations were made in both examples of gastric fistula cited above,
because in both cases we had under our eyes digestive phenomena in their
natural state. The fistula served only for seeing better and making observations under the most favorable conditions.

Experiment, according to the same physiologists, implies, on the
contrary, the idea of a variation or disturbance that an investigator brings
into the conditions of natural phenomena. This definition corresponds,
in fact, to a large group of experiments made in physiology, which might
be called experiments by destruction. This form of experimenting, which
goes back to Galen, is the simplest; it should suggest itself to the minds
of anatomists wishing to learn, in the living subject, the use of parts that
they have isolated by dissection in the cadaver. To do this, we suppress
an organ in the living subject, by a section or ablation; and from the

disturbance produced in the whole organism or in a special function, we deduce the function of the missing organ. This essentially analytic, experimental method is put in practice every day in physiology. For instance, anatomy had taught us that two principal nerves diverge in the face: the facial (seventh cranial) and the trigeminal (fifth cranial); to learn their functions, they were cut, one at a time. The result showed that section of the facial nerve brings about loss of movement, and section of the trigeminal, loss of sensation, from which it was concluded that the facial is the motor nerve of the face, and the trigeminal the sensory nerve.

We said that, in studying digestion by means of a fistula, we merely make an observation, according to the definition which we are examining. But after we have established the fistula, if we go on to cut the nerves of the stomach, in order to see the changes which result in the digestive function, then, according to the same way of thinking, we make an experiment, because we seek to learn the function of a part from the disturbance which its suppression involves. And this may be summed up by saying that in experimentation we make judgments by comparing two facts, one normal, the other abnormal.

This definition of experiment necessarily assumes that experimenters must be able to touch the body on which they wish to act, whether by destroying it or by altering it, so as to learn the part which it plays in the phenomena of nature. As we shall later see, it is on this very possibility of acting, or not acting, on a body that the distinction will exclusively rest between sciences called sciences of observation and sciences called experimental.

But if the definition of experiment which we have just given differs from the definition examined in the first place in that it admits that we make an experiment only when we can vary or can dissociate phenomena by a kind of analysis, still it resembles the first in that it also always assumes an intentional activity on the experimenter's part, in producing a disturbance of the phenomena. Now it will be easy to show that the operator's intentional action can often be replaced by an accident. Here too, as in the first definition, we might distinguish between disturbances occurring intentionally and disturbances occurring spontaneously or unintentionally. Indeed taking again the example in which a physiologist cuts the facial nerve to learn its function, I assume that a ball, a sabre cut or a splinter of stone, has cut or destroyed the facial nerve; there will result fortuitously a paralysis of movement, i.e., a disturbance, exactly the same as that which the physiologist caused intentionally.

It is the same in the case of numberless pathological lesions which are real experiments, by which physicians and physiologists profit, without any purpose on their part to produce the lesions, which result from disease. I emphasize this idea now, because it will be useful to us later, to prove that medicine includes real experiments which are spontaneous, and not produced by physicians.

I will make one more remark by way of conclusion. If indeed we characterize experiment by a variation or disturbance brought into a phenomenon, it is only in so far as we imply that the disturbance must be compared with the normal state. As experiments indeed are only judgments, they necessarily require comparison between two things; and the intentional or active element in an experiment is really the comparison which the mind intends to make. Now, whether the alteration is produced by accident or otherwise, the experimenter's mind compares none the less. It is therefore unnecessary to regard as a disturbance one of the facts to be compared, especially as there is nothing disturbed or abnormal in nature; everything happens according to laws which are absolute, i.e., always normal and determined. Effects vary with the conditions which bring them to pass, but laws do not vary. Physiological and pathological states are ruled by the same forces; they differ only because of the special conditions under which the vital laws manifest themselves.

II. GAINING EXPERIENCE AND RELYING ON OBSERVATION IS DIFFERENT FROM MAKING EXPERIMENTS AND MAKING OBSERVATIONS

The general objection which I make to the preceding definitions is that they give words too narrow a meaning, by taking account of only the art of investigation, instead of considering observation and experiment at the same time as the two opposite extremes of experimental reasoning. So we find these definitions lacking in clearness and generality. To give the definition its full usefulness and value, therefore, I think that we must distinguish what pertains to the method of investigation, used to gather facts, from the characteristics of the intellectual method, which utilizes facts and makes them at once the support and the criterion of the experimental method.

In French the word *expérience* in the singular means, in general and in the abstract, the knowledge gained in the practice of life. When we apply to a physician the word experience in the singular, it means the information which he has gained in the practice of medicine. It is the same with the other professions; and it is in this sense that we say that a man has gained experience, or that he has experience. Subsequently the word *expérience* (experiment) in the concrete was extended to cover the facts which give us experimental information about things.

The word observation in the singular, in its general and abstract use, means noting a fact accurately with the help of appropriate studies and means of investigation. In the concrete the word observation has been extended to cover the facts noted; and it is in this sense that we speak of medical observations, astronomical observations, etc.

Speaking concretely, when we say "making experiments or making observations," we mean that we devote ourselves to investigation and to research, that we make attempts and trials in order to gain facts from which the mind, through reasoning, may draw knowledge or instruction.

Speaking in the abstract, when we say "relying on observation and gaining experience," we mean that observation is the mind's support in reasoning, and experience the mind's support in deciding, or still better, the fruit of exact reasoning applied to the interpretation of facts. It follows from this that we can gain experience without making experiments, solely by reasoning appropriately about well-established facts, just as we can make experiments and observations without gaining experience, if we limit ourselves to noting facts.

Observation, then, is what shows facts; experiment is what teaches about facts and gives experience in relation to anything. But as this teaching can come through comparison and judgment only, i.e., by sequence of reasoning, it follows that man alone is capable of gaining experience and perfecting himself by it.

"Experience," says Goethe, "disciplines man every day." But this is because man reasons accurately and experimentally about what he observes; otherwise he could not correct himself. The insane, who have lost their reason, no longer learn from experience; they no longer reason experimentally. Experience, then, is the privilege of reason. "Only man may verify his thoughts and set them in order; only man may correct, rectify, improve, perfect and so make himself every day more skilful, wise and fortunate. Finally for man alone does the art exist, that supreme art of which the most vaunted arts are mere tools and raw material: the art of reason, reasoning."

In experimental medicine, we shall use the word experience in the same general sense in which it is still everywhere used. Men of science learn every day from experience; by experience they constantly correct their scientific ideas, their theories; rectify them, bring them into harmony with more and more facts, and so come nearer and nearer to the truth.

We can learn,—i.e., gain experience of our surroundings, in two ways, empirically and experimentally. First there is a sort of teaching or unconscious and empirical experience, which we get from dealing with separate objects. But the knowledge which we gain in this way is also accompanied necessarily by vague experimental reasoning which we carry on quite unawares, and in consequence of which we bring together facts to make a judgment about them. Experience, then, may be gained by empirical and unconscious reasoning; but the obscure and spontaneous movement of the mind has been raised by men of science into a clear and reasoned method, which therefore proceeds consciously and more swiftly toward a definite goal. Such is the experimental method in the sciences by which experience is always gained by virtue of precise reasoning based on an idea born of observation and controlled by experiment. In all experimental knowledge, indeed, there are three phases: an observation made, a comparison established and a judgment rendered. By the experimental method, we simply make a judgment on the facts around us, by help of a criterion which is itself just another fact so arranged as to control the judgment and to afford experience. Taken in this general sense, experience is the one source of human knowledge. The mind in itself has only the feeling of a necessary relation between things: it can know the form of that relation only by experience.

Two things must, therefore, be considered in the experimental method: (1) The art of getting accurate facts by means of rigorous investigation; (2) the art of working them up by means of experimental reasoning, so as to deduce knowledge of the law of phenomena. We said that experimental reasoning always and necessarily deals with two facts

at a time: observation, used as a starting point; experiment, used as conclusion or control. In reasoning, however, we can distinguish between
actual observation and experiment only, as it were, by logical abstraction
and because of the position in which they stand.

But outside of experimental reasoning, observation and experiment
no longer exist in this abstract sense; there are only concrete facts in each,
to be got by precise and rigorous methods of investigation. We shall see,
further on, that the investigator himself must be analyzed into observer
and experimenter; not according to whether he is active or passive in producing phenomena, but according to whether he acts on them or not,
to make himself their master.

*"Facts are sterile until there are
minds capable of choosing between them and
discerning those which conceal something and recognizing that
which is concealed; minds which under the
bare fact see the soul of the fact."*

Henri Poincaré

1854 – 1912

THE SEARCH FOR THE INTERNAL
HARMONY OF THE UNIVERSE IS LAID
DOWN AS A CREED FOR THE SCIENTIST

The work of Poincaré in mathematics extended from the quantum theory to celestial mechanics, from abstractions in the field of differential equations to their application in the solution of problems in the mechanics of gravitation. Like Bernard, his output of important scientific contributions was very great: more than five hundred papers are credited to him. His essay, reproduced here, is in strange contrast with that of Bernard. The latter's is precise and formal; Poincaré is contemplative. Both are the converse of the diciplines they represent. The layman, at least, would have expected the formal analysis to come from the mathematician, whose symbols and processes have developed, in an almost unbroken stream of evolution from their antique roots, in a framework which leaves little room for vagueness. The physiologist, on the other hand, works in a field in which the development has been discontinuous, in which the opportunities for selection have been wider. Yet one feels that Bernard's prescriptions are definite and of more general application than Poincaré's.

72

For Poincaré the internal harmony of the world as conceived by thinking human beings is the harmony expressed by mathematical laws—"the sole objective reality, the only truth we can attain." To him, the great miracle of nature is its regularity. Hence, in his consideration of "Science and Method" it is not surprising to find his emphasis on the choice of facts which contribute best to the discovery of intellectual beauty. These facts are what he calls the simple ones, those which do not hide a "dreadful complexity."

Poincaré's thesis is by no means so simple as the elegant prose suggests; for—implicitly, at least—it is directed not to the common reader but to the scientific aristocracy. "It is needful . . . to think for those who love not thinking." Here we can detect some signs of that separation of the scientist from the practical man which characterized much of the nineteenth century. Given his environment, Poincaré would have been surprised, one feels, by the growth of science after his death and, particularly, by its spread, in the form of the industrial laboratory, among practical men. Since membership of the scientific brotherhood has been opened to an ever-increasing number, his emphasis on discrimination and selection has now a wider audience.

The selections are from G. B. Halstead's translation of *Science and Method* and *The Value of Science*.

THE VALUE OF SCIENCE

THE SEARCH for truth should be the goal of our activities; it is the sole end worthy of them. Doubtless we should first bend our efforts to assuage human suffering, but why? Not to suffer is a negative ideal more surely attained by the annihilation of the world. If we wish more and more to free man from material cares, it is that he may be able to employ the liberty obtained in the study and contemplation of truth.

But sometimes truth frightens us. And in fact we know that it is sometimes deceptive, that it is a phantom never showing itself for a moment except to ceaselessly flee, that it must be pursued further and ever further without ever being attained. Yet to work one must stop, as some Greek, Aristotle or another, has said. We also know how cruel the truth often is, and we wonder whether illusion is not more consoling, yea, even more bracing, for illusion it is which gives confidence. When it shall have vanished, will hope remain and shall we have the courage to achieve? Thus would not the horse harnessed to his treadmill refuse to go, were his eyes not bandaged? And then to seek truth it is necessary to be independent, wholly independent. If, on the contrary, we wish to act, to be strong, we should be united. This is why many of us fear truth; we consider it a cause of weakness. Yet truth should not be feared, for it alone is beautiful.

When I speak here of truth, assuredly I refer first to scientific truth; but I also mean moral truth, of which what we call justice is only one aspect. It may seem that I am misusing words, that I combine thus under the same name two things having nothing in common; that scientific truth, which is demonstrated, can in no way be likened to moral truth, which is felt. And yet I can not separate them, and whosoever loves the one can not help loving the other. To find the one, as well as to find the other, it is necessary to free the soul completely from prejudice and from passion; it is necessary to attain absolute sincerity. These two sorts of truth when discovered give the same joy; each when perceived beams with the same splendor, so that we must see it or close our eyes. Lastly, both attract us and flee from us; they are never fixed: when we think to have reached them, we find that we have still to advance, and he who pursues them is condemned never to know repose. It must be added that those who fear the one will also fear the other; for they are the ones who in everything are concerned above all with consequences. In a word, I liken the two truths, because the same reasons make us love them and because the same reasons make us fear them.

If we ought not to fear moral truth, still less should we dread scientific truth. In the first place it can not conflict with ethics. Ethics and science have their own domains, which touch but do not interpenetrate. The one shows us to what goal we should aspire, the other, given the goal, teaches us how to attain it. So they can never conflict since they can never meet. There can no more be immoral science than there can be scientific morals.

But if science is feared, it is above all because it can not give us happiness. Of course it can not. We may even ask whether the beast does not suffer less than man. But can we regret that earthly paradise where man brute-like was really immortal in knowing not that he must die? When we have tasted the apple, no suffering can make us forget its savor. We always come back to it. Could it be otherwise? As well ask if one who has seen and is blind will not long for the light. Man, then, can not be happy through science, but to-day he can much less be happy without it.

But if truth be the sole aim worth pursuing, may we hope to attain it? It may well be doubted. Readers of my little book 'Science and Hypothesis' already know what I think about the question. The truth we are permitted to glimpse is not altogether what most men call by that name. Does this mean that our most legitimate, most imperative aspiration is at the same time the most vain? Or can we, despite all, approach truth on some side? This it is which must be investigated.

In the first place, what instrument have we at our disposal for this conquest? Is not human intelligence, more specifically the intelligence of the scientist, susceptible of infinite variation? Volumes could be written without exhausting this subject; I, in a few brief pages, have only touched it lightly. That the geometer's mind is not like the physicist's or the naturalist's, all the world would agree; but mathematicians themselves do not resemble each other; some recognize only implacable logic, others appeal to intuition and see in it the only source of discovery. And this would be a reason for distrust. To minds so unlike can the mathematical theorems themselves appear in the same light? Truth which is not the same for all, is it truth? But looking at things more closely, we see how these very different workers collaborate in a common task which could not be achieved without their cooperation. And that already reassures us.

Next must be examined the frames in which nature seems enclosed and which are called time and space. In 'Science and Hypothesis' I have already shown how relative their value is; it is not nature which imposes them upon us, it is we who impose them upon nature because we find them convenient. But I have spoken of scarcely more than space, and particularly quantitative space, so to say, that is of the mathematical relations whose aggregate constitutes geometry. I should have shown that it is the same with time as with space and still the same with 'qualitative space'; in particular, I should have investigated why we attribute three dimensions to space. I may be pardoned then for taking up again these important questions.

Is mathematical analysis, then, whose principal object is the study of these empty frames, only a vain play of the mind? It can give to the physicist only a convenient language; is this not a mediocre service, which, strictly speaking, could be done without; and even is it not to be feared that this artificial language may be a veil interposed between reality and the eye of the physicist? Far from it; without this language most of the intimate analogies of things would have remained forever unknown to us; and we should forever have been ignorant of the internal harmony of the world, which is, we shall see, the only true objective reality.

The best expression of this harmony is law. Law is one of the most recent conquests of the human mind; there still are people who live in the presence of a perpetual miracle and are not astonished at it. On the contrary, we it is who should be astonished at nature's regularity. Men demand of their gods to prove their existence by miracles; but the eternal marvel is that there are not miracles without cease. The world is divine because it is a harmony. If it were ruled by caprice, what could prove to us it was not ruled by chance?

This conquest of law we owe to astronomy, and just this makes the grandeur of the science rather than the material grandeur of the objects it considers. It was altogether natural, then, that celestial mechanics should be the first model of mathematical physics; but since then this science has developed; it is still developing, even rapidly developing. And it is already necessary to modify in certain points the scheme from which I drew two chapters of 'Science and Hypothesis.' In an address at the St. Louis exposition, I sought to survey the road traveled; the result of this investigation the reader shall see farther on.

The progress of science has seemed to imperil the best established principles, those even which were regarded as fundamental. Yet nothing shows they will not be saved; and if this comes about only imperfectly, they will still subsist even though they are modified. The advance of science is not comparable to the changes of a city, where old edifices are pitilessly torn down to give place to new, but to the continuous evolution of zoologic types which develop ceaselessly and end by becoming unrecognizable to the common sight, but where an expert eye finds always traces of the prior work of the centuries past. One must not think then that the old-fashioned theories have been sterile and vain.

Were we to stop there, we should find in these pages some reasons for confidence in the value of science, but many more for distrusting it; an impression of doubt would remain; it is needful now to set things to rights.

Some people have exaggerated the rôle of convention in science; they have even gone so far as to say that law, that scientific fact itself, was created by the scientist. This is going much too far in the direction of nominalism. No, scientific laws are not artificial creations; we have no reason to regard them as accidental, though it be impossible to prove they are not.

Does the harmony the human intelligence thinks it discovers in nature exist outside of this intelligence? No, beyond doubt a reality completely independent of the mind which conceives it, sees or feels it, is an impossibility. A world as exterior as that, even if it existed, would for us be forever inaccessible. But what we call objective reality is, in the last analysis, what is common to many thinking beings, and could be common to all; this common part, we shall see, can only be the harmony expressed by mathematical laws. It is this harmony then which is the sole objective reality, the only truth we can attain; and when I add that the universal harmony of the world is the source of all beauty, it will be understood what price we should attach to the slow and difficult progress which little by little enables us to know it better.

SCIENCE AND METHOD

THE CHOICE OF FACTS

TOLSTOI somewhere explains why 'science for its own sake' is in his eyes an absurd conception. We can not know *all* facts, since their number is practically infinite. It is necessary to choose; then we may let this choice depend on the pure caprice of our curiosity; would it not be better to let ourselves be guided by utility, by our practical and above all by our moral needs; have we nothing better to do than to count the number of lady-bugs on our planet?

It is clear the word utility has not for him the sense men of affairs give it, and following them most of our contemporaries. Little cares he for industrial applications, for the marvels of electricity or of automobilism, which he regards rather as obstacles to moral progress; utility for him is solely what can make man better.

For my part, it need scarce be said, I could never be content with either the one or the other ideal; I want neither that plutocracy grasping and mean, nor that democracy goody and mediocre, occupied solely in turning the other cheek, where would dwell sages without curiosity, who, shunning excess, would not die of disease, but would surely die of ennui. But that is a matter of taste and is not what I wish to discuss.

The question nevertheless remains and should fix our attention; if our choice can only be determined by caprice or by immediate utility, there can be no science for its own sake, and consequently no science. But is that true? That a choice must be made is incontestable; whatever be our activity, facts go quicker than we, and we can not catch them; while the scientist discovers one fact, there happen milliards of milliards in a cubic millimeter of his body. To wish to comprise nature in science would be to want to put the whole into the part.

But scientists believe there is a hierarchy of facts and that among them may be made a judicious choice. They are right, since otherwise there would be no science, yet science exists. One need only open the eyes to see that the conquests of industry which have enriched so many practical men would never have seen the light, if these practical men alone had existed and if they had not been preceded by unselfish devotees who died poor, who never thought of utility, and yet had a guide far other than caprice.

As Mach says, these devotees have spared their successors the trouble of thinking. Those who might have worked solely in view of an immediate application would have left nothing behind them, and, in face of a new need, all must have been begun over again. Now most men do not love to think, and this is perhaps fortunate when instinct guides them, for most often, when they pursue an aim which is immediate and ever the same, instinct guides them better than reason would guide a pure intelligence. But instinct is routine, and if thought did not fecundate it, it would no more progress in man than in the bee or ant. It is needful then to think for those who love not thinking, and, as they are numerous, it is needful that each of our thoughts be as often useful as possible, and this is why a law will be the more precious the more general it is.

This shows us how we should choose: the most interesting facts are those which may serve many times; these are the facts which have a chance of coming up again. We have been so fortunate as to be born in a world where there are such. Suppose that instead of 60 chemical elements there were 60 milliards of them, that they were not some common, the others rare, but that they were uniformly distributed. Then, every time we picked up a new pebble there would be great probability of its being formed of some unknown substance; all that we knew of other pebbles would be worthless for it; before each new object we should be as the new-born babe; like it we could only obey our caprices or our needs. Biologists would be just as much at a loss if there were only individuals and no species and if heredity did not make sons like their fathers.

In such a world there would be no science; perhaps thought and even life would be impossible, since evolution could not there develop the preservational instincts. Happily it is not so; like all good fortune to which we are accustomed, this is not appreciated at its true worth.

Which then are the facts likely to reappear? They are first the simple facts. It is clear that in a complex fact a thousand circumstances are united by chance, and that only a chance still much less probable could reunite them anew. But are there any simple facts? And if there are, how recognize them? What assurance is there that a thing we think simple does not hide a dreadful complexity? All we can say is that we ought to prefer the facts which *seem* simple to those where our crude eye discerns unlike elements. And then one of two things: either this simplicity is real, or else the elements are so intimately mingled as not to be distinguishable. In the first case there is chance of our meeting anew this same simple fact, either in all its purity or entering itself as element in a complex manifold. In the second case this intimate mixture has likewise more chances of recurring than a heterogenous assemblage; chance knows how to mix, it knows not how to disentangle, and to make with multiple elements a well-ordered edifice in which something is distinguishable, it must be made expressly. The facts which appear simple, even if they are not so, will therefore be more easily revived by chance. This it is which justifies the method instinctively adopted by the scientist, and what justifies it still better, perhaps, is that oft-recurring facts appear to us simple, precisely because we are used to them.

But where is the simple fact? Scientists have been seeking it in the two extremes, in the infinitely great and in the infinitely small. The astronomer has found it because the distances of the stars are immense, so great that each of them appears but as a point, so great that the qualitative differences are effaced, and because a point is simpler than a body which has form and qualities. The physicist on the other hand has sought the elementary phenomenon in fictively cutting up bodies into infinitesimal cubes, because the conditions of the problem, which undergo slow and continuous variation in passing from one point of the body to another, may be regarded as constant in the interior of each of these little cubes. In the same way the biologist has been instinctively led to regard the cell as more interesting than the whole animal, and the outcome has shown his wisdom, since cells belonging to organisms the most different are more alike, for the one who can recognize their resemblances, than are these organisms themselves. The sociologist is more embarrassed; the elements, which for him are men, are too unlike, too variable, too capricious, in a word, too complex; besides, history never begins over again. How then choose the interesting fact, which is that which begins again? Method is precisely the choice of facts; it is needful then to be occupied first with creating a method, and many have been imagined, since none imposes itself, so that sociology is the science which has the most methods and the fewest results.

Therefore it is by the regular facts that it is proper to begin; but after the rule is well established, after it is beyond all doubt, the facts in full conformity with it are erelong without interest since they no longer teach us anything new. It is then the exception which becomes important. We cease to seek resemblances; we devote ourselves above all to the differences, and among the differences are chosen first the most accentuated, not only because they are the most striking, but because they will be the most instructive. A simple example will make my thought plainer: Suppose one wishes to determine a curve by observing some of its points. The practician who concerns himself only with immediate utility would observe only the points he might need for some special object. These points would be badly distributed on the curve; they would be crowded in certain regions, rare in others, so that it would be impossible to join them by a continuous line, and they would be unavailable for other applications. The scientist will proceed differently; as he wishes to study the curve for itself, he will distribute regularly the points to be observed, and when enough are known he will join them by a regular line and then he will have the entire curve. But for that how does he proceed? If he has determined an extreme point of the curve, he does not stay near this extremity, but goes first to the other end; after the two extremities the most instructive point will be the mid-point, and so on.

So when a rule is established we should first seek the cases where this rule has the greatest chance of failing. Thence, among other reasons, come the interest of astronomic facts, and the interest of the geologic past; by going very far away in space or very far away in time, we may find our usual rules entirely overturned, and these grand overturnings aid us the better to see or the better to understand the little changes which may happen nearer to us, in the little corner of the world where we are called to live and act. We shall better know this corner for having traveled in distant countries with which we have nothing to do.

But what we ought to aim at is less the ascertainment of resemblances and differences than the recognition of likenesses hidden under apparent divergences. Particular rules seem at first discordant, but looking more closely we see in general that they resemble each other; different as to matter, they are alike as to form, as to the order of their parts. When we look at them with this bias, we shall see them enlarge and tend to embrace everything. And this it is which makes the value of certain facts which come to complete an assemblage and to show that it is the faithful image of other known assemblages.

I will not further insist, but these few words suffice to show that the scientist does not choose at random the facts he observes. He does not, as Tolstoi says, count the lady-bugs, because, however interesting lady-bugs may be, their number is subject to capricious variations. He seeks to condense much experience and much thought into a slender volume; and that is why a little book on physics contains so many past experiences and a thousand times as many possible experiences whose result is known beforehand.

But we have as yet looked at only one side of the question. The scientist does not study nature because it is useful; he studies it because he delights in it, and he delights in it because it is beautiful. If nature were not beautiful, it would not be worth knowing, and if nature were not worth knowing, life would not be worth living. Of course I do not here speak of that beauty which strikes the senses, the beauty of qualities and of appearances; not that I undervalue such beauty, far from it, but it has nothing to do with science; I mean that profounder beauty which comes from the harmonious order of the parts and which a pure intelligence can grasp. This it is which gives body, a structure so to speak, to the iridescent appearances which flatter our senses, and without this support the beauty of these fugitive dreams would be only imperfect, because it would be vague and always fleeting. On the contrary, intellectual beauty is sufficient unto itself, and it is for its sake, more perhaps than for the future good of humanity, that the scientist devotes himself to long and difficult labors.

It is, therefore, the quest of this especial beauty, the sense of the harmony of the cosmos, which makes us choose the facts most fitting to contribute to this harmony, just as the artist chooses from among the features of his model those which perfect the picture and give it character and life. And we need not fear that this instinctive and unavowed prepossession will turn the scientist aside from the search for the true. One may dream a harmonious world, but how far the real world will leave it behind! The greatest artists that ever lived, the Greeks, made their heavens; how shabby it is beside the true heavens, ours!

And it is because simplicity, because grandeur, is beautiful, that we preferably seek simple facts, sublime facts, that we delight now to follow the majestic course of the stars, now to examine with the miscroscope that prodigious littleness which is also a grandeur, now to seek in geologic time the traces of a past which attracts because it is far away.

We see too that the longing for the beautiful leads us to the same choice as the longing for the useful. And so it is that this economy of thought, this economy of effort, which is, according to Mach, the constant tendency of science, is at the same time a source of beauty and a practical advantage. The edifices that we admire are those where the architect has known how to proportion the means to the end, where the columns seem to carry gaily, without effort, the weight placed upon them, like the gracious caryatids of the Erechtheum.

Whence comes this concordance? Is it simply that the things which seem to us beautiful are those which best adapt themselves to our intelligence, and that consequently they are at the same time the implement this intelligence knows best how to use? Or is there here a play of evolution and natural selection? Have the peoples whose ideal most conformed to their highest interest exterminated the others and taken their places? All pursued their ideals without reference to consequences, but while this quest led some to destruction, to others it gave empire. One is tempted to believe it.

If the Greeks triumphed over the barbarians and if Europe, heir of Greek thought, dominates the world, it is because the savages loved loud colors and the clamorous tones of the drum which occupied only their senses, while the Greeks loved the intellectual beauty which hides beneath sensuous beauty, and this intellectual beauty it is which makes intelligence sure and strong.

Doubtless such a triumph would horrify Tolstoi, and he would not like to acknowledge that it might be truly useful. But this disinterested quest of the true for its own beauty is sane also and able to make man better. I well know that there are mistakes, that the thinker does not always draw thence the serenity he should find therein, and even that there are scientists of bad character. Must we, therefore, abandon science and study only morals? What! Do you think the moralists themselves are irreproachable when they come down from their pedestal?

*"A law of nature becomes a better law
when we can predict the exceptions to it."*

Gilbert N. Lewis

1875 – 1946

SOME ASPECTS OF THE ANATOMY OF
SCIENCE ARE ANALYZED

Gilbert N. Lewis's lecture (from *The Anatomy of Science,*
Yale University Press) is in strange contrast to Poincaré's
essay. The voice of the man entranced by the mechanics of the
universe, the scientific aristocrat, is replaced by a quieter, more
humble, human person, closer to our own conception of the
scientist as an integral part of our society. For Lewis, the difficulty
of the modern scientist is the rate at which new observations and
experiments are being made; things move so rapidly that there
is less chance to catch up with them and produce theories which
are "nearer to an adequate interpretation of our knowledge."
Whereas Poincaré looks for the similarities among apparently
diverse facts, Lewis delights in the challenge of the paradoxes.
The common man, if not the scientist, can find consolation in
his recognition that the process of abstraction (analysis and synthesis) is "an organic process which accompanies thought but is
not altogether subject to our own volition." Perhaps like Molière's
character who discovers that he had been speaking prose all his
life, we are all scientists in embryo.

It is not surprising that Lewis built himself a reputation as
a stimulating teacher. His work in thermodynamics, valence, and
atomic structure advanced our knowledge of the state of matter.

His theory of valency explained the power which the atom possesses to combine with a definite number of other atoms and opened up the possibilities of creating new products by new combinations of atoms; he isolated heavy water, of so much importance to the utilization of atomic energy. Yet, in spite of all this specialization in the higher reaches of physics, he asserts his lack of patience with those who "identify science with measurement" and so exclude areas of investigation which are capable of less precision.

Here is a man who, with his basic respect for any student in search of the "proximate," rejects the idea of a scientific aristocracy. He makes it possible for even the humblest research worker to realize his part in the great work of science.

METHODS OF SCIENCE; NUMBERS

THE STRENGTH of science lies in its naïveté. Science is like life itself; if we could foresee all the obstacles that lie in our path we would not attack even the first, but would settle down to self-centered contemplation. The average scientist unequipped with the powerful lenses of philosophy, is a nearsighted creature, and cheerfully attacks each difficulty in the hope that it may prove to be the last. He is not given to minute analysis of his own methods. Indeed, if he should become too self-conscious he might lose his power, like the famous centipede who, after too profound analysis of his own method of locomotion, found he could no longer walk.

Yet, as the artist, after painstaking effort, steps back from his easel to view his picture as a whole, so it may not be unprofitable for the scientist to forsake from time to time his own specialty and survey the general trend of science.[1] Mach[2] says, "Every philosopher has his own private science and every scientist his private philosophy," intimating that both are rather

[1] "These kinds of contemplation should therefore be alternated and taken by turns, so that the understanding may be rendered at once penetrating and comprehensive. Francis Bacon, *Novum Organum*.

[2] Ernst Mach, *Erkenntniss und Irrtum*.

crude affairs. May we not make of these two a blend, retaining a little of the creativeness of science, even with some of its naïveté, and of the breadth of philosophy, even with some of its scepticism?

To give any sort of historical account of the development of scientific concepts would require more space than is allotted to these pages and a competence far surpassing my own. What I shall attempt to present will be a kind of contemporaneous cross section showing the inner structure of science. Such a presentation must of necessity have a somewhat personal bias. I know that I shall say many things that have been said before, often by authors unknown to me, but I shall console myself with the hope that one or two of the things that I say here will, in their turn, be said again.

I should have liked to use the word 'metaphysics' in the title of this book, but there are certain words which have accumulated such evil implications that they must either be abandoned, or withdrawn for a period of purification. Two such words, 'phlogiston' and 'ether,' we shall have occasion to discuss in later lectures. However, in its best sense metaphysics might well be defined as the study of the major abstractions of the human mind, such as space, time, matter, life, love, duty, patriotism,—we need not enumerate further. A more or less complete list of our major and minor abstractions is furnished by any unabridged dictionary. There is not a word that we use which is not a product of the remarkable process of abstraction which is always associated with thought, and which perhaps *is* thought. This process of abstracting or idealizing or refining the raw material of experience is one which we shall have frequent occasion to discuss.

When we speak of the major abstractions we mean those which have been derived from a great mass of raw material through a vast number of these refining processes. The same material of which cheese is made is also used for making chess sets, but in the latter case the nature of the raw material is of little importance. The value of the chess set depends upon the amount of human effort which has gone into its making. So we have some ideas that are freshly derived from experience, while others have passed through so elaborate and prolonged a system of refinement that we no longer know from what raw material they came. But instead of saying categorically that this idea is objective, that is subjective, may we not say merely that one idea is more subjective than another, recognizing all gradations in the extent of operation of our process of abstraction? Indeed, it will be our policy not to emphasize those classifications of ideal and real, false and true, and the like, which often give too smug a view of natural philosophy; but rather to point out from time to time the artificialities of the boundaries which these classifications set up.

When we consider those ideas which we have called the major abstractions, we find that a large group, dealing with the relations of man with man and of man with God, cannot be discussed with the same freedom from prejudice and passion as those which are less intimately human or social. The hardest study of mankind is man. Perhaps a tiger beetle or a tarantula could undertake the study with less prejudice, but perhaps also they might be distracted by wondering whether a creature with only one third or one fourth of the harmonious number of legs could possess real intelligence.

Human beings cannot be persuaded to regard themselves as mere natural phenomena. It is an alluring thought that the true, the beautiful and the good are merely embodiments of a single idea, but it is a thought which makes little appeal to a man with an ulcerated tooth. We go on nailing up the scaffolding of our joint temple to Goodness, Beauty and Truth until a hammer hits our own thumb, and our enthusiasm for this kind of architecture rapidly wanes. If, then, by common consent we agree to segregate the natural from the social sciences it is because stars and electrons and chromosomes do not bring us so near to the quick of human feeling as religion and society and man.

The methods of natural science are not unique. If we ask how long ago the great group of Indo-European languages were only local dialects of neighboring tribes, or how long ago some fossil was embedded in a sedimentary rock, the two problems present the same kind of difficulty. In both cases we recognize that there have been periods of rapid accretion or rapid erosion, and other periods of stagnancy, but by observing rates of growth of present levels, or rates of change of living languages, an estimate can be made.

I take it that the scientific method, of which so much has been heard, is hardly more than the native method of solving problems, a little clarified from prejudice and a little cultivated by training. A detective with his murder mystery, a chemist seeking the structure of a new compound, use little of the formal and logical modes of reasoning. Through a series of intuitions, surmises, fancies, they stumble upon the right explanation, and have a knack of seizing it when it once comes within reach. I have no patience with attempts to identify science with measurement, which is but one of its tools, or with any definition of the scientist which would exclude a Darwin, a Pasteur or a Kekulé.

The scientist is a practical man and his are practical aims. He does not seek the *ultimate* but the *proximate*. He does not speak of the last analysis but rather of the next approximation. His are not those beautiful structures so delicately designed that a single flaw may cause the collapse of the whole. The scientist builds slowly and with a gross but solid kind of masonry. If dissatisfied with any of his work, even if it be near the very foundations, he can replace that part without damage to the remainder. On the whole, he is satisfied with his work, for while science may never be wholly right it certainly is never wholly wrong; and it seems to be improving from decade to decade.

The theory that there is an ultimate truth, although very generally held by mankind, does not seem useful to science except in the sense of a horizon toward which we may proceed, rather than a point which may be reached. If there were an absolute truth of to-day, would it be the absolute truth of to-morrow? The trenchant Remy de Gourmont[3] writes: "There is no truth since the world is perpetually changing. You have acquired the notion of evolution . . . but you have wished at the same time to preserve the notion of truth." We have all been merry at the expense of the preacher who began his prayer, "Paradoxical as it may seem to Thee, O Lord," but our laughter is due to the very assumption that we are now questioning, that there is an absolute truth free from paradox. If we adopt the view that ideas are constantly evolving to meet an ever changing environment, the hope of attaining a perfect fit between the two may be illusory.

In science a period of extreme activity in observation and experimentation is a period in which many contradictions seem to appear, old theories have to be discarded or modified, and the readjustment cannot keep pace with the new data. The physical sciences are now in such an "awkward age" of rapid growth. On the other hand, in a period in which few new observations are made, our theories have a chance of coming nearer to an adequate interpretation of our knowledge.

A paradox is never very terrifying to the scientist. Faraday wrote to

[3] Remy de Gourmont, *A Night in the Luxembourg.*

Tyndall,[4] "The more we can enlarge the number of anomalous facts and consequences the better it will be for the subject, for they can only remain anomalies to us while we continue in error." The scientist recognizes that he is always in the midst of paradoxes and that it is his duty to resolve them. He knows that the science of the future will also have its paradoxes, but believes that every individual paradox can be resolved, that this process of resolution will lead not to greater complexity but to greater simplicity, and that out of discord a more perfect harmony will evolve. This I take to be the universal *credo* of science.

Perhaps, indeed, the scientist in his attitude toward paradox is a little more reverent than those who are constantly grumbling because some flaw has been found in a preëstablished harmony. After all, is it necessary to decide as to the existence of all these ultimates and absolutes, and especially as to the existence of an absolute truth? If we once get out of the child-like notion that every act is either right or wrong, that every statement is either true or false, that every question may be answered with a 'yes' or a 'no,' we still recognize that with our present knowledge there are some statements which are more probable than others.

If we arrange various statements according to our estimate of their probability, we get the idea of a continuum, ranging from no probability to complete certainty. But whether or not any of these statements are situated exactly upon one or the other of the terminals of this continuous range may not be of great consequence. At any rate, the scientist must practice economy of thought, not only in his mode of thinking but also in deciding what to think about. He does not find it economical to think about ultimates, and yet it must be confessed that in spite of himself he often sees them creeping insidiously into scientific thought.

Lightly as we have touched upon the problem of absolute truth, we must pass even more rapidly over the age-old problem of the real and the ideal; the objective and the subjective. If we had not studied the motion of the planets we know that someone else would, with like results; and while we turn our telescopes upon the moon, children are crying for that same moon and dogs are baying at it. On the other hand, we realize that even in the act of registering our sense impressions they are being profoundly modified owing to the instincts that have come to us from long

[4] Tyndall, *Diamagnetism.*

heredity, owing to our individual memories, to our sensations, and above all, to our communications with other human beings.

How different your dog Towser would look to you if you had never seen him before, and especially if you had never seen any dog before. The word 'dog' is an abstraction from many Towsers, and as we cull the traits of similarity from a larger and larger mass of observations we proceed from the special to the general. Towser, dog, mammal, vertebrate, animal, living thing, object,—these are successive products of the great process of abstraction. Often as we proceed in the direction of greater abstraction and idealization, we eliminate little by little the empirical material from which the abstractions were derived, but it seems probable that the empirical is never wholly eliminated. So men gather beet roots, and, subjecting the juices to various arts of refining, obtain a sugar which still contains some traces of its earthy origin. Perhaps we know what we mean by a pure chemical, but no one has ever seen one; and I doubt if we shall ever see a pure abstraction.

It would be far from my purpose to enter upon an exhaustive study of the difficult problems in the theory of knowledge. As is remarked by Edgar Allan Poe,[5] himself a remarkable thinker, "The mental features discoursed of as the analytical, are, in themselves, but little capable of analysis." Nevertheless, if we are to discuss the concepts of science we must at least have a partial realization of the mode of their evolution.

I say evolution rather than manufacture in order to accentuate the point of view that I here present. I am suggesting that the combined analysis and synthesis which we call the process of abstraction, and by which we assimilate and metabolize our observations, may best be regarded as an organic process which accompanies thought, but is not altogether subject to our own volition. We cannot make a vine grow, but we can train it in its growth. So also we can train this mental process until we call it reason, but the process itself is going on willy-nilly in the mind of a Darwin or a Jukes. Presumably we see the same process in the mind of a dog who, in recognizing the call to dinner as meaning not always meat or dog biscuit but always something to eat, is, in his turn, abstracting and generalizing.

Anyone who has once acquired the habit of regarding this process of abstraction as a living, growing thing, with creative and procreative power

[5] Edgar Allan Poe, *Murders in the Rue Morgue.*

of its own, will never, I think, return to the idea of stagnant, man-made concepts which are but wax models of a vital and fragrant flower. Thought is a luxuriant growth, redundant and wasteful, from which here and there we may cut a branch or a twig and whittle it to our purpose.

With this view of the process of thought as a prolific growth which we can neither start nor stop, but may sometimes direct and bend to our purpose, we no longer heed such sterile dicta as those which say that nothing comes from a process of reasoning except that which is put into it. As well might we tell the farmer that nothing comes out of the ground except what goes into it. Every thought, every statement, throws out its tentacles to search the neighboring territory. We cannot state a rule without wondering whether the converse is true. If I write down the numbers 1, 3, 5, 7, you are all expecting me next to write down 9. If I slowly draw a curve upon the blackboard, you begin to predict whether this curve will take an upward or downward direction. In some measure our thought is always directed by our previous knowledge; and when the process of reaching out from given data is no longer a random search but is given a quite definite direction, we call the process *extrapolation.*

Now there are many kinds of thought and processes of abstraction which have little to do with the particular objective that we call science, yet, as I have already intimated, the methods are often very like those which lead to our sciences. A warlike people, during peaceful interludes, amuse themselves by playing at war. Armies, with their horses and elephants, are brought together for the great manœuvres, which, however, prove to be costly things, so that wooden replicas of men and horses and elephants come to be used on a smaller ground. Then the nature of the ground and the movement of the pieces become conventionalized, and convention succeeds convention until finally we have that remarkably compact and perfect abstraction called chess.

Here is a concrete illustration of the abstracting process which may serve as an introduction to our study of the growth of scientific concepts. As we now proceed to discuss these concepts one by one, this examination of concrete cases will give us a better idea of the power and also of the limitations of the scientific method. We shall begin with the oldest of the mathematical sciences,—arithmetic, the science of numbers.

*"The most incomprehensible thing about the world
is that it is comprehensible."*

Albert Einstein

1879 – 1955

SOME PHILOSOPHIC CONSIDERATIONS
CONCERNING THE METHODS OF SCIENCE
ARE OFFERED

Einstein's major contribution to physics, the theory of relativity, changed classical Newtonian concepts of time and space in relation to matter in motion. This is no place to show the consequences of Einstein's theories of the interconnection between and interdependence of space and time, or the significance of his hypothesis that the interval of space between two objects and the interval of time between two events are not absolute, but relative, changing according to the circumstances of the observer.

What is of interest in the present context is the immediate stimulus to Einstein's discovery. It came from his consideration of an experiment which failed to demonstrate what logic had deduced from other observations. Assume that light travels at a uniform speed of y miles per second. If an observer sends out a beam of light toward a mirror in space, in one second of time, the light would travel y miles; but, because the earth has moved at the same time, say x miles, then, at the end of one second, the light would be only $y - x$ miles from the earth. The true speed second. The homeward trip of the reflected beam would be faster (relative to the observer), since the distance to be traversed would be reduced by another x miles. But when two Americans, Michelson and Morley, tried, in 1887, to demonstrate this by experiment, they were unsuccessful. Although their failure was later attributed to a shrinking of the object in the direction of its motion, a principle already established by Maxwell's electromagnetic theory, it was left to Einstein's concept of relativity to provide the all-inclusive explanation.

The point of interest here is the way in which Einstein first approached the problem of the unsuccessful experiments: he asserted that "it is impossible to determine the speed of motion through space by any experiment whatever" because the laws of nature made it impossible. The phenomena of nature are determined by us and our experiences rather than by a mechanical universe outside of us and independent of us.

The stylistic difficulties of these extracts from "General Considerations Concerning the Method of Science" (reproduced from the *Journal of the Franklin Institute,* 1936) are, then, to be expected from an intellect of such great dimensions as Einstein's, and they are, perhaps, exaggerated by literal translation from the German. The "method" consists in the refinement of data from the arbitrary selection of "certain repeatedly occurring complexes of sense impressions," through a series of "layers" in which the system is increasingly "poorer in concepts and relations" until we reach "the system of greater conceivable unity." The intermediate layers "represent problematic partial success"; the goal is the attainment of a definite system. And to achieve his goal, the scientist has to be prepared to analyze not only the concepts of his own specific field but also the nature of everyday thinking. His own great discovery shows best how Einstein achieved a solution by cutting through two hundred years of preconceptions based on the extension of Newtonian axioms.

GENERAL CONSIDERATION CONCERNING THE METHOD OF SCIENCE

IT HAS OFTEN BEEN SAID, and certainly not without justification, that the man of science is a poor philosopher. Why then should it not be the right thing for the physicist to let the philosopher do the philosophizing? Such might indeed be the right thing at a time when the physicist believes he has at his disposal a rigid system of fundamental concepts and fundamental laws which are so well established that waves of doubt can not reach them; but, it can not be right at a time when the very foundations of physics itself have become problematic as they are now. At a time like the present, when experience forces us to seek a newer and more solid foundation, the physicist cannot simply surrender to the philosopher the critical contemplation of the theoretical foundations; for, he himself knows best, and feels more surely where the shoe pinches. In looking for a new foundation, he must try to make clear in his own mind just how far the concepts which he uses are justified, and are necessities.

The whole of science is nothing more than a refinement of every day thinking. It is for this reason that the critical thinking of the physicist cannot possibly be restricted to the examination of the concepts of his own specific field. He cannot proceed without considering critically a much more difficult problem, the problem of analyzing the nature of everyday thinking.

On the stage of our subconscious mind appear in colorful succession sense experiences, memory pictures of them, representations and feelings. In contrast to psychology, physics treats directly only of sense experiences and of the "understanding" of their connection. But even the concept of the "real external world" of everyday thinking rests exclusively on sense impressions.

Now we must first remark that the differentiation between sense impressions and representations is not possible; or, at least it is not possible with absolute certainty. With the discussion of this problem, which affects also the notion of reality, we will not concern ourselves but we shall take the existence of sense experiences as given, that is to say as psychic experiences of a special kind.

I believe that the first step in the setting of a "real external world" is the formation of the concept of bodily objects and of bodily objects of various kinds. Out of the multitude of our sense experiences we take, mentally and arbitrarily, certain repeatedly occurring complexes of sense impression (partly in conjunction with sense impressions which are interpreted as signs for sense experiences of others), and we attribute to them a meaning—the meaning of the bodily object. Considered logically this concept is not identical with the totality of sense impressions referred to; but it is an arbitrary creation of the human (or animal) mind. On the other hand, the concept owes its meaning and its justification exclusively to the totality of the sense impressions which we associate with it.

The second step is to be found in the fact that, in our thinking (which determines our expectation), we attribute to this concept of the bodily object a significance, which is to a high degree independent of the sense impression which originally gives rise to it. This is what we mean when we attribute to the bodily object "a real existence." The justification of such a setting rests exclusively on the fact that, by means of such concepts and mental relations between them, we are able to orient ourselves in the labyrinth of sense impressions. These notions and relations, although free statements of our thoughts, appear to us as stronger and more unalterable than the individual sense experience itself, the character of which as anything other than the result of an illusion or hallucination is never completely guaranteed. On the other hand, these concepts and relations, and indeed the setting of real objects and, generally speaking, the existence of "the real world," have justification only in so far as they are connected with sense impressions between which they form a mental connection.

The very fact that the totality of our sense experiences is such that by means of thinking (operations with concepts, and the creation and use of definite functional relations between them, and the coordination of sense experiences to these concepts) it can be put in order, this fact is one which leaves us in awe, but which we shall never understand. One may say "the eternal mystery of the world is its comprehensibility." It is one of the great realizations of Immanuel Kant that the setting up of a real external world would be senseless without this comprehensibility.

In speaking here concerning "comprehensibility," the expression is used in its most modest sense. It implies: the production of some sort of order among sense impressions, this order being produced by the creation of general concepts, relations between these concepts, and by relations between the concepts and sense experience, these relations being determined in any possible manner. It is in this sense that the world of our sense experiences is comprehensible. The fact that it is comprehensible is a miracle.

In my opinion, nothing can be said concerning the manner in which the concepts are to be made and connected, and how we are to coordinate them to the experiences. In guiding us in the creation of such an order of sense experiences, success in the result is alone the determining factor. All that is necessary is *the statement* of a set of rules, since without such rules the acquisition of knowledge in the desired sense would be impossible. One may compare these rules with the rules of a game in which, while the rules themselves are arbitrary, it is their rigidity alone which makes the game possible. However, the fixation will never be final. It will have validity only for a special field of application (i.e. there are no final categories in the sense of Kant).

The connection of the elementary concepts of every day thinking with complexes of sense experiences can only be comprehended intuitively and it is unadaptable to scientifically logical fixation. The totality of these connections—none of which is expressible in notional terms—is the only thing which differentiates the great building which is science from a logical but empty scheme of concepts. By means of these connections, the purely notional theorems of science become statements about complexes of sense experiences.

We shall call "primary concepts" such concepts as are directly and intuitively connected with typical complexes of sense experiences. All other notions are—from the physical point of view—possessed of meaning, only in so far as they are connected, by theorems, with the primary notions. These theorems are partially definitions of the concepts (and of the statements derived logically from them) and partially theorems not derivable from the definitions, which express at least indirect relations between the "primary concepts," and in this way between sense experiences. Theorems of the latter kind are "statements about reality" or laws of nature, i.e. theorems which have to show their usefulness when applied to sense experiences comprehended by primary concepts. The question as to which of the theorems shall be considered as definitions and which as natural laws will depend largely upon the chosen representation. It really becomes absolutely necessary to make this differentiation only when one examines the degree to which the whole system of concepts considered is not empty from the physical point of view.

STRATIFICATION OF THE SCIENTIFIC SYSTEM

The aim of science is, on the one hand, a comprehension, as *complete* as possible, of the connection between the sense experiences in their totality, and, on the other hand, the accomplishment of this aim *by the use of a minimum of primary concepts and relations.* (Seeking, as far as possible, logical unity in the world picture, i.e. paucity in logical elements.)

Science concerns the totality of the primary concepts, i.e. concepts directly connected with sense experiences, and theorems connecting them. In its first stage of development, science does not contain anything else. Our everyday thinking is satisfied on the whole with this level. Such a state of affairs cannot, however, satisfy a spirit which is really scientifically minded; because, the totality of concepts and relations obtained in this manner is utterly lacking in logical unity. In order to supplement this deficiency, one invents a system poorer in concepts and relations, a system retaining the primary concepts and relations of the "first layer" as logically derived concepts and relations. This new "secondary system" pays for its higher logical unity by having, as its own elementary concepts (concepts of the second layer), only those which are no longer directly connected with complexes of sense experiences. Further striving for logical unity brings us to a tertiary system, still poorer in concepts and relations, for the deduction of the concepts and relations of the secondary (and so indirectly of the primary) layer. Thus the story goes on until we have arrived at a system of the greatest conceivable unity, and of the greatest poverty of concepts of the logical foundations, which are still compatible with the observation made by our senses. We do not know whether or not this ambition will ever result in a definite system. If one is asked for his opinion, he is inclined to answer no. While wrestling with the problems, however, one will never give up the hope that this greatest of all aims can really be attained to a very high degree.

An adherent to the theory of abstraction or induction might call our layers "degrees of abstraction"; but, I do not consider it justifiable to veil the logical independence of the concept from the sense experiences. The relation is not analogous to that of soup to beef but rather of wardrobe number to overcoat.

The layers are furthermore not clearly separated. It is not even absolutely clear which concepts belong to the primary layer. As a matter of fact, we are dealing with freely formed concepts, which, with a certainty sufficient for practical use, are intuitively connected with complexes of sense experiences in such a manner that, in any given case of experience, there is no uncertainty as to the applicability or non-applicability of the statement. The essential thing is the aim to represent the multitude of concepts and theorems, close to experience, as theorems, logically deduced and belonging to a basis, as narow as possible, of fundamental concepts and fundamental relations which themselves can be chosen freely (axioms). The liberty of choice, however, is of a special kind; it is not in any way similar to the liberty of a writer of fiction. Rather, it is similar to that of a man engaged in solving a well designed word puzzle. He may, it is true, propose any word as the solution; but, there is only *one* word which really solves the puzzle in all its forms. It is an outcome of faith that nature—as she is perceptible to our five senses—takes the character of such a well formulated puzzle. The successes reaped up to now by science do, it is true, give a certain encouragement for this faith.

The multitude of layers discussed above corresponds to the several stages of progress which have resulted from the struggle for unity in the course of development. As regards the final aim, intermediary layers are only of temporary nature. They must eventually disappear as irrelevant. We have to deal, however, with the science of today, in which these strata represent problematic partial successes which support one another but which also threaten one another, because today's systems of concepts contain deep seated incongruities which we shall meet later on.

II

Technology
Before Science

II

*"Research in applied science leads
to improvements but research in pure science leads
to revolutions."*
—J. J. Thomson

TECHNOLOGY BEFORE SCIENCE

Technology is the application of the physical and mathematical sciences to the arts and trades; in other words, the use of scientific discovery to satisfy the needs of man. In our time we are apt to associate the term with "improvement"—an application of science to make life easier (as a washing machine makes use of electrical energy to eliminate physical labor) or safer (as radio waves are employed to guide an airplane pilot) or more secure (as the deepfreeze permits the storage of food against a lean harvest). How, then, can we talk of technology *before* science? No one can say when systematized knowledge began to be accumulated and science organized; if we rely on the strict definition of our terms, we could easily become involved in the kind of argument in which the Schoolmen delighted. What we are concerned with is those aspects of the practical life of man which we associate with the term *arts:* the application of human skills to the satisfaction of man's needs.

We assume that, during the long ages before recorded history began, man's struggle for survival gave him no time to meditate upon his achievements and to discover in them a "scientific" principle. Yet, to stand in the center of a prehistoric ceremonial circle of stones, such as is found in many places in the world, is to realize that our unknown forefathers had among them men capable of "organizing verified facts to provide a guide to further action." Remote from any known source of scientific knowledge, they solved problems of transportation and construction equal to those encountered by the Egyptians or the Romans.

One agrees, therefore, with Sarton, who ignores the implications of the word "technology" and places the beginnings of science at the point "whenever and wherever men tried to solve the innumerable problems of life." If, in the nineteenth century, scientists asserted the gap between themselves and the practical men, let us credit them not with snobbery but with anxiety for preservation of a true scientific method. They may have pretended to despise the "practical men," but, in fact, they depended on them more than they would then admit. For the Industrial Revolution, from which modern industry developed, began at the hands of practical men, who improvised change much as did their prehistoric ancestors. The science of metals began with the observations of the humble brass founder rather than with the laws of metallurgical science. Did not the science of rotary motion, for example, have its origins in the same simple way?

When we think of prescientific technology, our first picture is of the buildings which have been discovered and identified as belonging to preclassical times. The ceremonial circles mentioned above, such as Stonehenge in England, are simple in design and crude in execution; but how was it possible for such primitive men to move stones weighing hundreds of tons over several hundred miles, to plant them vertically and firmly on the ground, and to lay a line of similar stones along their summits? No answer can yet be given. It is easier to explain the construction of the Pyramids in Egypt, by interpretation of the written records left by the Egyptians and by analysis of the Greek texts which were inspired by Egyptian practical mathematicians. What impresses us about the structures whose origins are not recorded is the ability of primitive man to resolve problems that combined mass with design.

The tomb of Agamemnon at Mycenae is an even more exciting example of this mystery. An earth mound encloses a conical stone structure, perfect in symmetry, made up of interlocking stone slabs. The entrance portal at the foot of a ramp approach is ten feet wide and twenty feet long, the roof a single stone slab two feet thick. Even in comparison with the Empire State Building this is one of the wonders of the world; its construction would challenge a modern contractor. Perhaps it was the contemplation of such achievements as this that inspired the early Greek scientists to study forces and motion. Perhaps Archimedes's theory of the lever and his invention of the compound pulley were inspired by Agamemnon's tomb.

But these are the things that survived. What of the smaller matters, those that affected the everyday life of the common man? Our knowledge of these has greatly increased in the last century or so, for excavations have brought to light writings and artifacts which have shown us how the domestic arts came into being. The tools used by the smith, by the spinner and the weaver, by the carpenter and the potter, can be described in considerable detail. As the gaps in knowledge are filled in by new discoveries of the archeologists, our appreciation of the ingenuity of early man increases.

Perhaps the greatest lesson to be learned from a study of the evolution of man's basic tools is that "invention" is not often the quasi-miraculous discovery of an individual endowed with special gifts; nor is it necessarily the result of the deliberate search of the research scientist to which we have become accustomed today. Attempts to satisfy man's daily needs must have led to some kind of division of labor even among the most primitive and nomadic societies. The men hunted; the women cooked the flesh for food and prepared the skins of animals and fashioned clothing out of them. Simple routines were evolved, and their repetition led to the discovery of ways to economize time and effort. The women soon learned how best to commence the skinning of an animal, what shape of stone would scrape it best, how long it should be cured in the sun, and what herbs would give it smoothness and suppleness. Succeeding generations inherited and improved upon these techniques and evolved new ones to deal with new products as they were found. The selection and harvesting of wild grains, the predecessor of our wheat, rye, and barley, were patiently systematized in similar ways.

From these primitive crafts—and accidental discoveries

which introduced man to the significance of metals—the structure of the domestic arts was evolved. Until communities grew
and village or town life became established, progress was slow.
Traditional ways were difficult to change. Larger communities,
however, enforced specialization in varying degrees because relatively larger outputs became necessary. The trades which were
known to Homer and mentioned in the *Odyssey* (composed,
probably, in the ninth century before Christ) were representative
of this expansion of the arts beyond the confines of the family
circle. One specialization led to another. An improvement in
security would lead to exploration of the possibilities of other
arts. The smith, freed temporarily from forging weapons, could
experiment with decorative ironwork. Time could be found for
the manipulation of scarce metals into decorative objects, the
making of which needed new skills. New dyes were found for
textiles; experiments were carried out in sculpture and in the
manufacture of ceramics and glass.

It is beyond the scope of this book to do more than suggest
the outlines of the development of technology. Its growth continued as something distinct from what we now call applied
science almost to our own era—if, indeed, we can say that it has
yet stopped. The improvisations of a farmer remote from industrial facilities will often amount to an invention owing little to
the achievements of modern science. An interesting example of
this is found in the solutions to the problem of how to keep a
gate closed in a field fence. There are many ingenious and effective designs to be seen that have rarely been repeated and certainly never patented.

Today we agree that science and technology go hand in
hand, the one suggesting innovations, the other proving their
effectiveness; but there has always been a strong undercurrent
of initiative coming from the practical side of life which has
provided the initial impetus to science. "Yankee ingenuity" is
an American term for just this process. Increased wealth and
more time for reflection have fostered the growth of science, but
the exigencies of everyday life will continue to force solutions,
too, as they have since the emergence of man as a rational being.

"My main interest, almost the only one,
is the love of truth, whether pleasant or not, whether useful
or not. Truth is self-sufficient, and there is nothing
to which it can be subordinated without loss."

George Sarton
1884 – 1956

A CONSIDERATION OF THE DAWN
OF SCIENCE AND A FEW OF ITS
EARLY MANIFESTATIONS

It seems a presumption, in introducing these readings in the history of science, to relegate George Sarton's work to the category of a mere selection. Sarton's position in the history of science is unique and, from some points of view, regrettably so, for he left no successor as broadly qualified by study and enthusiasm to carry on the work in which he was a pioneer.

Trained at the University of Ghent in natural science, with specialization in chemistry, crystallography, mathematics, and celestial mechanics (his doctoral dissertation was on the mechanical principles of Newton), Sarton gave his whole life to two objectives: the compilation of a complete history of science and the publication of a scientific journal devoted to this subject. The journal, *Isis,* now half a century old, flourishes. The major work, although incomplete, is justly described as monumental. Entitled *Introduction to the History of Science,* its three volumes, with more than four thousand pages, cover everything that is known about science from the time of Homer through the fourteenth century. To include an area of which little was previously

known, Sarton studied Arabic and not only interpreted the Arab
texts to provide a unique account of their science but also came
to know the Arab mind as few Westerners have done. Sarton
was interested in the human aspects of science; the wide range
of his other publications, which carried him far beyond the fourteenth century, show the depth of this interest. World War I
drove Sarton out of Belgium to the United States in 1915. As a
"research associate" of the Carnegie Institution, he began his history and resumed the publication of *Isis*. Almost all of his aca-
demic life in America was centered at Harvard, first in the Wide-
ner Library and, later, as Professor of the History of Science.

Sarton's moment of discovery is to be found in his decision
to establish a new science—the history of science. The results of
his observations are as pertinent to the study of science as are
those of the "natural philosophers," though time—and more
historians of science—will be needed to provide the synthesis.

The reading is taken from Volume I of Sarton's *A History
of Science,* published by Harvard University Press in 1952.

THE DAWN OF SCIENCE

When did science begin? Where did it begin? It began whenever and
wherever men tried to solve the innumerable problems of life. The first
solutions were mere expedients, but that must do for a beginning. Gradually the expedients would be compared, generalized, rationalized, simpli-
fied, interrelated, integrated; the texture of science would be slowly woven.
The first solutions were petty and awkward but what of it? A *Sequoia
gigantea* two inches high may not be very conspicuous, but it is a *Sequoia*
all the same. It might be claimed that one cannot speak of science at all
as long as a certain degree of abstraction has not been reached, but who
will measure that degree? When the first mathematician recognized that
there was something in common between three palm trees and three don-
keys, how abstract was his thought? Or when primitive theologians conceived the invisible presence of a supreme being and thus seemed to reach

an incredible degree of abstraction, was their idea really abstract, or was it concrete? Did they postulate God or did they see Him? Were the earliest expedients nothing but expedients or did they include reasonings, religious or artistic cravings? Were they rational or irrational? Was early science wholly practical and mercenary? Was it pure science, such as it was, or a mixture of science with art, religion or magic?

Such queries are futile, because they lack determination and the answers cannot be verified. It is better to leave out for the nonce the consideration of science as science, and to consider only definite problems and their solutions. The problems can be imagined, because we know the needs of man; he must be able to feed himself and his family, to find a shelter against the inclemencies of the weather, the attacks of wild beasts or fellow men, and so on. Our imaginations are not arbitrary, for they are guided by a large number of observed facts. To begin with, archaeologic investigations reveal monuments which help us to realize the kind of objects and tools that our forefathers created and even to understand their methods of using them, and to guess their intentions. The study of languages brings to light ancient words which are like fossil witnesses of early objects or early ideas. Anthropologists have made us familiar with the manners and customs of primitive men who were living under their own eyes. Finally, psychologists have analyzed the reactions of children or of undeveloped minds in the face of the very problems that primitive men had to solve. The amount of information thus obtained from several directions is so large that a scholar's life is too short to encompass it. There is no place here for a review of it, however brief, but only for a few hints.

In order to simplify our task a little, let us assume that the primitive men we are dealing with have already solved some of the most urgent problems, for otherwise their very existence would have remained precarious, not to speak of their progress, material or spiritual. Let us assume that they have discovered how to make a fire and have learned the rudiments of husbandry. They are already—that is, some of them are—learned people and technicians, and they may already be speaking of the good old days when life was more dangerous but simpler and a man did not have to remember so many things. I say "speaking," for by this time they have certainly developed a language, though they are still unable to write it; indeed, they are still unconscious of the possibility of doing so. At this stage, and for a long time to come, writing is neither essential nor necessary. Our own culture is so closely dependent on writing that it requires some effort to imagine one independent of it. Man can go very far without writing,[1] but not without language. Language is the bedrock upon which any culture is built. In the course of time it becomes the richest treasure house of that culture.

One of the greatest mysteries of life is that the languages of even the most primitive peoples, languages that have never been reduced to writing (except by anthropologists), are extremely complex. How did those languages develop as they did? The development was very largely unconscious and casual.

Our reference to investigations made today by field anthropologists is sufficient warning that when we speak of the dawn of science or of any prehistoric period we are not thinking in terms of a chronologic scale of universal application. There is no such scale. The dawn of science occurred ten thousand years ago or more in certain parts of the world; it can still be witnessed in other parts today; and irrespective of place we can observe it to some extent in the mind of any child.

EARLY TECHNICAL PROBLEMS

Let us consider rapidly the multitude of technical problems that early men had to solve if they wished to survive, and, later, to improve their condition and to lighten the burden of life. They had to invent the making of fire and experiment with it in various ways. Not only the husbandman but also the nomad needed many tools, for cutting and carving, flaying, abrading, smoothing, crushing, for the making of holes, for grasping and joining. Each tool was a separate invention, or rather the opening up of a new series of inventions, for each was susceptible of improvements which would be introduced one by one. In early times there was already room for key inventions, which might be applied to an endless group of separate problems and which ushered in unlimited possibilities. For example, there was the general problem of how to devise a handle and how to attach it firmly to a given tool. Many different solutions were found for that problem, one of the most ingenious being that of the Eskimos and Northern Indians, namely, the use of babiche (strings or thongs of rawhide) by

---

[1] Witness the Incas of Peru, whose civilization was very complex and advanced. They had an elaborate language but no system of writing [*Isis* 6, 219 (1923-24)].

means of which the tool and handle are bound together; as the hide dries it shrinks almost to half its length and the two objects are inseparable. A tighter fit could hardly be obtained otherwise.

The husbandman had to discover the useful plants one by one—plants to use as food, or as drugs, or for other domestic purposes—and this implied innumerable experiments. It was not enough for him to discover a plant; he had to select among infinite variations the best modalities of its use. He had to capture animals and to domesticate the very few that were domesticable, to build houses and granaries, to make receptacles of various kinds. There must have been somewhere a first potter, but the potter's art involved the conscious or unconscious coöperation of thousands of people. Heavy loads had to be lifted and transported, sometimes to great distances. How could that be done? Well, it had to be done and it was done. Ingenious people invented the lever, the simple pulley, the use of rollers, and later, much later, that of wheels. A potter of genius applied the wheel to his own art. How could a man cover his body to protect it from the cold or the rain or the burning sun? The use of hides was one solution, the use of leaves or bark another, but nothing equaled the materials obtained by the weaving of certain fibres. When this idea occurred to a great inventor, the textile industry was born. The earliest tools were made of stone or bones; when the practical value of metals was finally realized it became worth while to dig for their ores and to smelt them, to combine them in various ways; this was the beginning of mining and metallurgy. Each of the sentences of this paragraph could easily be expanded into a treatise.

In order to illustrate the almost uncanny ingenuity of "primitive" people, it may suffice to display the three following examples, taken in three parts of the world very distant from each other. The Australian boomerang is so well known that it hardly requires discussion; it is a missile weapon the curved shape of which is so cunningly devised that the weapon when thrown describes extraordinary curves and may even return to the sender. The South American tipiti is an elastic plaited cylinder of jacitara-palm bark which is used to express the juice of the cassava (or manioc); as the cylinder is lengthened, by the weight of a stone or otherwise, the internal pressure increases and the juice flows out. This invention is admirable in its simplicity and effectiveness, but what is more astonishing is that the Indians were able to discover the great nutritive value of cassava. The juice contains a deadly substance (hydrocyanic acid) which must be removed by cooking; otherwise, the consumer would be killed instead of nourished. How did the Indians find the treasure which could be enjoyed only after the poison spoiling it had been removed? My third example is the *li* 鬲 , a tripod used in China in prehistoric times. It is a three-legged cooking pot, the legs of which are shaped like cows' udders; various foods may be cooked in each leg with a single fire burning in the middle.

These examples might easily be multiplied. Selected as they have been in three corners of the world as remote from one another as could be, they illustrate the wide distribution of genius. We well know that whatever amount of civilization we enjoy today is the gift of many nations; we do not know so well that the same was already true thousands of years ago. Pre-historians have proved beyond doubt the existence of sophisticated cultures at very early times in many places. This does not disprove the monogenesis of mankind. It is highly probable that the new species *Homo sapiens* originated in a single place, but so long ago that by the time at which the earliest observable cultures flourished man had already invaded a good part of the world.

*"It is as futile to deplore the superstitions of the past
as it is to complain of the unsightly scaffolding essential to the
erection of a lovely building."*

V. Gordon Childe

1892 – 1957

THE CUMULATIVE AND PROGRESSIVE
EVOLUTION OF TOOLS AND MACHINES FOR
PRODUCING AND USING ROTARY MOTION
ARE DESCRIBED

The sources of our knowledge of man's first efforts to make life less hard, to warm himself and to cook his food, to build a shelter, are the excavations of the archeologist. Only within the last hundred years has archeology become a science in its own right—probably largely because, in our time, some of the Western nations accumulated economic resources well in excess of immediate needs, and some of these have been made available for investigations into the remote past. Using the discoveries of other sciences, including those of the atomic physicists, the archeologist provides us with accurate, dated information about his finds. Not infrequently, it becomes necessary to re-examine the history books in the light of these new discoveries.

V. Gordon Childe was a distinguished member of this comparatively new scientific discipline. Appropriately enough, he was a "digger," as Australians call themselves in recollection of their pioneer explorations for gold. From 1927 until 1946 he was Professor of Prehistoric Archeology at the University of Edinburgh, and from 1946 to 1956 he directed the Institute of

Archeology in London. Childe's excavations were made in Scotland, Northern Ireland, and the Orkney Islands. His systematic examination of the origins of rotary motion as a source of energy is a satisfying example of the achievements of archeological science and of scientific reporting.

The selection is taken from Volume I of *A History of Technology,* edited by C. Singer and published by the Oxford University Press.

ROTARY MOTION

I. NATURE OF ROTARY MOTION

ROTATING MACHINES for performing repetitive operations, driven by water, by thermal power, or by electrical energy, were the most decisive factors of the industrial revolution; and, from the first steamship till the invention of the jet plane, it is the application of rotary motion to transport that has revolutionized communications. The use of rotary machines, as of any other human tools, has been cumulative and progressive. The inventors of the eighteenth and nineteenth centuries were merely extending the applications of rotary motion that had been devised in previous generations, reaching back thousands of years into the prehistoric past. Hence a special section is devoted in this work to the initial and early stages of its use.

Rotary motion, in the form we know it in machines and vehicles, was a comparatively recent addition to man's equipment—recent, that is, as measured against the geological time-scale of prehistorians. The potter's wheel and the wheeled vehicle are a bare 6000 years old, the spindle has not been used for more (and perhaps much less) than 2000 years longer. . . . Men have been making tools, however, for perhaps some 500,000 years, and some of the tools employed in that vast period were probably already in a sense rotated or partially rotated. It is, therefore, convenient to introduce a distinction between continuous or true and complete rotary motion, and partial or discontinuous rotary motion.

For true rotary motion, the revolving part of the instrument must be free to turn in the same direction indefinitely. There are, however, a number of processes which involve a partial turn of the instrument; such are boring and drilling by hand. There are even machines like the bow-drill . . . or the pole-lathe, which allow a number, but only a limited number, of complete revolutions of the revolving part. Partial rotary motion of this sort has been used by man much longer than true rotary motion. Indeed, it began among his pre-human ancestors.

II. PARTIAL ROTARY MOTION

(a) *Boring.* It is a feature of the anatomy of the primates that the bony structure and the musculature of the forelimbs permit the execution of twisting movements. These depend on a partial rotation of the lower end of the radius around the fixed lower end of the ulna. . . . As soon as some subhuman primate began to supplement his powers by manipulating bits of stone or wood, he could turn these in a boring movement. It was after *homo faber* had begun to modify such ready-made tools into artifacts more suited to his needs that he must have begun to shape them to serve for boring and other purposes.

The earliest recognizable standardized tool, the hand-axe . . . is an all-purposes tool. It could be used for boring—although there is no evidence that it was so used, nor in fact how it was used at all—but if employed for digging up roots and grubs it could hardly fail to be given a twist in the process. Among the Lower Palaeolithic flake-tools of the Clactonian industry, standardized tools cannot be recognized, but there are flakes which would serve very well for boring holes in wood or hides, though no products thus perforated survive or indeed would have been likely to survive. . . .

The first perforated objects of antler, bone, ivory, and shell that survive are from the Upper Palaeolithic phase, which also yields perforated stone objects. Stone may have been perforated by percussion, but the antler has certainly been bored, while small holes in bones, shells, or teeth were quite probably drilled. From the Aurignacian, we have already sections of reindeer antler pierced with holes about 2 cm in diameter. The use of these so called *bâtons de commandement* . . . is disputed, but that the holes were pierced by boring through the antler is generally agreed. In fact, stout flint tools trimmed to a point survive from this period, and are probably correctly termed tap-bores.

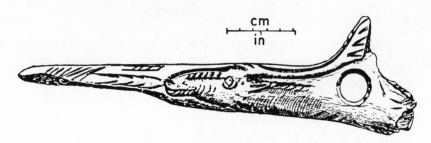

Upper Palaeolithic *bâtons de commandement* made from a section of reindeer antler pierced with holes made by boring; from Dordogne, France.

For finer perforations, a new implement not at first involving the use of other muscles was developed. Awls for piercing leather and similar materials were probably first made from splinters of bone or antler. . . . They may have been utilized as early as Lower Palaeolithic times, but only in the Upper Palaeolithic phases did men invent techniques for working bone by grinding and polishing. They were thus able to make sharp but relatively tough pointed implements. Such piercers must have been worked like bores, by twisting from the wrist. For perforating harder materials, such as shell, bone, and ivory, bone was unsuitable, and flint blades, trimmed by bi-lateral flaking to a sharp point, were manufactured. Very probably, these were soon mounted at the end of a wooden shaft, and in this state they can perhaps be more accurately described as drill-bits. . . .

A. Flint borer from Clacton-on-Sea; Lower Palaeolithic. This could be used for boring holes in wood or in hides. *B.* Antler awl from Torquay; Upper Palaeolithic.

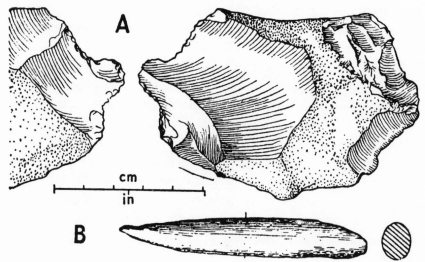

(*b*) *Hand-drill.* A smooth cylindrical stick armed at one end with a flint point can be set in motion by a different set of muscular movements. It can be made to revolve by rubbing between the palms. This motion is used even today by savage and barbarous tribes to actuate the simplest drills, and is and was used for other purposes than making holes. The ancient Maya and many other peoples used the simplest form of drill, rotated between the palms, for making fire. . . .

There are living or recent peoples of a low cultural level who use indirectly operated drills which deserve the name of machines and, in effect, convert to-and-fro horizontal motion into rotary motion. These drills are still driven by human muscle-power, but the driver pulls, or pushes and pulls, with the forearm instead of twisting with his wrist. Thus in the strap-drill the spindle is rotated by pulling backwards and forwards a sinew or thong twisted round it. This device is very widely distributed today, and must be very old, though little direct evidence of its former use is likely to have survived. . . .

(*c*) *Bow-drill.* This may be regarded as an improvement on the strap-drill. . . . In it, the ends of the cord, sinew, or strap are attached to the extremities of a bow, and the spindle is made to rotate by moving the bow back and forth. The bow-drill is very widely distributed, and was used even in Europe for most drilling operations until supplemented by the brace in the Middle Ages. It is still occasionally used in Turkey. It is represented in Egypt from 2500 B.C. onwards, and is probably as old as the bow and goes back to Palaeolithic times; but as the first Upper Palaeolithic populations in Europe, the Aurignacians and Gravettians, are not definitely known to have used the bow, we cannot confidently attribute the bow-drill to them. . . . Both strap-drill and bow-drill require a handle

Egyptian carpenters and beadmakers. (The bead-driller uses a triple drill; behind him the beads are threaded, and beneath his right arm a finished necklace is outlined.) From a tomb at Thebes, *c.* 1450 B.C.

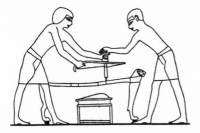

in which the spindle can rotate freely, for the driller must hold the head of the instrument and press it into the work. In point of fact, the head of the strap-drill is often grasped in the mouth. . . . Clearly, the left hand or other organ that holds the drill must be protected from direct contact with the revolving shaft, so that the handle is at the same time a sort of socket. Among the Eskimo it is made of ivory. The ancient Egyptians employed the hollow horn of a gazelle as the handle for the machine used in stone-boring . . . but the commonest form of socket is probably a knob of hard stone 2·5–6 cm in diameter. The revolving butt of the drill will gradually wear a convenient socket in the underside of such a stone knob.

(d) *Pump-drill.* The pump-drill may conveniently be mentioned here, though there is no evidence for its use before Roman times. It is a more complicated machine than any of the foregoing. Though still driven by human muscle-power, it involves, at least in its perfected form, the use of a fly-wheel to preserve the momentum imparted to the spindle by the human driving-force. It will be noticed that the cross-piece introduces a second type of bearing, serving to steady the spindle. . . .

Pump-drill from Nias, Indonesia, with a stone-filled coconut as fly-wheel.

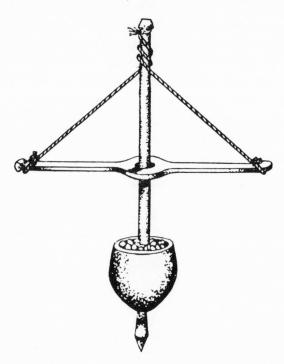

Perforated shells, teeth, stone beads, and even bone needles adequately attest the use of some sort of drill throughout Upper Palaeolithic times. An exuberant use of drilling—even for ornamenting bone implements— among the Maglemoseans of northern Europe may perhaps be taken as evidence that the bow-drill was already in use, at least by Mesolithic times.

Among the peasant societies of the New Stone Age and the succeeding Palaeometallic or Bronze Age, many improvements in drilling and boring are attested by their results, without having any demonstrable bearing on the development of rotary motion. Thick blocks of hard stone were perforated with shaft-holes to serve as mace-heads, axes, or hammers. . . . Of course, in this and similar operations the actual perforating agent was an abrasive, usually sand, for no hard steel bits were available. At first, the abrasive was moved by a solid bit, and the maker had laboriously to grind to powder a whole cylinder of hard stone exactly equal in volume to the perforation desired. Generally, when the hole had been driven half-way through the block, this was turned over and grinding begun at the opposite end. The result is a very characteristic bi-conical hole. . . . In most cases, the accuracy is so astonishing that some centring device is usually postulated, and elaborate drilling machines have been imagined, providing both centring and downward pressure on the spindle.

Such reconstructions, though frequently illustrated and logically plausible, are completely imaginary. One labour-saving device is, however, well attested—the hollow borer (drill). In this tool, the bit is tubular, and only a thin tube of the stone need actually be ground to powder. As soon as the tube has pierced the block, out drops the bore-core—a little cylinder of solid stone equivalent to at least two-thirds of what would have been completely pulverized under the older system. . . . The best bits for hollow boring are, of course, metallic tubes, such as the tubes of folded copper sheet used by pre-Columbian tribes in America . . . but even these would grind only with the aid of an abrasive. In practice, a hollow reed or bone will work quite well, though the operator will have to keep changing his bit, and must provide himself with a stock of reeds of equal diameter before starting any big operation. Even using the tubular drill, it was the normal practice to turn the block over, if it was at all thick, and continue on the opposite side.

The most relevant of the boring operations is that involved in the manufacture of the stone vases which were used extensively in the Near

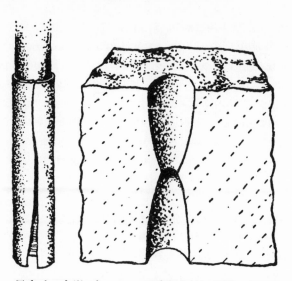

Tubular drill of copper, and bi-conical bore-hole.

East from the Neolithic stage onwards. No doubt at first hollowed merely by percussion, by early metallic times these vases were drilled out. From Egypt in particular, the processes are well documented by vessels in all stages of manufacture, by a variety of bits, and best of all by lively pictures from Old Kingdom and later tombs. . . . The actual grinding was still done by an abrasive — sand or sometimes emery (corundum, aluminium oxide). The bits were of flint fixed into cleft sticks. For hollowing out globular vessels, a series of graded flint crescents were employed succes-

A. Detail of an Egyptian relief showing the grinding of a vase, from a tomb at Saqqara, *c.* 2500 B.C. *B.* Two protodynastic examples of the flint bits thus used. *C.* Hieroglyph representing the drill.

sively as the operation proceeded. The tomb pictures show that the requisite pressure was obtained by tying a pair of heavy stones to the spindle. The hieroglyphic symbol is a picture of this device with its weights and crescent bit fixed in the forked stick. The craftsman's left hand grasps the top of the stick while the right hand turns it, apparently by pushing on the weights.

In the early pictures the upper end of the stick seems curved, and this has suggested that it was used as a sort of crank handle. The swing of the arms to and fro would then be converted into rotary motion. If this interpetation is correct, the ancient Egyptians were applying true rotary motion to one sort of drilling before 2500 B.C. There seems no other evidence for the use of anything like a crank for nearly two millennia, and then only for turning true wheels. As for the brace, it is nowhere attested before the Middle Ages. This obvious interpretation of the Egyptian pictures is probably wrong. The curved piece at the top of the spindle is very likely not part of the spindle at all, but a handle of hollow horn in which the spindle turns freely. It is always depicted grasped in the operator's left hand, while one would expect him to turn the drill with his right. This hand is, however, shown directed toward the weights.

(e) *The Earliest Form of Lathe.* There is a set of machines which in practice provided discontinuous rotary motion, though in principle they were as capable of revolving in one direction as the Egyptian vase-borer. The lathe works on the same essential principles as the drill, but differs from it in two respects. In the lathe, the work, and not the cutting tool, is rotated, and the spindle is horizontal, not vertical. The horizontal arrangement of the spindle almost inevitably involves the use of a second bearing or support, in addition to the socket in which the butt may turn. Moreover, the simplest sort of lathe, the so-called pole-lathe, generally operates by some force independent of the operator though originally generated by his own exertions. It is, in fact, driven by a belt or strap wrapped round the spindle, one end of which is attached to a weight raised by the operator, or to a supple piece of wood which the operator has bent. It is the fall of the weight by gravity, or the recoil of the strained timber, that turns the spindle, which undergoes two or more, but a limited number of, complete revolutions. While this device is geographically fairly widespread, there is no direct evidence for its use till classical times.[1] Its employment is in any

---

[1] I believe, but cannot definitely prove, that it was in use in the Bronze Age in Mesopotamia and the Indus valley.

case later than that of the potter's wheel, which provides continuous rotary motion.

(*f*) *Door-sockets*. Before discussing wheels, which are essential constituents of all machines producing true rotary motion, and which imply bearings, it is necessary to refer to another device, with no direct relation to rotary motion but one which, together with the drill-handle, may have played a part in inspiring the earliest bearings.

Until metal hinges came into use, doors were swung on poles projecting slightly above and below the margins of the door-frame. The upper end hung freely in a loop of hide fixed to the door-post, the lower stood in a hollow in the threshold, or in a stone embedded in the floor at the foot of the door-post. Wooden thresholds equipped with such sockets have been found in Neolithic houses preserved in peat bogs in central Europe. In a slightly more advanced technological stage, but in an earlier period of time, stone door-sockets were used in Hither Asia. As early as the pro-

Stone socket for lower pivot of door. The inscription records the restoration of a temple by Gudea, Prince of Lagash, Sumer, *c*. 2500 B.C.

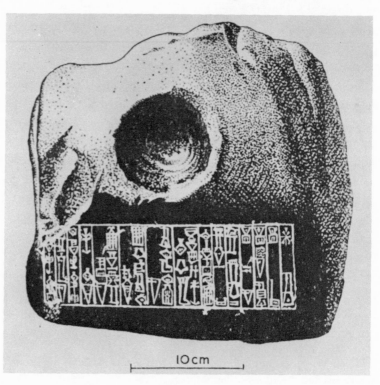

10 cm

tochalcolithic village of Hassuna in Assyria, that is, by 4500 B.C., we find the characteristic socket stone—a block of stone fixed in the floor of the doorway, with a cup-like depression in the upper surface. At a later date, similar door-sockets were very widely used. They are attested quite early throughout Hither Asia and the Aegean, and before the beginning of our era we find socket stones of the familiar form in Scottish structures that are still 'prehistoric'.

In Mesopotamia, where stone was scarce, door-sockets were always valuable articles. They were not regarded as part of a house; the tenant renting a dwelling unfurnished would bring his own door-socket as much as his own couch. In temples and palaces they were regular vehicles for inscriptions. . . . Often the socket was lined with copper or bronze, and the pivot of the gate was coated with the same metal. In the prehistoric Harappa civilization of the Indus valley the stone socket was generally replaced by one of kiln-fired brick.

(g) *Spinning*. The earliest application of continuous rotary motion to an industrial purpose involves the use of a different set of human muscles from those employed in boring and drilling—twirling between finger and thumb. Spinning was practised almost from the beginning of the Neolithic revolution. Thus it is substantially older than the more complicated machines for partial rotary motion that have just been discussed.

All Neolithic societies seem to have woven fabrics from spun threads, either of flax, wool, or, in some cases, cotton. In spinning, the threads are wound on a rotating spindle as they are drawn out. The spindle is just a straight stick held vertically between finger and thumb at the upper end. A perforated disk of stone or pottery, termed a whorl, is generally attached to act as a fly-wheel and to maintain the momentum of the spin. . . . The spin is started by twirling with the finger and thumb, and this motion must be constantly repeated. As the winding is always in one direction, spinning must rank as true rotary motion, but, from its invention in Neolithic times throughout antiquity and well into the Middle Ages, the spindle was always operated by finger and thumb and worked without bearings.

III. TRUE OR CONTINUOUS ROTARY MOTION

(a) *Wheels*. All effective industrial applications of rotary motion have developed from some sort of wheel—ideally a disk equipped with bearings to allow it to spin freely. The manufacture of a disk requires in itself the performance of another rotary motion, namely, tracing a circle. This can be accurately executed only with an appropriate instrument. A true circle can be traced by a length of string, one end of which is fixed, or by a forked stick or bone (a wish-bone for example), one prong of which is rotated on the other as a fixed point. Neither device is likely to survive in the archaeological record, or to be recognized if it did. Yet it is certain that illiterate barbarians in Britain and Ireland, long before 1000 B.C., were accurately marking out large ceremonial circles over 50 metres in diameter, like Grange (Limerick), and Stonehenge. This must have been done with some sort of rope pegged at the centre. Contemporary artists incised smaller but truer circles on stone or metal. These must have been described with a sort of compass, which after all is but a forked stick.

Save for a minute instrument, adjustable in the manner of a beam-compass, from a Bronze Age site in central Italy, no compass survives from earlier than classical times, but hard-pointed, if not necessarily hinged, compasses can be inferred reliably from circles precisely inscribed on bone or clay before 3000 B.C. Most conclusive are some pot-sherds and bricks from the Harappan cities of the Indus basin. On these, soon after 2500 B.C., the impressions of points, almost certainly metallic, can be discerned both at the centre and on the circumference. Slight discrepancies between the diameters of intersecting circles show that the arms of the instrument were movable.

Disks revolving freely on a fixed axis, or with an axle free to turn in a bearing, were in use in both the ceramic and the transport industries between 3500 and 3000 B.C. The earliest reliably dated evidence comes from Sumer and Susiana. Wheels and their essential appurtenances were at first of wood, and consequently can only exceptionally survive. In this respect, however, the potter's wheel is slightly better placed than the vehicular, for it may leave on the pot characteristic striations which an expert can recognize even on a fragment. Though pots are easily broken, pottery is practically indestructible. As a result, the first evidence for potter's wheels seems a little earlier than that for wheeled vehicles, and their distribution can be plotted much more accurately. This apparent priority of the potter's wheel may be adventitious.

(b) The Potter's Wheel: Definitions and Ethnographic Data. In pottery manufacture the function of the wheel is to supply centrifugal force to a lump of still plastic clay accurately 'thrown' on its centre. Such a well centred lump when spinning fast—100 revolutions per minute at least are required—needs only light guiding-pressure from the potter's hand to rise and assume any sectionally circular form he may wish to impose upon it. Instead of expending his own muscular energy in pressing, moulding, or coiling the clay, he merely directs energy imparted to it. Till the machine age, however, that energy was supplied by human effort and was no more derived from a non-human source of power than that of the bow or the pole-lathe.

Potters' wheels, ancient and modern, are made almost entirely of wood. No ancient ones have survived complete. The striations on wheel-made vases tell hardly anything of the machine that was used in making them, and even the few surviving stone bearings and pottery disks supply at best ambiguous testimony. To get some idea of the first potters' wheels we must examine the folk-industries of the less highly mechanized peoples. Among them we encounter two kinds of machine capable of imparting the requisite spin to the well centred clay. Both are correctly termed wheels, but they are described in French by distinct terms, *tournette* and *tour* respectively. The former name is also applied to another device, the turn-table, that cannot fulfil the distinctive function of a wheel as just defined, though in theory it may be the precursor of the wheel.

In building up a large pot by hand, many barbarian potters set the vessel on a movable base—a mat, a stone slab, a sherd—which can be turned as required, to bring the several segments of the pot within convenient reach of the hand. To facilitate turning, the base is occasionally pivoted. The result will be called a turn-table here, and is that described by some French writers as a *tournette*. For example, the Gelib potters in Italian Somaliland use a stout wooden disk, planted firmly on the ground, from the upper surface of which projects a boss. On the boss, a second wooden disk is poised at the centre, and the pot is built up on its upper face. . . . Its underside is generally slightly hollowed out at the centre, but not always enough to deserve the name of socket, while the boss is domed, not pointed. Pots are built up on this machine by coiling, the upper disk being slowly turned round by the foot, as the process advances, but never set spinning. It doubtless could be made to spin, though the disk is not heavy enough to maintain its momentum. The true wheel might have developed out of some such device, but there is no evidence for the priority of turn-tables; indeed, no turn-table is known until a time when the wheel had been long in use.

Undocumented speculations as to how wheels might have developed having no place in a history, the turn-table might have been left without further reference. Unfortunately, English archaeological literature has been bedevilled by the translation of the French *tournette* by the self-contradictory term 'slow-wheel'. The term *tournette* should properly be restricted to turn-tables on which the pot is built, not thrown, by the potter. Both the simplest and more complex forms of the potter's wheel are wheels which may be made to spin fast enough to impart centrifugal force to a centred lump of clay. The distinction concerns not the speed, but the source, of the motion. The simple wheel is normally set spinning by the thrower himself, but keeps spinning by its own momentum, like a top. In contrast, the compound wheel consists of two wheels, fixed one above the other on a common axle, so that the thrower can move the lower wheel with his foot, leaving both his hands free to manipulate the clay, which is centred on the upper wheel or head. The compound wheel is, therefore, often called the footwheel.

(c) *The Simple Wheel.* The simple wheel is essentially a centrally pivoted disk of wood, stone, or clay on a wooden frame. The wheel must be heavy enough to retain its momentum when set spinning. It may be started with the bare hand of the thrower or an assistant, by a jerk with a stick that engages in a notch or hollow near the rim of the disk, or by pulling a strap wound round the rim of the disk or its axle, as in the strap-drill. Once started, even by a jerk from a stick, such a wheel will spin long enough for the thrower to complete a small pot, though for larger pots he may have to use the stick again.

There are two varieties of the simple wheel, which may be termed respectively the socketed and the pivoted disk. In the first, the wheel revolves freely on a fixed pivot which fits into the socket on the underside of the disk. . . . Alternatively, the pivot projects from the underside of the disk or is mortised firmly into it, but turns in a fixed socket—generally a stone hollowed out like a door-socket and embedded in the ground. . . . In the second type, the pivot, when not in one piece with the disk, may be elongated to become an axle, but then an additional bearing is required above the socket, to support the axle yet allow it to revolve. The socketed disk is used today in south-east Asia—India outside the

Indus basin, China, and Japan—and has been reported from the Congo. The pivoted disk, on the other hand, is still used by village potters in Crete, but only to supplement the foot-wheel and mainly as a turn-table in the manufacture of large jars. Finally, the foot-wheel is employed today in Sindh and the Punjab (where it is termed the Pathan wheel), in Iraq, Palestine, Crete, and in the less industrialized countries of continental Europe. It can obviously be regarded as an improvement on the pivoted disk in which a second wheel has been attached to the pivot after it had been elongated into an axle. The survival of the two types side by side, as in the Cretan industry, lends some support to this theory of genetic connexion. Both require a support to steady the axle, which in the foot-wheel comes between the two wheels. All these machines impose severe strain on the bearings, which must support the weight of a disk heavy enough to maintain its momentum for from five to seven minutes.

The fire-drill . . . if it helped to suggest the idea of a fixed socket, would have given the first wheelwrights an obvious warning of the friction generated by rapid rotary motion. Ideally, the pivot or spindle should be of metal, or at least cased in metal at its tip, but in practice hard wood is still used both in India and in China. The socket, too, should be metal-lined, like the sockets of temple doors in Babylonia, but no metal linings have been reported. In China, a hard porcelain cup is used as a lining, while in India a flint pebble, concave on one face, is inserted in the underside of the disk. The support needed to steady the axle of the foot-wheel, or of the simple wheel with elongated pivot, is most readily furnished by a horizontal plank perforated with a hole through which the axle passes, but further friction will arise between its edges and the revolving shaft. On the other hand, the socketed disk and the short-pivoted disk will require some support while at rest. When in full spin, each would doubtless remain horizontal, but friction with the support is liable to retard starting-up. At these points lubricants—fats, vegetable oils, or bitumen—might be helpful.

III

The Beginnings
of the
Scientific Approach

III

*"Whoever makes a close study of the scientific world
of Ancient Greece cannot but be filled with veneration and his
veneration will but increase, the more he realizes that,
beyond all difference and change, the cosmos
of the Greeks is still the rock from which
our own cosmos has been hewn."*

—S. Sambursky

THE BEGINNINGS OF THE
SCIENTIFIC APPROACH

We have indications that the civilization of Greece reached
the peak of its intellectual development in the fifth century
B.C.E. We know that, during two thousand years before the
Greeks, man was solving the problems of practical life with
but few attempts to explain why things happened as they did.
The Babylonians and Egyptians left their marks as construction
engineers capable of solving formidable problems; they systematized methods of counting and measurement; they observed the
rhythms of the sun and planets and made calendars. The Egyptians made progress in the art of medicine.

The climax of Greek achievement was followed by another
era in which the practical man reigned supreme. The Romans—
soldiers, administrators, lawyers—whose conquests absorbed the
Greeks and the body of Greek knowledge, concerned themselves
with the practical affairs of their vast Empire. They, in turn, were
conquered; cultural growth throughout Europe as we now know
it was suspended. The Arabs and the Jews carried on the Greek

125

scientific tradition while the Christian Church struggled for survival and occupied itself with the rationalization of its philosophy. For a thousand years, science remained dormant among the peoples north of the Mediterranean.

What might have happened if the course of history had been diverted? Let us suppose that the Romans had been more modest in their ambitions and had concentrated on building up their strength to a point where they could resist the encroachments of the barbarians. The Greeks among them, inheritors of the great traditions of Aristotle and Archimedes, would have had more opportunity to impress the Romans with their ideas of the scientific approach. Instead of the word "How?" more would have been heard of "Why?" And, as in our modern civilization, in which the "Why?" of the scientist is constantly stimulated by the results of technological progress, Roman empiricism would have been enriched by scientific questioning. Had the Roman era lasted longer than five or six hundred years, is it not possible that the exploitation of the vast natural resources of their Empire (even a smaller empire, more capable of protection against the invader) would have given some Greek citizen, perhaps a follower of Hero, the opportunity to discover how the power of steam could be employed to move a machine? Might not the astrologers have broken loose from superstition and, with the help of Arabic knowledge of glass, found ways to observe the stars and so arrive at those discoveries which, in fact, had to await the coming of Galileo a thousand years later?

It is, indeed, a great mystery why, under the impact of the constant needs for war materiel, the Roman economy did not call on its scientists—even its Greek scientists—for greater contributions, as we have done, particularly during the last twenty years. Why, for instance, were the alchemists not induced to extend their experiments; to defer attempts to transform base metals into gold and to find a way of making an iron capable of taking a keener edge—in fact, to make cheaper steel?

Attempts to explain the Romans' failure to make use of the specialists among them must take into account a great array of influences that discouraged inquiry. Perhaps, as in the Middle

Ages, too much emphasis was placed on religion. Education was the privilege of the few, and the fundamentals upon which they could have exercised their ingenuity were withheld from *hoi polloi*. Perhaps even among the Greeks themselves this exclusiveness of education took its toll, limiting the development of inquiring minds. Another theory, proposed by Sarton, suggests that the decline of science was the inevitable result of a basic lack of moral character among the Greeks.

Whatever the explanation, the fact remains that the structure of scientific accomplishment built up by the Greeks disappeared. Modern science had to be laboriously rebuilt from its foundations, while men argued, often wastefully, as to the meaning of the words the Greeks had left behind them. A great gap was created in the steady stream of progress.

Are these inquiries into the "what might have been" justified? How valuable, after all, was the Greek contribution to science? Were the foundations they laid actually as sound as this approach assumes? Is it possible that the modern reader of the classical writings, too much influenced by his inherited fund of knowledge, attributes too high an accomplishment to the Greeks by reading into the writings more than is, in fact, there?

In order to assess the value of the Greek contributions to science, we must recall that the idea of positive activity is implicit in the definition of the term *contribution*. Science does not develop from mere observation; the scientist must pursue an objective, study and select his data, organize it systematically, and attempt a synthesis. As we have seen in our discussion of Claude Bernard, even a wrong hypothesis may be useful to the scientist by leading him into a better method of obtaining his experimental data. There can be a contribution to science, therefore, even if the conclusions are incorrect, provided the scientist or his successor is prepared always to question the results and to proceed from one stage to another toward the truth. By this standard, the Greeks could be described, correctly, as scientists. They made mistakes, but, within their own era, progress can be observed; and, perhaps more significantly, the records of their work provided the impetus to a resumption of scientific work when Europe at last found time not only to study but also to criticize them.

Sarton's great *Introduction to the History of Science* lists hundreds of Greeks who contributed, in one way or another, to the growth of science. We can cite but a few. A hundred years before Hippocrates, the subject of our first selection in Part I, the Ionian school of natural philosophy came into being, founded by Thales (*c.* 624-*c.* 548 B.C.). Thales had lived in Egypt, and he set up the first system of abstract geometry out of the practice of mathematics and astronomy which he learned there. His was the first attempt to provide a general explanation of the universe. He is said to have predicted the eclipse of the sun that occurred in 585 B.C. One of his pupils, Anaximander (610-*c.* 545 B.C.), attempted to explain organic evolution and produced a map of the world, perhaps the first Greek to do so.

Farther west, in the Greek colony in Southern Italy, Pythagoras (*c.* 566-*c.* 497 B.C.) founded his brotherhood, which developed into a scientific school. The Egyptians had discovered how to lay out a right angle, a necessary preliminary to building a pyramid, but it was Pythagoras who produced the first deductive proof —the *pons asinorum* of schooldays—that the square on the hypotenuse of a right-angled triangle is equal to the sum of the squares on the other two sides. The Pythagoreans placed such emphasis on the theory of numbers that the school ultimately found itself involved in a world of mystical abstractions. Their influence was felt especially in the period of scholasticism, when their conception of a numbered order in geometry, arithmetic, music, and astronomy caused these four subjects to become the fundamental courses in medieval education. More immediately, their ideas were a powerful influence on Plato; however, before discussing him, we should note a trio of experimenters whose work represents a peak in this first period of Greek science.

Empedocles (*c.* 493-*c.* 433 B.C.), physicist and physician as well as poet and philosopher, recognized four elements (fire, air, water, and earth) over combinations of which two moving forces (love and strife) ruled; but he also developed a theory of the movement of the blood to and from the heart and made the first reference in Greek literature to the use of water-clocks. Democritus (*c.* 470-*c.* 400 B.C.), renowned for his atomic theory, is dealt with in more detail below, in the introduction to Lucretius's poetic description of his teachings. Hippocrates, the first great medical scientist, has already been mentioned. These men were important influences in medieval studies, and, by the standard we have suggested, they clearly rank as scientists entitled to their position in the great evolution of the species.

With Socrates and Plato came a pause in the rate of development. The former (470-399 B.C.) developed in his philosophical discussions the idea of the inductive method in science. Although, like his pupil Plato (427-347 B.C.), he distrusted experimentation, he taught the virtues of clear definition and reasoned skepticism. Plato, more interested in mathematics and much influenced by Pythagorean ideas, is said to have regarded experiments as offensive to the gods. His theories, especially those recorded in the *Timaeus,* had a tremendous influence on medieval thought and brought him into a later disrepute which sometimes overshadowed his real contributions to mathematics and astronomy. Equally known for his development of the analytical method, in which one assumes the problem solved and then works back through the various presumptions until one reaches a premise, the truth or falsehood of which is known, he showed, in effect, that analysis as well as synthesis is an important tool of scientific investigation.

Aristotle and Theophrastus, who followed Plato, will also be discussed below in the introductions to their writings.

After these men, the center of interest shifts from Athens to the new center of Mediterranean culture, Alexandria. We read below of the work of two of the many scientists who worked in the great library there. Archimedes propounded one of the few quantitative laws that came from Greek mathematical studies— the law of the lever. From a later Alexandrian, Hero (who lived sometime between 100 B.C.E. and 150 A.D.), came compilations of existing knowledge which have provided a source of much information about Greek mechanics, and the discovery of new precision instruments used in surveying.

The thread that connects all the Greek writings is the attempt to explain the nature of matter and of the universe. The Greek scientists were always susceptible to the philosophical urge, and sometimes the results of experiment and induction were subordinated to grand hypotheses about gods and men; but, in astronomy, cosmology, and mathematics and especially in geometry, they maintained with increasing integrity the purity of their studies.

*"Science arises whenever from a multitude of
notions given in experience a universal conception
is formed comprising all similar cases. . . . The reason for
this is that experience is knowledge of individual
cases, whereas science is knowledge of
universal principles."*

Aristotle
384 – 322 B.C.

THE HABITS OF A NUMBER OF MARINE
ANIMALS ARE DESCRIBED

Aristotle's position in the history of science is paradoxical. In him is synthesized all that was great in classical Greek science. Possessed of an extraordinary mind and a remarkable capacity for teaching, he brought together in one place, and added to in a lifetime of his own research, the accumulated knowledge of the ancient world. Yet, because his influence was so great, he can be accused of holding up the progress of science for hundreds of years. The fault was not his, as we shall soon see, but rather that of an accident of history intervening to retard the natural growth of the tree that he planted.

Aristotle's life spanned those of two of the great kings of Greece, Philip II of Macedonia (359-336 B.C.) and Alexander the Great (356-323 B.C.). His father was physician to the first, and he became the tutor of the second. He was, no doubt, given his basic training in the mysteries of medicine under the influence of the Hippocratic school. As a tutor, he inspired a military conqueror with an interest in science; for Alexander's conquests brought back not only plunder but also knowledge of cultures of the East, from as far as India, to stimulate the scholars of Alexandria.

Aristotle, in his early life, was a student of Plato—philosopher, mathematician, and the founder of jurisprudence. Aristotle's training as a mathematician was less important to his later teaching than his realization of the value of observation in the study of natural history, a direct contradiction to the teachings of Plato, who regarded experiment as an impiety. One suspects that his formal studies in Plato's Academy in Athens were often interrupted by days spent on the clear waters of the Mediterranean and on the nearby rocks of the Attic coast. Those days were not spent indolently; his observation of the habits of marine animals were systematically recorded, and so good was his work that modern knowledge can add little to his descriptions of such phenomena as the breeding of the octopus or the catfish. Here began, no doubt, his interest in biology, in botanical and anatomical studies that have come down to us in his *Histories about Animals, On the Generation of Animals,* and *On the Parts of Animals* from which we have selected readings (from D. W. Thompson's translation, published by Oxford University Press).

Aristotle's curiosity may have led him to practice vivisection; certainly, he dissected, and his studies in anatomy were well done even by modern standards. If, as we shall see later in Part V, his conclusions were sometimes wrong and his errors remained undetected by later medieval scholars, the fault lies not with him but with them. His system of organized research was as significant as the principles of logic that he established. The error of the Schoolmen was to concern themselves too much with argument under Aristotelian rules and too little with his inductive method.

Aristotle did not follow the experimental method consistently, especially in his studies of the nature of matter and of the physical world around him. Because the atomic ideas of Democritus conflicted with his own ideas of nature, he rejected them and adopted an older conception of matter that assumed the existence of four elements—earth, water, air, and fire—which, in various combinations, formed different substances. To these he added a fifth, called aether, as the component of the celestial bodies. Aristotle's explanation of the universe, unverified by experiment or observation, attained dignity by virtue of his other more substantial additions to scientific knowledge and method; unfortunately, it retained its influence until the time of Galileo. However, against this negative contribution we must measure his investigations of the theories of geometry, which influenced its later systematization.

The medieval scholars who, in effect, misused Aristotle's writings when they were rediscovered in the twelfth century were, as we have seen, too much concerned with maintaining the purity of the Christian doctrines. Theirs was a closed world—one of religious contemplation, different in every respect from the stimulating atmosphere infused by the bright sun and transparent, sparkling waters of Greece.

Aristotle's "Lyceum," founded in 335 B.C., in Athens, provided the training ground for many of the scholars who were later established in Alexander's new city of Alexandria. The Library there, one of the wonders of the world, was to become the link between Greek culture and that of the Arabs and was to see the further development of that inductive approach to science of which Aristotle was the earliest and greatest exponent.

HISTORIA ANIMALIUM

In marine creatures, also, one may observe many ingenious devices adapted to the circumstances of their lives. For the accounts commonly given of the so-called fishing-frog are quite true; as are also those given of the torpedo. The fishing-frog has a set of filaments that project in front of its eyes; they are long and thin like hairs, and are round at the tips; they lie on either side, and are used as baits. Accordingly, when the animal stirs up a place full of sand and mud and conceals itself therein, it raises the filaments, and, when the little fish strike against them, it draws them in underneath into its mouth. The torpedo narcotizes the creatures that it wants to catch, overpowering them by the power of shock that is resident in its body, and feeds upon them; it also hides in the sand and mud, and catches all the creatures that swim in its way and come under its narcotizing influence. This phenomenon has been actually observed in operation. The sting-ray also conceals itself, but not exactly in the same way. That the creatures get their living by this means is obvious from the fact that, whereas they are peculiarly inactive, they are often caught with mullets in their interior, the swiftest of fishes. Furthermore, the fishing-frog is unusually thin when he is caught after losing the tips of his filaments, and the torpedo is known to cause a numbness even in human beings. Again, the hake, the ray, the flat-fish, and the angel-fish burrow in the sand, and after concealing themselves angle with the filaments on their mouths, that fishermen call their fishing-rods, and the little creatures on which they feed swim up to the filaments taking them for bits of sea-weed, such as they feed upon.

Wherever an anthias-fish is seen, there will be no dangerous creatures in the vicinity, and sponge-divers will dive in security, and they call these signal-fishes 'holy-fish'. It is a sort of perpetual coincidence, like the fact that wherever snails are present you may be sure there is neither pig nor partridge in the neighbourhood; for both pig and partridge eat up the snails.

The sea-serpent resembles the conger in colour and shape, but is of lesser bulk and more rapid in its movements. If it be caught and thrown away, it will bore a hole with its snout and burrow rapidly in the sand; its snout, by the way, is sharper than that of ordinary serpents. The so-called sea-scolopendra,[1] after swallowing the hook, turns itself inside out until it ejects it, and then it again turns itself outside in. The sea-scolopendra, like the land-scolopendra, will come to a savoury bait; the creature does not bite with its teeth, but stings by contact with its entire body, like the so-called sea-nettle. The so-called fox-shark, when it finds it has swallowed the hook, tries to get rid of it as the scolopendra does, but not in the same way; in other words, it runs up the fishing-line, and bites it off short; it is caught in some districts in deep and rapid waters, with night-lines.

The bonitos swarm together when they espy a dangerous creature, and the largest of them swim round it, and if it touches one of the shoal they try to repel it; they have strong teeth. Amongst other large fish, a

[1] It is not clear what animal Aristotle was describing here. [Ed. note.]

lamia-shark, after falling in amongst a shoal, has been seen to be covered with wounds.

Of river-fish, the male of the sheat-fish is remarkably attentive to the young. The female after parturition goes away; the male stays and keeps on guard where the spawn is most abundant, contenting himself with keeping off all other little fishes that might steal the spawn or fry, and this he does for forty or fifty days, until the young are sufficiently grown to make away from the other fishes for themselves. The fishermen can tell where he is on guard: for, in warding off the little fishes, he makes a rush in the water and gives utterance to a kind of muttering noise. He is so earnest in the performance of his parental duties that the fishermen at times, if the eggs be attached to the roots of water-plants deep in the water, drag them into as shallow a place as possible; the male fish will still keep by the young, and, if it so happen, will be caught by the hook when snapping at the little fish that come by; if, however, he be sensible by experience of the danger of the hook, he will still keep by his charge, and with his extremely strong teeth will bite the hook in pieces.

* * *

Of molluscs the sepia is the most cunning, and is the only species that employs its dark liquid for the sake of concealment as well as from fear: the octopus and calamary make the discharge solely from fear. These creatures never discharge the pigment in its entirety; and after a discharge the pigment accumulates again. The sepia, as has been said, often uses its colouring pigment for concealment; it shows itself in front of the pigment and then retreats back into it; it also hunts with its long tentacles not only little fishes, but oftentimes even mullets. The octopus is a stupid creature, for it will approach a man's hand if it be lowered in the water; but it is neat and thrifty in its habits: that is, it lays up stores in its nest, and, after eating up all that is eatable, it ejects the shells and sheaths of crabs and shell-fish, and the skeletons of little fishes. It seeks its prey by so changing its colour as to render it like the colour of the stones adjacent to it; it does so also when alarmed. By some the sepia is said to perform the same trick; that is, they say it can change its colour so as to make it resemble the colour of its habitat. The only fish that can do this is the angel-fish, that is, it can change its colour like the octopus.

* * *

The dolphin, the whale, and all the rest of the Cetacea, all, that is to say, that are provided with a blow-hole instead of gills, are viviparous. That is to say, no one of all these fishes is ever seen to be supplied with eggs, but directly with an embryo from whose differentiation comes the fish, just as in the case of mankind and the viviparous quadrupeds.

The dolphin bears one at a time generally, but occasionally two. The whale bears one or at the most two, generally two. The porpoise in this respect resembles the dolphin, and, by the way, it is in form like a little dolphin, and is found in the Euxine; it differs, however, from the dolphin as being less in size and broader in the back; its colour is leaden-black. Many people are of opinion that the porpoise is a variety of the dolphin.

All creatures that have a blow-hole respire and inspire, for they are provided with lungs. The dolphin has been seen asleep with his nose above water, and when asleep he snores.

The dolphin and the porpoise are provided with milk, and suckle their young. They also take their young, when small, inside them. The young of the dolphin grows rapidly, being full-grown at ten years of age. Its period of gestation is ten months. It brings forth its young in summer, and never at any other season; [and, singularly enough, under the Dog-star it disappears for about thirty days]. Its young accompany it for a considerable period; and, in fact, the creature is remarkable for the strength of its parental affection. It lives for many years; some are known to have lived for more than twenty-five, and some for thirty years; the fact is fishermen nick their tails sometimes and set them adrift again, and by this expedient their ages are ascertained.

The seal is an amphibious animal: that is to say, it cannot take in water, but breathes and sleeps and brings forth on dry land—only close to the shore—as being an animal furnished with feet; it spends, however, the greater part of its time in the sea and derives its food from it, so that it must be classed in the category of marine animals. It is viviparous by immediate conception and brings forth its young alive, and exhibits an after-birth and all else just like a ewe. It bears one or two at a time, and three at the most. It has two teats, and suckles its young like a quadruped. Like the human species it brings forth at all seasons of the year, but especially at the time when the earliest kids are forthcoming. It conducts its young ones, when they are about twelve days old, over and over again during the day down to the sea, accustoming them by slow degrees to the water. It slips down steep places instead of walking, from the fact that it cannot steady itself by its feet. It can contract and draw itself in, for it is fleshy and soft and its bones are gristly. Owing to the flabbiness of its body it is difficult to kill a seal by a blow, unless you strike it on the temple. It looks like a cow. The female in regard to its genital organs resembles the female of the ray; in all other respects it resembles the female of the human species.

So much for the phenomena of generation and of parturition in animals that live in water and are viviparous either internally or externally.

"A plant has the power of germination
in all its parts, for it has life in them all. . . .
The methods of generation are these: spontaneous, from
a seed, a root, a piece torn off, a branch, a twig,
pieces of wood cut off small, or
from the trunk itself."

Theophrastus

c. 372 – 287 B.C.

SOME METHODS OF PLANT PROPAGATION
AND GROWTH ARE DESCRIBED

The fact that Theophrastus was but twelve years younger than his master, Aristotle, gives us an idea of the atmosphere of the Lyceum. Here master and pupils walked together in the gardens during the hours of study (hence the name *Peripatetics,* applied to the members of the Lyceum from the Greek word meaning "to walk around"). The "pupils" were evidently of all ages — from Theophrastus — almost as old as Aristotle — to Alexander, afterwards the King—perhaps no more than twenty. Aristotle assigned research projects to his students, and, in consequence, many compilations of ancient knowledge were added to Aristotle's library, which was later to become the nucleus of the famous Library at Alexandria. Theophrastus did this work of compilation in natural philosophy; similar "papers" were written in medicine, mathematics, and astronomy. Thus a more or less complete history of science became available as the working tool of the Lyceum.

Theophrastus, who succeeded Aristotle as the head of the Lyceum, took an intellectual position often independent of that of his master. Whereas Aristotle accepted a teleological view (that developments are due to the purpose that will in fact be fulfilled by them; as, for example, the assumption that plants and animals exist only for their use to human beings), Theophrastus seems to have preferred to leave such questions to be decided by the evidence.

Theophrastus's work in botany, which established the basic concepts of botanical science, is unusual for the extent of his observations, his interest in scientific agriculture, and, especially, for the data he accumulated on the strange (to the Greeks) new specimens from India. Of these, he collected his information from Alexander and his officers, and it is considered that the quality of this work meets the standards of description required by modern science. Theophrastus wrote on climate, minerals, and geography; but he is best known for his work on plant propagation and seed germination. Theophrastus restored the Hippocratic assumption that the brain was the center of intelligence. (Aristotle had decreed that the seat of the intelligence was the heart, the brain providing it with a cooling system by secreting phlegm.) His work in arithmetic and geometry, of which he is believed to have written a history, has been lost, but we know that he had no sympathy for the idea that natural phenomena could be expressed in the artificial language of mathematics.

The selection is from the A. Hort translation of *The History of Plants* in the Loeb Classical Library.

PROPAGATION: GERMINATION AND GROWTH

1. The ways in which trees and plants in general originate are these: spontaneous growth, from seed, from a root, from a piece torn off, from a branch or twig, from the trunk itself; or again from small pieces into which the wood is cut up (for some trees can be produced even in this manner).

Of these methods spontaneous growth comes first, one may say, but growth from seed or root would seem most natural; indeed these methods too may be called spontaneous; wherefore they are found even in wild kinds, while the remaining methods depend on human skill or at least on human choice.

However all plants start in one or other of these ways, and most of them in more than one. Thus the olive is grown in all the ways mentioned, except from a twig; for an olive-twig will not grow if it is set in the ground, as a fig or pomegranate will grow from their young shoots. Not but what some say that cases have been known in which, when a stake of olive-wood was planted to support ivy, it actually lived along with it and became a tree; but such an instance is a rare exception, while the other methods of growth are in most cases the natural ones. The fig grows in all the ways mentioned, except from root-stock and cleft wood; apple and pear grow also from branches, but rarely. However, it appears that most, if not practically all, trees may grow from branches, if these are smooth, young, and vigorous. But the other methods, one may say, are more natural, and we must reckon what may occasionally occur as a mere possibility.

In fact there are quite few plants which grow and are brought into being more easily from the upper parts, as the vine is grown from branches; for this, though it cannot be grown from the "head," yet can be grown from the branch, as can all similar trees and under-shrubs, for instance, as it appears, rue, gilliflower, bergamot-mint, tufted thyme, calamint. So the commonest ways of growth with all plants are from a piece torn off or from seed; for all plants that have seeds grow also from seed. And they say that the bay too grows from a piece torn off, if one takes off the young shoots and plants them; but it is necessary that the piece torn off should have part of the root or stock attached to it. However, the pomegranate and "spring apple" will grow even without this, and a slip of almond grows if it is planted. The olive grows, one may say, in more ways than any other plant; it grows from a piece of the trunk or of the stock, from the root, from a twig, and from a stake, as has been said. Of other plants the myrtle also can be propagated in several ways; for this too grows from pieces of wood and also from pieces of the stock. It is necessary, however, with this, as with the olive, to cut up the wood into pieces not less than a span long and not to strip off the bark.

Trees then grow and come into being in the above-mentioned ways;

for as to methods of grafting and inoculation, these are, as it were, combinations of different kinds of trees; or at all events these are methods of growth of quite different class and must be treated of at a later stage.

2. Of under-shrubs and herbaceous plants the greater part grow from seed or a root, and some in both ways; some of them also grow from cuttings, as has been said, while roses and lilies grow from pieces of the stems, as also does dog's-tooth grass. Lilies and roses also grow when the whole stem is set. Most peculiar is the method of growth from an exudation; for it appears that the lily grows in this way too, when the exudation that has been produced has dried up. They say the same of alexanders, for this too produces an exudation. There is a certain reed also which grows if one cuts it in lengths from joint to joint, and sets them sideways, burying it in dung and soil. Again they say that plants which have a bulbous root are peculiar in their way of growing from the root.

The capacity for growth being shown in so many ways, most trees, as was said before, originate in several ways; but some come only from seed, as silver-fir, fir, Aleppo pine, and in general all those that bear cones; also the date-palm, except that in Babylon it may be that, as some say, they take cuttings from it. The cypress in most regions grows from seed but in Crete from the trunk also, for instance in the hill country about Tarra; for there grows the cypress which they clip, and when cut it shoots in every possible way, from the part which has been cut, from the ground, from the middle, and from the upper parts; and occasionally, but rarely, it shoots from the roots also.

About the oak accounts differ; some say it only grows from seed, some from the root also, but not vigorously, others again that it grows from the trunk itself, when this is cut. But no tree grows from a piece torn off or from a root except those which make sidegrowths.

*"Give me a place to stand and
I will move the world."*

Archimedes

287 – 212 B.C.

THE LAW OF THE LEVER IS DEVELOPED
AND SOME APPLICATIONS OF THIS
PRINCIPLE ARE SET FORTH

There was an implicit conflict between Plato and Aristotle that derived from the deductive methods of the one and the experimental, or inductive, methods of the other. In Archimedes we find a synthesis. Combining mathematics with experiment, he was able to set up hypotheses with respect to limited aspects of the problem, to make deductions therefrom, and, finally, to test the results against further observation. As he was clearly a pioneer in the modern scientific method, so he was a leader in applying science to contemporary problems. His life is surrounded with legend; but much of it accords with the capacity of this great mathematician and inventor.

Archimedes was born and died in Syracuse, on the island of Sicily. He may have been a relative of its king, Hieron II (*c.* 306-215 B.C.). He may have studied in Alexandria, or had close contacts with the scholars there and made use of its publishing facilities. Many of his practical discoveries are associated with King Hieron; for him he invented the water screw, which, turning in a tightly fitting cylinder, would raise water from the hold of a ship or, as in Egypt, from the river Nile.

When Hieron suspected that his craftsmen had stolen some

of the gold intended for his crown and had alloyed the remainder with silver in order to cover the theft, he called on Archimedes to examine the case. The incident supposedly led to the observations from which Archimedes evolved the concept of relative density of bodies. It is said that Archimedes noticed, when he entered his bath, that he displaced a volume of water equal to that of his own body. From this he went on to show, by experiment, that when a body is immersed in a liquid, its weight is diminished by the weight of the water displaced; when a body floats, its weight is equal to the weight of the liquid displaced. Archimedes was able to exonerate the craftsmen from Hiero's charge and went on to demonstrate some general principles, which he deduced mathematically, as to the nature of fluids. From these came laws of hydrostatics and the means of making hydrometers, used today for measuring the density of liquids. Archimedes's skills were also applied to the arts of war; for example, he invented a catapult which was used in defending Syracuse for three years against the besieging Romans. When the city was finally stormed, Archimedes was slain by a soldier who came upon him while he was studying a geometrical problem he had drawn in the sand.

From Archimedes's original work in mathematics, we obtained our everyday value of the term π for determining the area of a circle (πr^2). His work on the measurement of the sphere and the cylinder was so significant to his contemporaries that these figures were cut into his tombstone.

The reading included here is from his *Physical Treatises* (from the translation by T. L. Heath, published by Cambridge University Press). It shows his analysis of the equilibrum of planes and the center of gravity, from which he established the law of the lever. Here we see Archimedes as an inventor, demonstrating that geometry had a practical application. In this he is to be contrasted with his predecessor, Euclid, who contented himself with summarizing the accumulated knowledge of geometry.

ON THE EQUILIBRIUM OF PLANES OR THE CENTRES OF GRAVITY OF PLANES

"I POSTULATE the following:

1. Equal weights at equal distances are in equilibrium, and equal weights at unequal distances are not in equilibrium but incline towards the weight which is at the greater distance.

2. If, when weights at certain distances are in equilibrium, something be added to one of the weights, they are not in equilibrium but incline towards that weight to which the addition was made.

3. Similarly, if anything be taken away from one of the weights, they are not in equilibrium but incline towards the weight from which nothing was taken.

4. When equal and similar plane figures coincide if applied to one another, their centres of gravity similarly coincide.

5. In figures which are unequal but similar the centres of gravity will be similarly situated. By points similarly situated in relation to similar figures I mean points such that, if straight lines be drawn from them to the equal angles, they make equal angles with the corresponding sides.

6. If magnitudes at certain distances be in equilibrium, (other) magnitudes equal to them will also be in equilibrium at the same distances.

7. In any figure whose perimeter is concave in (one and) the same direction the centre of gravity must be within the figure."

PROPOSITION 1

Weights which balance at equal distances are equal.

For, if they are unequal, take away from the greater the difference between the two. The remainders will then not balance [*Post.* 3]; which is absurd.

Therefore the weights cannot be unequal.

PROPOSITION 2

Unequal weights at equal distances will not balance but will incline towards the greater weight.

For take away from the greater the difference between the two. The equal remainders will therefore balance [*Post.* 1]. Hence, if we add the difference again, the weights will not balance but incline towards the greater [*Post.* 2].

PROPOSITION 3

Unequal weights will balance at unequal distances, the greater weight being at the lesser distance.

Let *A*, *B* be two unequal weights (of which *A* in the greater) balancing about *C* at distances *AC*, *BC* respectively.

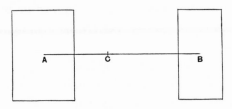

Then shall *AC* be less than *BC*. For, if not, take away from *A* the weight (*A* − *B*.) The remainders will then incline towards *B* [*Post.* 3]. But this is impossible, for (1) if *AC* = *CB*, the equal remainders will balance, or (2) if *AC* > *CB*, they will incline towards *A* at the greater distance [*Post.* 1].

Hence *AC* < *CB*.

Conversely, if the weights balance, and *AC* < *CB*, then *A* > *B*.

PROPOSITION 4

If two equal weights have not the same centre of gravity, the centre of gravity of both taken together is at the middle point of the line joining their centres of gravity.

PROPOSITION 5

If three equal magnitudes have their centres of gravity on a straight line at equal distances, the centre of gravity of the system will coincide with that of the middle magnitude. [This follows immediately from Prop. 4.]

Cor. 1. *The same is true of any odd number of magnitudes if those which are at equal distances from the middle one are equal, while the distances between their centres of gravity are equal.*

Cor. 2. *If there be an even number of magnitudes with their centres of gravity situated at equal distances on one straight line, and if the two middle ones be equal, while those which are equidistant from them (on each side) are equal respectively, the centre of gravity of the system is the middle point of the line joining the centres of gravity of the two middle ones.*

PROPOSITION 6, 7

Two magnitudes, whether commensurable [Prop. 6] *or incommensurable* [Prop. 7], *balance at distances reciprocally proportional to the magnitudes.*

I. Suppose the magnitudes A, B to be commensurable, and the points A, B to be their centres of gravity. Let DE be a straight line so divided at C that.

$$A : B = DC : CE.$$

We have then to prove that, if A be placed at E and B at D, C is the centre of gravity of the two taken together.

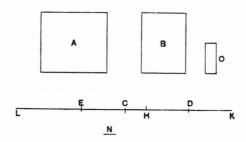

Since A, B are commensurable, so are DC, CE. Let N be a common measure of DC, CE. Make DH, DK each equal to CE, and EL (on CE produced) equal to CD. Then $EH = CD$, since $DH = CE$. Therefore LH is bisected at E, as HK is bisected at D.

Thus LH, HK must each contain N an even number of times.

Take a magnitude O such that O is contained as many times in A as N is contained in LH, whence

$$A : O = LH : N.$$

But
$$B : A = CE : DC$$
$$= HK : LH.$$

Hence, *ex aequali*, $B : O = HK : N$, or O is contained in B as many times as N is contained in HK.

Thus O is a common measure of A, B.

Divide LH, HK into parts each equal to N, and A, B into parts each equal to O. The parts of A will therefore be equal in number to those of

LH, and the parts of B equal in number to those of HK. Place one of the parts of A at the middle point of each of the parts N of LH, and one of the parts of B at the middle point of each of the parts N of HK.

Then the centre of gravity of the parts of A placed at equal distances on LH will be at E, the middle point of LH [Prop. 5, Cor. 2], and the centre of gravity of the parts of B placed at equal distances along HK will be at D, the middle point of HK.

Thus we may suppose A itself applied at E, and B itself applied at D.

But the system formed by the parts O of A and B together is a system of equal magnitudes even in number and placed at equal distances along LK. And, since $LE = CD$, and $EC = DK$, $LC = CK$, so that C is the middle point of LK. Therefore C is the centre of gravity of the system ranged along LK.

Therefore A acting at E and B acting at D balance about the point C.

II. Suppose the magnitudes to be incommensurable, and let them be $(A + a)$ and B respectively. Let DE be a line divided at C so that

$$(A + a) : B = DC : CE.$$

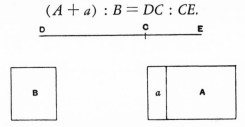

Then, if $(A + a)$ placed at E and B placed at D do not balance about C, $(A + a)$ is either too great to balance B, or not great enough.

Suppose, if possible, that $(A + a)$ is too great to balance B. Take from $(A + a)$ a magnitude a smaller than the deduction which would make the remainder balance B, but such that the remainder A and the magnitude B are commensurable.

Then, since A, B are commensurable, and

$$A : B < DC : CE,$$

A and B will not balance [Prop. 6], but D will be depressed.

But this is impossible, since the deduction a was an insufficient deduction from $(A + a)$ to produce equilibrium, so that E was still depressed.

Therefore $(A + a)$ is not too great to balance B; and similarly it may be proved that B is not too great to balance $(A + a)$.

Hence $(A + a)$, B taken together have their centre of gravity at C.

PROPOSITION 8

If AB be a magnitude whose centre of gravity is C, and AD a part of it whose centre of gravity is F, then the centre of gravity of the remaining part will be a point G on FC produced such that

$$GC : CF = (AD) : (DE).$$

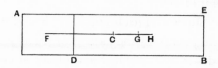

For, if the centre of gravity of the remainder (DE) be not G, let it be a point H. Then an absurdity follows at once from Props. 6, 7.

PROPOSITION 9

The centre of gravity of any parallelogram lies on the straight line joining the middle points of opposite sides.

Let $ABCD$ be a parallelogram, and let EF join the middle points of the opposite sides AD, BC.

If the centre of gravity does not lie on EF, suppose it to be H, and draw HK parallel to AD or BC meeting EF in K.

Then it is possible, by bisecting ED, then bisecting the halves, and so on continually, to arrive at a length EL less than KH. Divide both AE and ED into parts each equal to EL, and through the points of division draw parallels to AB or CD.

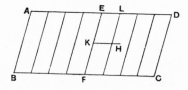

We have then a number of equal and similar parallelograms, and, if any one be applied to any other, their centres of gravity coincide [*Post.* 4]. Thus we have an even number of equal magnitudes whose centres of gravity lie at equal distances along a straight line. Hence the centre of gravity of the whole parallelogram will lie on the line joining the centres of gravity of the two middle parallelograms [Prop. 5, Cor. 2].

But this is impossible, for *H* is outside the middle parallelograms. Therefore the centre of gravity cannot but lie on *EF*.

PROPOSITION 10

The centre of gravity of a parallelogram is the point of intersection of its diagonals.

For, by the last proposition, the centre of gravity lies on each of the lines which bisect opposite sides. Therefore it is at the point of their intersection; and this is also the point of intersection of the diagonals.

Alternate proof.

Let *ABCD* be the given parallelogram, and *BD* a diagonal. Then the triangles *ABD*, *CDB* are equal and similar, so that [*Post.* 4], if one be applied to the other, their centres of gravity will fall one upon the other.

Suppose *F* to be the centre of gravity of the triangle *ABD*. Let *G* be the middle point of *BD*. Join *FG* and produce it to *H*, so that *FG* = *GH*.

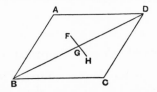

If we then apply the triangle *ABD* to the triangle *CDB* so that *AD* falls on *CB* and *AB* on *CD*, the point *F* will fall on *H*.

But [by *Post.* 4] *F* will fall on the centre of gravity of *CDB*. Therefore *H* is the centre of gravity of *CDB*.

Hence, since *F*, *H* are the centres of gravity of the two equal triangles, the centre of gravity of the whole parallelogram is at the middle point of *FH*, i.e. at the middle point of *BD*, which is the intersection of the two diagonals.

"If the extent of the
Atlantic Ocean were not an obstacle,
we might easily pass by sea from Iberia to India,
keeping in the same parallel."

Eratosthenes

c. 275 – 194 B. C.

A METHOD IS DESCRIBED FOR MEASURING
THE CIRCUMFERENCE OF THE EARTH

The expeditions of Alexander opened up a new world to
the botanist Theophrastus, and his founding of the great center
of learning at Alexandria provided a place for the study of the
results of the botanist's terrestrial observations. The librarian
appointed in the year 235 B.C. was Eratosthenes, who proved
to be the first great geographer and the founder of the science
of geography. He made maps, conceived the idea of projections
(by means of which the map surface on a globe may be presented on a plane surface), and compiled a general treatise on
geography. He is best known for his highly successful attempt
to measure the circumference of the globe, which is described
in the reading that follows. This comes not from his own account, which has disappeared, but from that of a Greek astronomer, Cleomedes, writing a hundred years or so later.

It should be noted that Eratosthenes exposed himself to
error by making two basic assumptions: first, that Alexandria
and Syene were on the same meridian, and second, that Syene
was on the Tropic of Cancer. He was slightly incorrect in both
assumptions; but this does not invalidate the essential accuracy

150

of his discovery that the angle between Alexandria and Syene, as measured by the angle of the noon sun on midsummer day, was exactly one-fiftieth of the 360° circle. We do not know the modern equivalent of Eratosthenes's unit of linear measurement, the *stade*. If, as George Sarton says, it is .157 miles, Eratosthenes measured the circumference of the earth as 24,662 miles, with a corresponding diameter of 7850 miles, or only 50 miles less than the actual diameter at the poles. The technique of measurement depended on two other propositions, remarkable for the period when they were made: that the earth was a sphere and that the rays of the sun, when they strike the earth, are, for all practical purposes, parallel.

Eratosthenes is said to have relied mostly on data in books for his studies, and this often led him to inaccurate conclusions. His reputation seems to be justified, however, by the conclusions he reached when he had accurate data with which to work.

The reading is from the T. L. Heath translation from Cleomedes, in *Greek Astronomy,* published by Dent in 1932.

THE MEASUREMENT OF THE CIRCUMFERENCE OF THE EARTH

About the size of the earth the physicists, or natural philosophers, have held different views, but those of Posidonius and Eratosthenes are preferable to the rest. The latter shows the size of the earth by a geometrical method; the method of Posidonius is simpler. Both lay down certain hypotheses, and, by successive inferences from the hypotheses, arrive at their demonstrations.

* * *

The method of Eratosthenes depends on a geometrical argument and gives the impression of being slightly more difficult to follow. But his statement will be made clear if we premise the following. Let us suppose, in this case too, first, that Syene and Alexandria lie under the same meridian circle; secondly, that the distance between the two cities is 5,000 stades; and thirdly, that the rays sent down from different parts of the sun on different parts of the earth are parallel; for this is the hypothesis on which geometers proceed. Fourthly, let us assume that, as proved by the geometers, straight lines falling on parallel straight lines make the alternate angles equal, and fifthly, that the arcs standing on (i.e., subtended by) equal angles are similar, that is, have the same proportion and the same ratio to their proper circles—this, too, being a fact proved by the geometers. Whenever, therefore, arcs of circles stand on equal angles, if any one of these is (say) one-tenth of its proper circle, all the other arcs will be tenth parts of their proper circles.

Any one who has grasped these facts will have no difficulty in understanding the method of Eratosthenes, which is this. Syene and Alexandria lie, he says, under the same meridian circle. Since meridian circles are great circles in the universe, the circles of the earth which lie under them are necessarily also great circles. Thus, of whatever size this method shows the circle on the earth passing through Syene and Alexandria to be, this will be the size of the great circle of the earth. Now Eratosthenes asserts, and it is the fact, that Syene lies under the summer tropic. Whenever, therefore, the sun, being in the Crab at the summer solstice, is exactly in the middle of the heaven, the gnomons (pointers) of sundials necessarily throw no shadows, the position of the sun above them being exactly vertical; and it is said that this is true throughout a space three hundred stades in diameter. But in Alexandria, at the same hour, the pointers of sundials throw shadows, because Alexandria lies further to the north than Syene. The two cities lying under the same meridian great circle, if we draw an arc from the extremity of the shadow to the base of the pointer of the sundial in Alexandria, the arc will be a segment of a great circle in the (hemispherical) bowl of the sundial, since the bowl of the sundial lies under the great circle (of the meridian). If now we conceive straight lines produced from each of the pointers through the earth, they will meet at the centre of the earth. Since then the sundial at Syene is vertically under the sun, if we conceive a straight line coming from the sun to the top of the pointer of the sundial, the line reaching from the sun to the centre of the earth will be one straight line. If now we conceive another straight line drawn upwards from the extremity of the shadow of the pointer of the sundial in Alexandria, through the top of the pointer to the sun, this straight line and the aforesaid straight line will be parallel, since they are straight lines coming through from different parts of the sun to different parts of the earth. On these straight lines, therefore, which are parallel, there falls the straight line drawn from the centre of the earth to the pointer at Alexandria, so that the alternate angles which it makes are equal. One of these angles is that formed at the centre of the earth, at the intersection of the straight lines which were drawn from the sundials to the centre of the earth; the other is at the point of intersection of the top of the pointer at Alexandria and the straight line drawn from the extremity of its shadow to the sun through the point (the top) where it meets the pointer. Now on this latter angle stands the arc carried round from the extremity of the shadow of the pointer to its base, while on the angle at the centre of the earth stands the arc reaching from Syene to Alexandria. But the arcs are similar, since they stand on equal angles. Whatever ratio, therefore, the arc in the bowl of the sundial has to its proper circle, the arc reaching from Syene to Alexandria has that ratio to *its* proper circle. But the arc in the bowl is found to be one-fiftieth of its proper circle. Therefore the distance from Syene to Alexandria must necessarily be one-fiftieth part of the great circle of the earth. And the said distance is 5,000 stades; therefore the complete great circle measures 250,000 stades. Such is Eratosthenes' method.

"This ultimate stock we have devised to name
Procreant atoms, matter, seeds of things,
Or primal bodies, as primal to the world."

Lucretius

c. 95 – 55 B.C.

THE ATOMIC THEORY OF THE NATURE OF
THINGS, ACCORDING TO THE IDEAS OF
DEMOCRITUS AND EPICURUS,
IS SET FORTH

De Rerum Natura has been described by George Sarton
as the greatest philosophical poem of all time. Whatever its
literary merits, it stands as evidence of the manner in which
Greek scientific thinking was absorbed by the Romans, for it is,
for the most part, an exposition of the views of Democritus
(470-400 B.C.) and Epicurus (341-270 B.C.), whose lives
overlapped that of Aristotle at either end. A contemporary of
Marcus Tullius Cicero (himself a popularizer of Greek philosophy) and of Caius Julius Caesar, Lucretius, the Epicurean, helped
to bring the knowledge of atomism to the scholars of the Middle
Ages and thus was instrumental in its general acceptance by such
men as Galileo and Newton. Lucretius's views had their origins
in a period preceding Aristotle, but their influence during the
revival of learning makes them a worthy climax to this account
of the beginnings of the scientific approach.

Democritus was caught up in the effort to explain the origin
of matter in terms other than those of the sensations. He denied,
in effect, that reality can be described by the human comprehen-

154

sion of it. To describe a thing as sweet or bitter was inadequate to account for its essential being, for such a description was subjective and gave no clue to the problem of why there is "the stuff for plenishing the world."

For him the explanation lay in the concept of atoms, indivisible particles existing from the infinite and incapable of destruction. They combined in various ways and in sundry shapes and sizes to form objects with differing properties. In a similar way, atoms combined to form the innumerable worlds of the universe. The universe, indeed, consisted of atoms—and a vacuum.

Aristotle rejected Democritus's atomic theory and, in particular, the concept of the possibility of the vacuum, but Epicurus revived the theory and it survived to be an important influence on sixteenth-century thinkers. Though it was a primitive idea, the atomic theory came closer to modern explanations of the structure of matter than any other concept of the Greek or later thinkers. The poem of Lucretius presents the ideas in a form unusual for a collection of readings in science; but it could hardly be clearer or more logical in its expression. If the theories recorded here have no direct connection with modern atomic theory, there remains the possibility that such men as John Dalton (1766-1844), with whom the modern study begins, may have been inspired by them.

The selection is taken from the William Ellery Leonard translation of *De Rerum Natura,* in the Everyman edition of 1916.

NOTHING EXISTS per se *EXCEPT ATOMS AND THE VOID*

But, now again to weave the tale begun,
All nature, then, as self-sustained, consists
Of twain of things: of bodies and of void
In which they're set, and where they're moved around.

For common instinct of our race declares
That body of itself exists: unless
This primal faith, deep-founded, fail us not,
Naught will there be whereunto to appeal
On things occult when seeking aught to prove
By reasonings of mind. Again, without
That place and room, which we do call the inane,
Nowhere could bodies then be set, nor go
Hither or thither at all—as shown before.
Besides, there's naught of which thou canst declare
It lives disjoined from body, shut from void—
A kind of third in nature. For whatever
Exists must be a somewhat; and the same,
If tangible, however light and slight,
Will yet increase the count of body's sum,
With its own augmentation big or small;
But, if intangible and powerless ever
To keep a thing from passing through itself
On any side, 'twill be naught else but that
Which we do call the empty, the inane.
Again, whate'er exists, as of itself,
Must either act or suffer action on it,
Or else be that wherein things move and be:
Naught, saving body, acts, is acted on;
Naught but the inane can furnish room. And thus,
Beside the inane and bodies, is no third
Nature amid the number of all things—
Remainder none to fall at any time
Under our senses, nor be seized and seen
By any man through reasonings of mind.
Name o'er creation with what names thou wilt,
Thou'lt find but properties of those first twain,
Or see but accidents those twain produce.
    A property is that which not at all
Can be disjoined and severed from a thing
Without a fatal dissolution: such,

Weight to the rocks, heat to the fire, and flow
To the wide waters, touch to corporal things,
Intangibility to the viewless void.
But state of slavery, pauperhood, and wealth,
Freedom, and war, and concord, and all else
Which come and go whilst nature stands the same,
We're wont, and rightly, to call accidents.
Even time exists not of itself; but sense
Reads out of things what happened long ago,
What presses now, and what shall follow after:
No man, we must admit, feels time itself,
Disjoined from motion and repose of things.
Thus, when they say there "is" the ravishment
Of Princess Helen, "is" the siege and sack
Of Trojan Town, look out, they force us not
To admit these acts existent by themselves,
Merely because those races of mankind
(Of whom these acts were accidents) long since
Irrevocable age has borne away:
For all past actions may be said to be
But accidents, in one way, of mankind,—
In other, of some *region* of the world.
Add, too, had been no matter, and no room
Wherein all things go on, the fire of love
Upblown by that fair form, the glowing coal
Under the Phrygian Alexander's breast,
Had ne'er enkindled that renownèd strife
Of savage war, nor had the wooden horse
Involved in flames old Pergama, by a birth
At midnight of a brood of the Hellenes.
And thus thou canst remark that every act
At bottom exists not of itself, nor is
As body is, nor has like name with void;
But rather of sort more fitly to be called
An accident of body, and of place
Wherein all things go on.

CHARACTER OF THE ATOMS

Bodies, again,
Are partly primal germs of things, and partly
Unions deriving from the primal germs.
And those which are the primal germs of things
No power can quench; for in the end they conquer
By their own solidness; though hard it be
To think that aught in things has solid frame;
For lightnings pass, no less than voice and shout,
Through hedging walls of houses, and the iron
White-dazzles in the fire, and rocks will burn
With exhalations fierce and burst asunder.
Totters the rigid gold dissolved in heat;
The ice of bronze melts conquered in the flame;
Warmth and the piercing cold through silver seep,
Since, with the cups held rightly in the hand,
We oft feel both, as from above is poured
The dew of waters between their shining sides:
So true it is no solid form is found.
But yet because true reason and nature of things
Constrain us, come, whilst in few verses now
I disentangle how there still exist
Bodies of solid, everlasting frame—
The seeds of things, the primal germs we teach,
Whence all creation around us came to be.
First since we know a twofold nature exists,
Of things, both twain and utterly unlike—
Body, and place in which all things go on—
Then each must be both for and through itself,
And all unmixed: where'er be empty space,
There body's *not*; and so where body bides,
There not at all exists the void inane.
Thus primal bodies are solid, without a void.
But since there's void in all begotten things,
All solid matter must be round the same;
Nor, by true reason canst thou prove aught hides
And holds a void within its body, unless

Thou grant what holds it be a solid. Know,
That which can hold a void of things within
Can be naught else than matter in union knit.
Thus matter, consisting of a solid frame,
Hath power to be eternal, though all else,
Though all creation, be dissolved away.
Again, were naught of empty and inane,
The world were then a solid; as, without
Some certain bodies to fill the place held,
The world that is were but a vacant void.
And so, infallibly, alternate-wise
Body and void are still distinguished,
Since nature knows no wholly full nor void.
There are, then, certain bodies, possessed of power
To vary forever the empty and the full;
And these can nor be sundered from without
By beats and blows, nor from within be torn
By penetration, nor be overthrown
By any assault soever through the world—
For without void, naught can be crushed, it seems,
Nor broken, nor severed by a cut in twain,
Nor can it take the damp, or seeping cold
Or piercing fire, those old destroyers three;
But the more void within a thing, the more
Entirely it totters at their sure assault.
Thus if first bodies be, as I have taught,
Solid, without a void, they must be then
Eternal; and, if matter ne'er had been
Eternal, long ere now had all things gone
Back into nothing utterly, and all
We see around from nothing had been born—
But since I taught above that naught can be
From naught created, nor the once begotten
To naught be summoned back, these primal germs
Must have an immortality of frame.
And into these must each thing be resolved,
When comes its súpreme hour, that thus there be
At hand the stuff for plenishing the world.

* * *

So primal germs have solid singleness,
Nor otherwise could they have been conserved
Through æons and infinity of time
For the replenishment of wasted worlds.
Once more, if nature had given a scope for things
To be forever broken more and more,
By now the bodies of matter would have been
So far reduced by breakings in old days
That from them nothing could, at season fixed,
Be born, and arrive its prime and top of life.
For, lo, each thing is quicker marred than made;
And so whate'er the long infinitude
Of days and all fore-passèd time would now
By this have broken and ruined and dissolved,
That same could ne'er in all remaining time
Be builded up for plenishing the world.
But mark: infallibly a fixèd bound
Remaineth stablished 'gainst their breaking down;
Since we behold each thing soever renewed,
And unto all, their seasons, after their kind,
Wherein they arrive the flower of their age.
    Again, if bounds have not been set against
The breaking down of this corporeal world,
Yet must all bodies of whatever things
Have still endured from everlasting time
Unto this present, as not yet assailed
By shocks of peril. But because the same
Are, to thy thinking, of a nature frail,
It ill accords that thus they could remain
(As thus they do) through everlasting time,
Vexed through the ages (as indeed they are)
By the innumerable blows of chance.
    So in our programme of creation, mark
How 'tis that, though the bodies of all stuff
Are solid to the core, we yet explain
The ways whereby some things are fashioned soft—
Air, water, earth, and fiery exhalations—

And by what force they function and go on:
The fact is founded in the void of things.
But if the primal germs themselves be soft,
Reason cannot be brought to bear to show
The ways whereby may be created these
Great crags of basalt and the during iron;
For their whole nature will profoundly lack
The first foundations of a solid frame.
But powerful in old simplicity,
Abide the solid, the primeval germs;
And by their combinations more condensed,
All objects can be tightly knit and bound
And made to show unconquerable strength.
Again, since all things kind by kind obtain
Fixed bounds of growing and conserving life;
Since nature hath inviolably decreed
What each can do, what each can never do;
Since naught is changed, but all things so abide
That ever the variegated birds reveal
The spots or stripes peculiar to their kind,
Spring after spring: thus surely all that is
Must be composed of matter immutable.
For if the primal germs in any wise
Were open to conquest and to change, 'twould be
Uncertain also what could come to birth
And what could not, and by what law to each
Its scope prescribed, its boundary stone that clings
So deep in Time. Nor could the generations
Kind after kind so often reproduce
The nature, habits, motions, ways of life,
Of their progenitors.
               And then again,
Since there is ever an éxtreme bounding point

              *   *   *

Of that first body which our senses now
Cannot perceive: That bounding point indeed
Exists without all parts, a minimum
Of nature, nor was e'er a thing apart,

As of itself,—nor shall hereafter be,
Since 'tis itself still parcel of another,
A first and single part, whence other parts
And others similar in order lie
In a packed phalanx, filling to the full
The nature of first body: being thus
Not self-existent, they must cleave to that
From which in nowise they can sundered be.
So primal germs have solid singleness,
Which tightly packed and closely joined cohere
By virtue of their minim particles—
No compound by mere union of the same;
But strong in their eternal singleness,
Nature, reserving them as seeds for things,
Permitteth naught of rupture or decrease.

    Moreover, were there not a minimum,
The smallest bodies would have infinites,
Since then a half-of-half could still be halved,
With limitless division less and less.
Then what the difference 'twixt the sum and least?
None: for however infinite the sum,
Yet even the smallest would consist the same
Of infinite parts. But since true reason here
Protests, denying that the mind can think it,
Convinced thou must confess such things there are
As have no parts, the minimums of nature.
And since these are, likewise confess thou must
That primal bodies are solid and eterne.
Again, if Nature, creatress of all things,
Were wont to force all things to be resolved
Unto least parts, then would she not avail
To reproduce from out them anything;
Because whate'er is not endowed with parts
Cannot possess those properties required
Of generative stuff—divers connections,
Weights, blows, encounters, motions, whereby things
Forevermore have being and go on.

IV

The Bridge

The Bridge

IV

*"The defects of the scholastic method
are those that inevitably result from laying stress on 'dialectics.'
These defects are: indifference to facts and science, belief
in reasoning in matters which only observation
can decide, and an undue emphasis on
verbal distinctions and subtleties."*
—Bertrand Russell

THE BRIDGE

Between the decline of the Graeco-Roman civilization and the revival of learning and scientific inquiry, the Dark Ages intervened—for a period of roughly a thousand years before the birth of Leonardo da Vinci. We are apt to dismiss this period as one in which the urge to discover was at its lowest. The records are, naturally enough, not extensive for this period because they were in the form of manuscripts, limited in number and easily lost or destroyed. Moreover, any achievements of the period are apt to be overlooked because of our interest in the influence of the Schoolmen. Their efforts to reconcile Greek science with the teachings of the Church and their tendency to indulge in lengthy debates on what we now consider inconsequential points combined to obscure the positive contributions. Sarton's researches are a testimony to the extent of this work; his summary of the fourteenth century alone extends over one thousand pages. Not many of those who contributed to knowledge were of the stature of their successors of the fifteenth century and after, but there were enough men collecting information, compiling treatises, and speculating on scientific subjects to form an intellectual

163

bridge between the Classical and the Renaissance periods. The bridge was perhaps a narrow one, and some of its supports weak by later standards; but it was adequate to maintain a spirit of inquiry against the rigidities and conservatism of dogmatic scholars. The real struggle between the Schoolmen and the scientists reached its climax later, in the time of Copernicus and Galileo; but the conservatives had frequently indeed to invoke the power of the church against those whose ideas departed from accepted "truth."

The readings in Part IV cover a long period, extending from A.D. 23 to the beginning of the eighteenth century. The first three—examples of the work of Pliny the Elder, Ptolemy, and Galen—belong, in fact, to the Graeco-Roman period, whereas the selections from van Helmont and Georg Ernst Stahl are so clearly dated long after the Renaissance began that it may appear strange to include them with the truly medieval specimens from Geber and the Bestiary. The reasons for these choices are simple. The early writings are included to show the foundations upon which the medieval scholar continued his scientific work. Van Helmont and Stahl offer examples of the survival of the medieval approach in the modern period.

As we shall see, Ptolemy's systematic account of the universe was erroneous; but he evolved a workable structure that could be made to explain the heavenly phenomena in terms that could be applied to the needs of the time; and the medieval scholars thought more of perfecting his compilations than of criticizing them. The fact that his basic hypothesis was incorrect was, for practical purposes, of no importance as long as the needs of men required no more. The urge to oceanic exploration came much later, and only then did the Ptolemaic system require reexamination.

Pliny's *Natural History,* notwithstanding the rubbish it included, emphasized the value of recording observations. He inspired the later *Books of Beasts,* in which medieval scholars accumulated facts and fantasies with artistic gusto; yet they *did* collect facts. Galen attained an unfortunate influence over later medical men, but his observations, although inaccurate in some

respects, were nevertheless on record and inspired such research-
ers as Vesalius, of whom we shall read in Volume 2.

At the other end of the time span covered by these selections
are van Helmont and Stahl, whose failure to make real advances
in chemistry is to be attributed more to their preoccupation with
general explanations than to their failures in experimentation.
They sought a universal theory that would explain all the phenomena encountered in chemical reactions. Though their conclusions were erroneous, they succeeded in establishing workable
hypotheses which had considerable influence in stimulating experiment. They were useful indeed to such men as Henry Cavendish, Joseph Priestley, and Antoine Laurent Lavoisier, whose
work succeeded in establishing, at long last, a sound basis for
the study of chemistry.

The delayed emergence of chemistry as a factor in the
growth of science is one of the oddities of history. Although the
influence of the Schoolmen—or, better, of the theological approach to science—was effectively broken by the astronomers
and mathematicians early in the sixteenth century, the power of
those who hoped to discover the secret of making gold persisted
for two centuries more.

The inclusion of an extract from Agricola's *De Re Metallica*
("Of Minerals") reminds us that technological progress in the
Dark Ages must not be measured only by reference to the contributions of the scientists. Life continued in spite of wars and
controversies. People had to be fed and clothed; arms had to be
made. The wealthy demanded armor for themselves and jewelry
for their womenfolk. Travelers needed articles that they could
trade for food and lodging in strange countries. Horses had to
be shod and saddled. Ships had to be built, fields tilled and har-
vested. Trade became organized in the guilds, and knowledge
of improved methods could be disseminated without giving up
the secrets of the crafts to any and everybody.

It was suggested earlier that what we call the Industrial
Revolution began without the help of systematic science; and it
can be said of the medieval period that, in a similar way, modest
progress took place in the industrial arts without benefit of

scientific explanation of the phenomena involved. Agricola's vast researches into the practices of miners and refiners of metal show the extent to which this progress had occurred. Some of the methods he describes were efficient enough to remain unchanged until the end of the eighteenth century. His explanations of the manner in which metals were formed in the earth's crust showed the lack of scientific investigation; but the brass founder's skill in discerning the precise moment when zinc should be added to molten copper to make the alloy we call brass was a chemical "experiment" of a high order. It lacked an explanation, but the data remained available for the later scientist to think about.

To give a cutting edge to a weapon and to find the means of fashioning a complicated suit of armor that would be strong enough to ward off a blow from a sixteen-foot war lance implied experimental work. That we now think of such work as the method of trial and error in no way diminishes the credit due to the early craftsman.

When we look at a painting of the medieval period—say by Giotto (c. 1270-1336) — and note the brilliance of his centuries-old colors, we are reminded of the long research into the qualities of pigments, oil, and varnishes that Giotto inherited and developed. In the same period were built churches and cathedrals whose designs are copied by modern architects; the medieval craftsman solved problems involving load factors and stresses which today would need extensive mathematical knowledge; without benefit of scientific testing and analysis, they selected building materials which have withstood seven centuries of weathering.

These contributions to empirical knowledge must, of course, be considered in relation to their contribution to general welfare. Many of them affected only the wealthiest people. The advances that enabled the common man to enjoy better living were to be long deferred. Social change depended on many other factors. Yet the expanding class of craftsmen provided a channel through which the technical improvements that they evolved were translated into better living for more people.

Another factor distinguishes the medieval from the classical period: the steady increase in travel. The pilgrims who moved in a continuous stream to their national shrines or to Rome encountered travelers from other lands. The itinerant friars kept up the lines of communication between the houses of their respective orders. The Crusaders moved in relatively large groups whose needs had to be catered to, and hence the maintenance of armor, arms, and saddlery developed international characteristics. The sight of a Damascene sword would stimulate the envy and energy of an English or French smith. As the universities were established, the interchange of scholars brought constant infusions of knowledge of the arts to the hosts. At sea, sailors adapted primitive knowledge of the loadstone to the needs of navigation; thus, by at least the mid-thirteenth century, a compass was evolved.

Sooner or later these empirical developments, though small and, by our standards, insignificant, had to invade the cloisters. We have already read of Roger Bacon's call for more experiment; but, in general, philosophy, seeking, as Sarton says, "to unify knowledge and to harmonize it with one's religious creed," took most of the available intellectual energy.

Meanwhile, science continued to develop outside Western Europe. The founding of the essentially Greek city of Alexandria on the frontiers of the Arab world resulted in the translation into Arabic of Greek texts; these were to become a starting point for much original Arabic development. These Arabic translations came to the European medieval scholars through Moorish Spain and were rendered into Latin long before the original Greek manuscripts were rediscovered, thus bringing the Greek contributions into the mainstream of European scientific thought.

From the vast number of Arabic and Hebrew scholars whose works entered into the great interchange of knowledge of the eleventh and twelfth centuries, three figures stand out. Al Rhazi (Rhazes) (865-925), was the Arabic Hippocrates. His great learning in medicine he compiled into an encyclopedia (*al-Mansuri*), and he worked also in ophthalmic surgery and infectious diseases. He was interested, too, in physics and alchemy, and his applications of chemistry to medicine made him the forerunner of the iatrochemists of the sixteenth and seventeenth centuries—those who substituted chemical explanations of vital actions for the idea that "spirits" or "humors" governed man's bodily functions. Another prominent figure of the same period was Ibn Sina (980-1037), called, in Latin, Avicenna, whose codifications of medical knowledge are said to have offered strong competition to Galen. He translated Euclid and attacked the alchemists' theories on the transmutation of metals. A third Arab, contemporary also with Rhazes and Avicenna, was Alhazen (Ibn Al Haitham, c. 965-1039), whose work on optics influenced Roger Bacon and Kepler.

In astronomy, the Muslims developed the astrolabe, with which they located the position of the stars and determined their relative movements. They made advances in trigonometry which enabled them to make astronomical calculations. Their experiments in alchemy were distinguished by methodical observation and record keeping.

Muslim importance in these fields was at its peak from the middle of the eighth century to the end of the eleventh. If it took another three centuries for the Western mind to take up their work with the same vigor, it must be remembered that the bridge existed only in texts that had to be translated and comprehended. With all our modern resources, it has taken twenty years for the West to comprehend the extent of Russian scientific advances; the several centuries occupied in absorbing the ancient cultures seem inordinately long to us now but, from what we have seen of the period, it becomes clear that the transition was marvelously accomplished.

*"My purpose is to give a general description of everything
that is known to exist throughout the earth."*

Pliny the Elder
A.D. 23 – 79

THE PROPERTIES OF GOLD
ARE DESCRIBED

Not far from Naples is the crater of Vesuvius, the great
volcano whose erupting ash overwhelmed the cities of Pompeii
and Herculaneum in A.D. 79. In that ash lies the body of Pliny
the Elder, quite possibly preserved, as were many others discovered during recent excavations. Pliny died a victim of his own
curiosity, two years after publishing, in thirty-nine books, a remarkable encyclopedia containing all that was known about
science in his day. As a good scholar should, he cited all his authorities, 150 of them Roman and more than 300 Greek. He
was concerned mainly with nature—that is, with human beings,
animals, and birds, with metals, and with the whole range of
country activities: farming, wine-making, forestry. He wrote a
history of art and touched on chemistry, medicine, and astronomy. Some of his information is based on facts; some on legend
and superstition. Pliny's *Historia Naturalis* has been described
as "an old curiosity shop—precious early information side by
side with all the rubbish." The unicorn was included, for example, without any question as to its actual existence.

The importance of Pliny's work lies in the fact that it provided the early medieval scholars with a convenient primer of
Greek science. Indeed, as early as the end of the seventh century,

we find an Anglo-Saxon monk, Bede, making use of the *Natural History* for his own summary of Western European knowledge. It is said, too, that some of the medieval bestiaries drew imaginatively on some of Pliny's descriptions.

Pliny had views on the nature of the earth's structure: he thought for example, that people lived in the antipodes. He realized, too, that light travels faster than sound.

Pliny's description of the properties of gold is extraordinarily similar to those found in modern textbooks.

This selection is from the K.C. Bailey translation, *The Elder Pliny's Chapters of Chemical Subjects,* published by E. Arnold and Co. in 1932.

GOLD AND ITS PROPERTIES

I think that pride of place is given to this substance [gold], not by reason of its colour, for silver is brighter and more like sun-light (that is why it is more commonly used for military standards, since its gleaming is visible at a greater distance), and those who think it is the star-like hue of gold that charms are clearly mistaken, since no special importance is attached to such a colour in gems and other things; nor again is it preferred to the other metals by reason of its heaviness or its malleability, for in both it is surpassed by lead, but because it alone of all substances loses nothing on heating, and survives even conflagrations and the funeral pyre. In fact, the oftener it is heated the better it becomes, and ignition is the test for gold, that on heating till red hot it should still keep its colour. The test is called *obrussa*.

But the best proof of purity is a high melting-point. It is strange too that a substance unsubdued by charcoal, made from the most fiercely-burning wood, is swiftly heated by chaff, and that it is fused with lead to purify it.

Another and more important reason for holding gold in esteem is that it is least worn away by use. On the other hand, lines can be drawn with silver, copper, and lead, and the hands become soiled by the material that wears off. Again, nothing can be beaten into thinner leaves nor divided more finely, for an ounce of it is hammered out into seven hundred and fifty, or even more, gold-leaves measuring four fingers each way. The thickest of gold-leaves are called "leaf of Præneste," where the image of Fortune, gilded most faithfully, still helps to maintain the name. The next type of leaf is called "quæstorian." In Spain, nuggets of gold are called *striges.*

Above all, it alone is found in nuggets or fine dust. The other metals, after discovery in the mines, have to be perfected by roasting, but gold is gold straight off. Its substance is perfect when found in this way, for the gold in this case is pure; in the other cases which we shall describe it has to be extracted. Finally, neither rust nor verdigris nor anything else can waste its excellence or diminish its weight.

Again, brine and vinegar, the conquerors of matter, make no impression on it, and, more than any other metal, it is spun and woven like wool—even without wool.

According to Verrius, Tarquinius Priscus triumphed in a golden tunic, and we ourselves have seen Agrippina, wife of the Emperor Claudius, sitting beside him when he was exhibiting a mimic sea-fight, clad in a cloak woven of gold without other material. Indeed the method of weaving gold into Attalic cloth is old, and was invented by the kings of Asia.

On marble and other objects which cannot be heated white-hot, gold is laid on with white of egg; on wood with a glue called *leucophorum*, made in accordance with a certain formula. Its composition and preparation will be described in its proper place.

It was legal to gild copper by means of quicksilver or at least hydrargyrum, in place of which a fraudulent substitute has been devised, as we shall relate when we are describing their properties.

The copper is first subjected to the violence of fire; then when red-hot, quenched with brine, vinegar, or alum. The brightness of the surface is then used as a test whether the heating has been sufficiently prolonged, and the copper is dried again by heat so that, after polishing with a mixture of pumice and alum, it is fit to receive the gold-leaf laid on with mercury. Alum has purifying properties [in the case of copper] comparable to those already attributed to lead [in the case of gold].

*"The earth is a sphere, situated in the center of
the heavens; if it were not, one side of the heavens would appear
nearer to us than the other and the stars
would be larger there. . . ."*

Ptolemy
(Claudius Ptolemaeus)
90-168

THE HYPOTHESES OF THE GEOCENTRIC
UNIVERSE ARE SET DOWN

Not much is known about Claudius Ptolemaeus as a man
except that he was probably born in Egypt and most certainly
played an important part in the life of the great museum and
library of Alexandria. Ptolemy, the astronomer, geographer, and
mathematician, neglected to leave records of his own life, and
no one seems to have taken the trouble to record the exact date
of his death. Had his students known what was to be the extent
of Ptolemy's influence on the Western world, they might have
left a little more information about him. We do not know either
how much of the writings credited to him were actually his own.
Scholars agree, however, that whatever the source of his material,
Ptolemy's presentation is so skillful that he is entitled to full
credit.

Ptolemy cites enough references to show that his main
inspiration in the field of mathematics and astronomy was Hipparchus; in geography, Marinus of Tyre. Hipparchus probably

provided one of the links between Babylonian science and that of Greece, as is shown, for example, by his adoption of the Babylonian system of dividing the circumference of the circle into 360°. He was using, or perhaps actually invented, a number of the instruments subsequently discussed by Ptolemy. He constructed a celestial globe—the first we know of— and founded trigonometry.

Marinus of Tyre left no writings of his own, but the results of his work are included in Ptolemy's *Geographical Treatise.* Both of these men were of the generation preceding Ptolemy's, and they became his involuntary collaborators—not without advantage to the world of science.

Ptolemy provides us with an example of the useful incorrect hypothesis discussed by Claude Bernard in Part I. As we shall see, Ptolemy's authority was too strong in later centuries for the uncritical medieval scholars to question his basic assumptions; but, erroneous as some of his ideas were, Ptolemy produced a workable system that could be, and was, used successfully to explain the relationships of the stars and planets.

Ptolemy's work fell into two major divisions: the *Mathematical Treatise,* which has become known as the *Almagest,* and the *Geographical Treatise* already mentioned. Not enough is known about his work on optics, although it should be mentioned that Sarton regards it as "the most remarkable experimental research of antiquity." Ptolemy's astronomical work is included in both *Treatises,* the Geography containing mostly the latitudes and longitudes of the important places of the ancient world—slightly inaccurate, it is true, because of his reliance on incorrect estimates of the size of the globe. It is the *Almagest* with which we are principally concerned and from which the reading is selected.

The name *Almagest* is probably derived from an Arabic mispronunciation of a Greek word, *megali,* meaning "great," preceded by the Arabic article *al*—from the idea of the "great work" as opposed to the lesser work through which the students were introduced to the subject. The full title is translated as *The*

Mathematical Treatise or *The Great Treatise of Astronomy*. It is, in fact, an encyclopedia of astronomy, containing eleven books covering all the known knowledge on the subject. Our selection is taken from the introductory propositions, translated by T. L. Heath in *Greek Astronomy*. The work goes on to explain the motion of the planets and to deal with trigonometry as a tool of the astronomer, providing one of the earliest examples of work in applied mathematics. Ptolemy's catalogue of stars (he lists 1022), which he expanded from an earlier list of Hipparchus, is considered the most ancient accurate description of the heavens and the last one to be made for three hundred years.

Ptolemy's insistence on the absolute immobility of the earth and its position as the center of the universe proved to be strongly attractive to the medieval theologians, for whom man and his world were the sole object of creation. Thomas Aquinas qualified his acceptance of Ptolemy's theory by recognizing it as a working hypothesis only, but the Schoolmen made the theory a part of their general philosophy. Even after Copernicus published his theory in 1543, the Ptolemaic idea persisted. The principal factor in building up a case against Ptolemy proved to be the great maritime expeditions of the fifteenth century.

ON THE ORDER OF THE THEOREMS

2. The work which we have projected commences with a consideration of the general relation between the earth as a whole and the heavens as a whole. Of the special treatments that follow, the first part deals with the position of the ecliptic, the places inhabited by the human race, and the differences among the successive places, in each separate horizon, along the curvature of the earth's surface. The preliminary study of these relations makes easier the examination of the subsequent questions. The second part gives an account of the motion of the sun and the moon and of the phenomena that depend on these motions. For without the previous understanding of these matters it would be impossible to set forth a complete theory of the stars. Since the theory of the stars is contained, in accordance

with the general plan, in the concluding portion of this essay, the investigation of the sphere of the so-called fixed stars would properly find its place there, and the material on the five so-called planets would follow. We shall try to set forth all this material using as the basic foundations for knowledge the manifest phenomena themselves and those recorded observations of the ancients and the moderns about which there is no dispute; and we shall seek to fit the propositions together by geometrical proofs.

With respect to the general portion of the treatise the following preliminary assumptions are to be made: (1) that the heaven is spherical in form and rotates as a sphere; (2) that the earth, too, viewed as a complete whole, is spherical in form; (3) that it is situated in the middle of the whole heaven, like a center; (4) that by reason of its size and its distance from the sphere of fixed stars the earth bears to this sphere the relation of a point (5) that the earth does not participate in any locomotion. We shall say a few words by way of commentary on each of these propositions.

THAT THE HEAVEN ROTATES AS A SPHERE

3. It is reasonable to assume that the first ideas on these matters came to the ancients from observation such as the following. They saw the sun and the moon and the other stars moving from east to west in circles always parallel to each other; they saw the bodies begin to rise from below, as if from the earth itself, and gradually to rise to their highest point, and then, with a correspondingly gradual decline, to trace a downward course until they finally disappeared, apparently sinking into the earth. And then they saw these stars, once more, after remaining invisible for a time, make a fresh start and in rising and setting repeat the same periods of time and the same places of rising and setting with regularity and virtual similarity.

They were, however, led to the view of a spherical heaven chiefly by the observed circular motion described about one and the same center by those stars that are always above the horizon. For this point was, necessarily, the pole of the heavenly sphere, since the stars that are nearer this pole revolve in smaller circles, whereas those further away make larger circles, proportionately to their distance, until the distance reaches that of the stars not always visible. And of these latter they observed that those stars nearer the stars that are always visible remained invisible for a shorter time while those further away remained invisible for a correspondingly longer time. And so, from these phenomena alone they first conceived the afore-said idea, and then from the consideration of its consequences they adopted the other ideas that follow from it, since all the phenomena without quali-fication refuted the alternative hypotheses.

For example, if one should suppose, as some have, that the motion of the stars proceeds by a straight line without limit, how could one explain the fact that the daily motion of each star is always seen to begin from the same point? How could the stars in their unlimited motion turn back? And if they did turn back, how could this escape observation? Or how could they fail eventually to become altogether invisible, since they would appear ever smaller and smaller? In point of fact, however, they appear larger when near the region where they disappear, and are only gradually occulted and, as it were, cut off by the surface of the earth.

Again, the suggestion that the stars are kindled when they rise from the earth and again are snuffed out when they return to the earth is quite contrary to reason. For even if one should grant that the arrangement, size, and number of the stars, and their distances and intervals in space and time could have been the fulfillment of mere random and accidental procedure and that one part of the earth (the eastern part) had throughout it a kindling force, while the other (the western part) had an extinguish-ing force, or rather that the same part acted as a kindler from the point of view of some and as an extinguisher from the point of view of others, and that of the stars the very same ones were already kindled or extinguished, as the case might be, for some observers, but not yet for others—if, I repeat, one should grant all this, absurd as it is, what of the stars always visible, those that neither rise nor set? Why should the stars that are kindled and extinguished not rise and set everywhere? Why should those not sub-ject to such kindling and extinguishing always be above the horizon in all latitudes? For surely the stars which for some observers are always kindled and extinguished cannot be the same as those which for other observers are never kindled and extinguished. (Yet the proponents of the hypothesis of kindling would have to assume that they are the same) for it is quite evident that the same stars rise and set for some observers (i.e., those further south) whereas they neither rise nor set for others (i.e., those further north).

In a word, if one should suppose any other form of motion of the heavens save the spherical, the distances from the earth to the heavenly bodies would necessarily be unequal, however and wherever the earth itself might be supposed to lie situate. Consequently the sizes of the stars and their distances from one another would have to appear unequal to the same observers at each return, since the distances from the observers would sometimes be greater and at other times smaller. But this is not seen to be the case. For what makes the apparent size of a heavenly body greater when it is near the horizon is not its smaller distance but the vaporous moisture surrounding the earth between our eye and the heavenly body. It is the same as when objects immersed in water appear larger, and in fact the more deeply immersed the larger.

The hypothesis of spherical motion finds support also in the fact that on any other hypothesis save this one alone it is impossible that the instruments for measuring hours should be correct. There is also support in the following fact. Just as the motion of the heavenly bodies is completely without hindrance and the smoothest of all motions, and the most easily moved of all shapes is the circular for plane figures and the spherical for solids, so also since the polygon with the greater number of sides is the larger of regular polygons having equal perimeters, it follows that in the case of plane figures the circle is greater than any polygon of equal perimeter, and in the case of solid figures the sphere is greater. And the heaven is greater than all other bodies.

Various physical considerations, too, lead to the same conclusion. Thus the æther consists of finer and more homogeneous parts than does any other body. Now surfaces of bodies of homogeneous parts are themselves of homogeneous parts, and the circular surface in the case of plane figures and the spherical surface in the case of solid figures are the only surfaces that consist of homogeneous parts. The æther not being a plane surface but a solid may therefore be inferred to be of spherical form. A similar inference may be made from the fact that nature has constructed all earthly and destructible bodies entirely of circular forms but forms not having homogeneous parts, while she has constructed the divine bodies in the æther of spherical form having homogeneous parts. For if these bodies were flat or quoit-shaped their form would not appear circular to all observers at the same time from different places of the earth. Hence it is reasonable to infer that the æther which encloses the heavenly bodies, being of the same nature, is of spherical form, and, because of its composition out of homogeneous parts, moves with uniform circular motion.

THE ABSOLUTE IMMOBILITY OF THE EARTH

In the same way as before it can be proved that the earth cannot make any movement whatever in the aforesaid oblique direction, or ever change its position at all from its place at the centre; for the same results would, in that case, have followed as if it had happened to be placed elsewhere than at the centre. So I, for one, think it is gratuitous for any one to inquire into the causes of the motion towards the centre when once the fact that the earth occupies the middle place in the universe, and that all weights move towards it, is made so patent by the observed phenomena themselves. The ground for this conviction which is readiest to hand, seeing that the earth has been proved to be spherical and situated in the middle of the universe, is this simple fact: in all parts of the earth without exception the tendencies and the motions of bodies which have weight—I mean their own proper motions—always and everywhere operate at right angles to the (tangent) plane drawn evenly through the point of contact where the object falls. That this is so makes it also clear that, if the objects were not stopped by the surface of the earth, they would absolutely reach the centre itself, since the straight line leading to the centre is always at right angles to the tangent-plane to the sphere drawn through the intersection at the point of contact.

All who think it strange that such an immense mass as that of the earth should neither move itself nor be carried somewhere seem to me to look to their own personal experience, and not to the special character of the universe, and to go wrông through regarding the two things as analogous. They would not, I fancy, think the fact in question to be strange if they could realize that the earth, great as it is, is nevertheless, when compared with the enclosing body, in the relation of a point to that body. For in this way it will seem to be quite possible that a body relatively so small should be dominated and pressed upon with equal and similarly directed force on all sides by the absolutely greatest body formed of like constituents, there being no up and down in the universe any more than one would think of such things in an ordinary sphere. So far as the composite objects in the universe, and their motion on their own account and in their own nature are concerned, those objects which are light, being composed of fine particles, fly towards the outside, that is, towards the circumference, though their impulse seems to be towards what is for individuals "up," because with all of us what is over our heads, and is also called "up," points towards the bounding surface; but all things which are heavy, being composed of denser particles, are carried towards the middle, that is, to the centre, though they seem to fall "down," because, again, with all of us the place at our feet, called "down," itself points towards the centre of the earth, and they naturally settle in a position about the centre, under the action of mutual resistance and pressure which is equal and similar from all directions. Thus it is easy to conceive that the whole solid mass of the earth is of huge size in comparison with the things that are carried down to it, and that the earth remains unaffected by the impact of the quite small weights (falling on it), seeing that these fall from all sides alike, and the earth welcomes, as it were, what falls and joins it. But, of course, if as a whole it had had a common motion, one and the same with that of the weights, it would, as it was carried down, have got ahead of every other falling body, in virtue of its enormous excess of size, and the animals and all separate weights would have been left behind floating on the air, while the earth, for its part, at its great speed, would have fallen completely out of the universe itself. But indeed this sort of suggestion has only to be thought of in order to be seen to be utterly ridiculous.

Certain thinkers, though they have nothing to oppose to the above arguments, have concocted a scheme which they consider more acceptable, and they think that no evidence can be brought against them if they suggest for the sake of argument that the heaven is motionless, but that the earth rotates about one and the same axis from west to east, completing one revolution approximately every day, or alternatively that both the heaven and the earth have a rotation of a certain amount, whatever it is, about the same axis, as we said, but such as to maintain their *relative* situations.

These persons forget however that, while, so far as appearances in the stellar world are concerned, there might, perhaps, be no objection to this theory in the simpler form, yet, to judge by the conditions affecting ourselves and those in the air about us, such a hypothesis must be seen to be quite ridiculous. Suppose we could concede to them such an unnatural thing as that the most rarefied and lightest things either do not move at all or do not move differently from those of the opposite character—when it is clear as day that things in the air and less rarefied have swifter motions than any bodies of more earthy character—and that (we could further concede that) the densest and heaviest things could have a movement of their own so swift and uniform—when earthy bodies admittedly sometimes do not readily respond even to motion communicated to them by other things—yet they must admit that the rotation of the earth would be more violent than any whatever of the movements which take place about it, if it made in such a short time such a colossal turn back to the same position again, that everything not actually standing on the earth must have seemed to make one and the same movement always in the contrary sense to the earth, and clouds and any of the things that fly or can be thrown could never be seen travelling towards the east, because the earth would always be anticipating them all and forestalling their motion towards the east, insomuch that everything else would seem to recede towards the west and the parts which the earth would be leaving behind it.

For, even if they should maintain that the air is carried round with the earth in the same way and at the same speed, nevertheless the solid bodies in it would always have appeared to be left behind in the motion of the earth and air together, or, even if the solid bodies themselves were, so to speak, attached to the air and carried round with it, they could no longer have appeared either to move forwards or to be left behind, but would always have seemed to stand still, and never, even when flying or being thrown, to make any excursion or change their position, although we so clearly see all these things happening, just as if no slowness or swiftness whatever accrued to them in consequence of the earth not being stationary.

*"The art of healing was originally invented
and discovered by the logos [the reason] in conjunction with
experience. And today it can only be practiced excellently
and done well by one who employs both
of these methods. . . ."*

Galen

C. 129-C. 199

THE DISSECTION OF A BARBARY APE
PROVIDES THE MATERIAL FOR A
DESCRIPTION OF THE MUSCLES
OF THE FOREARM

Although Galen is recognized as one of the greatest scientific minds of his period and, indeed, of antiquity, it is well
to bear in mind his limitations as well as his accomplishments;
for his later influence on the medieval mind had often more to
do with his dogmatism than with his discoveries.

Galen was born in Asia Minor but practiced medicine in
Rome until his death around A.D. 200. As he was physician to
the greatest of the Roman Emperors, Marcus Aurelius, it is probable that he was under the influence of Stoics, whose philosophy
reached the climax of its influence at this time. If so, this would
account not only for his scientific interests—which Stoicism encouraged—but also for his teleological approach—that is, his
fundamental assumption that the body was designed to fulfill
the purposes of divine law. Galen's observations of bodily phenomena were, therefore, often interpreted in the light of this
assumption. His deductions, in voluminous and convincing style,

appealed to the Christians (and later the Muslims), who, in their formative years, were more concerned with theology than with science. As a consequence, Galen's explanations of the movement of the blood in the body suffered; and not only did his great interest in experiment fail to discover what in fact happened, but it actually misled his followers, even into the seventeenth century, into believing that his explanations were complete and final.

For Galen, the blood was formed in the liver and ebbed and flowed rather than circulated through the body. Mixed, in the heart, with "vital spirits," the blood flowed into the brain, where it was converted into "animal spirits" in a form capable of transmission through the nerves to stimulate the functions of the body. The general movement of the blood was from the veins into the arteries, a reversal of the actual system. So influential was Galen's teaching on this subject that it is said that medieval dissectors believed that the actual flows they observed were an effect on the body of the dissection itself. What they saw was abnormal; Galen's theory was the true one!

These negative aspects of Galen's work are emphasized for the reason already given: that his teaching had more importance than the body of experimental data he recorded. But he left a great mass of material that was valuable in all aspects of anatomy, physiology, and pathology. He brought together the existing Greek medical and anatomical knowledge and contributed further by his own experimentation and observation—adding to knowledge of the functions of the kidneys, the spinal cord, and the brain. Whether his concoction of stewed adders and opium, said to have been compounded for the Emperor, and the subject of two of Galen's treatises on pharmacy, can be reckoned as a useful contribution to medical knowledge depends, one supposes, on its effects on the Emperor. Its scientific value is probably less than Galen's explorations in anatomy (performed with the use of the Barbary ape, since human dissection was prohibited).

The present selection is a good sample of his style of exposition, which, even in translation, is clear and precise. Galen may have boasted; he certainly had a good deal of trust in the old god of medicine, Aesculepius; but, in spite of this, Galen represents the culmination of originality in Greek medieval literature and, perhaps, the last great name in medical science until Vesalius (1514-1564), Harvey (1578-1657), and other such men of the Renaissance. This translation of "On the Muscles Moving the Forearm" was done by O. Temkin and W. L. Straus, Jr., and published in the *Bulletin of the History of Medicine* in 1946.

THE MUSCLES OF THE FOREARM

You will not be able to observe accurately the movements of the forearm towards the upper arm, in flexion or in extension, before you lay the whole upper arm bare of all the surrounding muscles. So let us do it, keeping in mind that we said that the muscle lying upon the radius reaches up to the humerus and that the muscle underneath this one, viz. the muscle that inserts into the metacarpus before the index and middlefinger, also reaches up to the humerus a little distance away. As I said, it is better to preserve the heads of these muscles, or at least that of the one lying upon the radius. For it will only become clearly visible to you when you have laid bare the foremost muscle of the upper arm. You will expose this muscle by paying attention to the following two marks: the vein that runs along the whole upper arm and is called the "shoulder" vein, and the muscle that occupies the upper part of the shoulder—perhaps it would be better to say that "forms" the upper part of the shoulder, since it is the only muscle that lies upon this part. You should make the incision along the vein downwards and, of course, after having taken away the entire skin of this region, as well as all the membranes around the muscles. The incision in the upper part of the shoulder should be made by paying attention to the likeness and unlikeness of the fibres, whereby you will perceive that the whole circumference of the muscle reaches up to one apex and, like a triangle, is inserted into the upper arm. This muscle belongs to the shoulder joint, and it alone among the muscles moving the shoulder joint has now to be removed, in order that the double head of the foremost muscle of the upper arm become visible. . . .

The foremost muscle of the upper arm which, even before dissection, is clearly visible along the shoulder vein in all people, particularly in athletes, has two heads, one of which is attached to the rim of the neck of the scapula, the other to the apophysis which some people call ancyroeides [i.e. similar to an anchor], others coracoeides [i.e. similar to a raven's beak]. The ligament of each head is rather strong and not quite round. Now you should follow these heads as they extend downwards along the upper arm. For at the point where they unite, they produce this muscle which, however, is no longer lifted nor distant from the bones like its heads, but is forthwith grown to the bone of the upper arm, together with the other smaller muscle which lies underneath, and on top of which it rides as far as the elbow joint. Here it forms its aponeurosis and brings forth a strong tendon by means of which it grows to the radius. Moreover, it takes a share in the membranous ligament around the joint, by means of which it also flexes the joint, bending it slightly to the inner side.

If this muscle is taken away, you will find another one lying underneath. This muscle too clings to the upper arm from two fleshy origins, one in the back of the upper arm, the other one more in the front. The posterior head, however, reaches much higher. You will see that these heads also unite and form a muscle which becomes tendinous and, with the tendon produced, attaches to the ulnar bone, flexing the joint and bending it slightly outwards. But when both muscles function exactly, the flexion of the joint is not inclined to either side. Thus there are two anterior muscles which, as has been said, flex the elbow joint, while three others, grown to one another, extend this articulation. They should also be prepared as follows.

First one has to dissect the muscle which lies in the inner parts of the upper arm below the skin. It has its head near the limit of the posterior muscle of the arm-pit (whose nature will be discussed in the anatomy of the muscles moving the shoulder joint). Its end reaches the elbow joint near the inner condyle of the upper arm and is membranous and thin. After this muscle has been removed, study two origins of the muscles which extend the whole forearm. One of their origins grows out from the inside of the shoulder blade, not from the whole but from approximately half of its upper part. The other one grows out from the posterior part of the upper arm below its head. Advancing, these origins grow together at the upper arm and in their further advance they become attached to the bend of the ulna by means of a broad tendon. If you follow the fibres from above in a longitudinal direction, this tendon will appear double to you, taking its external part from the first muscle mentioned before, and the internal part from the second. If you separate them from each other and endeavor to pull each part of the muscle, you will see that each of them extends the whole forearm, but that there is a difference regarding lateral inclination. For the first of the muscles mentioned effects an oblique inclination outwards, the second inwards. Beneath this one there is another muscle which surrounds the bone of the upper arm. It is united with the second muscle and believed to be part of it by the anatomists. Thus it is if one considers this whole muscle as a double muscle. Nevertheless, it is possible to separate them from each other along the length of the fibres. And if you do this, you will find that this muscle remains entirely fleshy and grows into the posterior part of the elbow. If this muscle is pulled, sometimes a straight and direct tension around the elbow joint seemed to me to take place, sometimes it seemed to incline a little inwards.

"My wealth let sons and brethern part
Some things they cannot share—
My work well done, my noble heart,
These are my own to wear."

Jabir ibn Hayyan (Geber)
fl. 775

THE AIMS AND SOME OF THE METHODS
OF THE ALCHEMISTS ARE INDICATED

During the thirteenth century, there appeared some writings in Latin over the name of one "Geber." Although he is described by Charles Singer as "the father of Arabic alchemy," there is much doubt as to his date; moreover, he has sometimes been identified with an Arabic writer, Jabir ibn Hayyan, who flourished *c.* 775. Recent opinion, however, seems to be that Geber was the pseudonym of a Latin writer who assembled and translated various Arabic works, not necessarily those of Jabir only. Whatever the explanation of the mystery, the writings represent the continuation of the scientific tradition started by the Greeks —a link beween the ancient and modern scientific world in the field of chemistry.

The writings attributed to Geber show an interest in chemical methodology—including evaporation, distillation, filtration, melting, and so on. They discuss the manufacture of steel, the dyeing of cloth, and methods of preparing such chemicals as

186

sulfuric and nitric acids and *aqua regia* (in which gold may be dissolved).

The selection presented (taken from the R. Russell translation of *The Works of Geber,* re-edited in 1928 by E. Holmyard) consists of a short homily on the nature of the work of the chemist in his search for the philosopher's stone—that is, the substance sought by the alchemists that could transmute other metals into gold. The "most deep Search and Natural Industry," recommended as the greatest help to the artificer or alchemist, may suggest a higher level of experimental approach than was in fact the case. In other words, it is difficult to disentangle the effects of the hopeless search that preoccupied the alchemists from the truly scientific work that was incidental to it. The alchemists wrote in a mystical language that seems to have been directed only to members of their own circle. This passage contrasts strangely with the selection from Agricola, which follows it—and may exaggerate the difference between the industrial chemist of the day and the alchemists.

Geber's term *argentvive* means mercury. Geber believed, with the alchemists, that all metals are composed of "philosophic" sulfur, which from the time of the Arabian alchemists had been regarded as the principle of fire, and "philosophic" mercury. These could be released from the base metals by the art of the alchemist and, if they were sufficiently pure, could be recombined to make silver (if the sulfur were white) and gold (if the sulfur were red).

CHAPTER II

Of the Stone of Philosophers, that it is one only, for the White, and for the
Red, and from what Things it is extracted. And of the
Possibility and Way of Perfection.

We find Modern Artists to describe to us one only *Stone*, both for the *White* and for the *Red*; which we grant to be true: for in every *Elixir*, that is prepared, *White* or *Red*, there is no other Thing than *Argentvive* and *Sulphur*, of which, one cannot act, nor be, without the other: Therefore it is called, by *Philosophers*, one *Stone*, although it is extracted from many Bodies or Things. For it would be a foolish and vain thing to think to extract the same from a Thing, in which it is not, as some infatuated Men have conceited; for it never was the Intention of *Philosophers*: yet they speak many things by similitude. And because all *Metallick* Bodies are compounded of *Argentvive* and *Sulphur*, pure or impure, by accident, and not innate in their first Nature; therefore, by convenient *Preparation*, 'tis possible to take away such Impurity. For the *Expoliation of Accidents* is not impossible: therefore, the end of *Preparation* is, to take away *Superfluity*, and supply the *Deficiency* in Perfect Bodies. But *Preparation* is diversified according to the *Diversity* of things indigent. For experience hath taught us diverse ways of acting, *viz. Calcination, Sublimation, Descension, Solution, Distillation, Coagulation, Fixation* and *Inceration*: All which we sufficiently declare in the *Sum of the Perfection of the Magistery*. For these are Works helpful in *Preparation*.

*   *   *

CHAPTER V

The Conclusion of this First Part, containing the Qualifications of the Artificer.

Therefore, from what is abovesaid, we conclude, that the *Artificer* of this *Work* ought to be well skilled, and perfect in the *Sciences* of *Natural Philosophy*: because, how much *Money* soever he hath, and although he be endowed with a naturally profound *Wit* and *Desire* in his *Artifice*, yet he cannot attain his *End*, unless he hath by *Learning* acquired *Natural Philosophy*. For the defect of that which is not acquired by *Natural Ingenuity*, must be supplied by *Learning*. Therefore the *Artificer* must be helped by most deep *Search* and *Natural Industry*. For, by reason of his *Learning* only, how much soever of *Science* he hath acquired, unless he be also helped by *Natural Industry*, he will not be invited to so precious a *Banquet*. By his *Industry*, he must amend his *Errour* in the point, to which he will be ignorant how to apply a *Remedy*, if he rely only upon his *Learning*: so likewise, he may remedy his *Errour* in the *Point*, from his *Knowledg* acquired by *Natural Learning*, which by *Industry* only he cannot avoid; because *Art* is helped by *Ingenuity*, and *Ingenuity* by *Art* likewise.

Also it is necessary for him to be of a constant Will in his *Work,* that he may not presume to attempt this now, and that another time: because our *Art* consists not, nor is perfected in a Multitude of *Things.* For there is one *Stone,* one *Medicine,* in which the *Magistery* consists, to which we add not any extraneous *Thing,* nor remove we ought; except that in *Preparation* we take away *Superfluities.*

Also he must be diligent in the *Work,* persisting to the final *Consummation* thereof, that he leave not off obruptly; because he can acquire neither Knowledge nor Profit from a diminished *Work*; but shall rather reap *Desperation* and *Dammage.* It is also expedient he should know the *Principles* and Principal *Radixes* of this *Art,* which are essential to the *Work*: because, he that is ignorant of the *Beginnings,* cannot find the *End.* And we shew you all those *Principles* in a Discourse compleat, and sufficiently clear and manifest to wise Men, according to the exigency of this our Art. It is likewise expedient, the *Artist* should be temperate and slow to *Anger,* least he suddenly (through the force of *Rage*) spoil and destroy his *Works* begun.

Likewise also, he must keep his *Money,* and not presumptuously distribute it vainly, least he happen not to find the *Art,* and be left in *Misery,* and in the *Desperation* of *Poverty*; or at least, when (by his Diligent Endeavour) he is come near to the *End* of his *Magistery,* his *Money* being all spent, he be forced to leave the *End* (miserable Man as he is) uncompleated. For they, who in the *Beginning* prodigally waste their whole *Treasure,* when they draw nigh to the *End,* have not wherewith to Labour. Whence such Men are twofoldly overwhelmed with Grief, *viz.* because they spent their *Money* in Things unprofitable, and because they lose the most noble *Science* which they were in quest of. For you need not to consume your *Goods,* seeing you may come to the compleatment of the *Magistery* for a small price, if you be not ignorant of the *Principles of Art,* and rightly understand what we have declared to you. Therefore, if you waste your *Money,* not minding our Admonitions plain and manifest, written in this Little Book, inveigh not against Us; but impute what you suffer to your own *Ignorance* and *Presumption.* For this *Science* agrees not well with a *Man* poor and indigent, but is rather inimical and adverse to him.

Nor should the *Artist* endeavour to find the *Sophistical* end of his *Work,* but be intent on the true *Compleatment* only; because our *Art* is reserved in the *Divine Will* of *God,* and is given to, or with-held from, whom he will; who is *Glorious*, *Sublime*, and full of all *Justice* and *Goodness*. And perhaps, for the punishment of your *Sophistical Work*, he denies you the *Art*, and lamentably thrusts you into the *By-Path* of *Error*, and from your *Error* into perpetual *Infelicity* and *Misery*: because he is most miserable and unhappy, to whom (after the *End* of his *Work* and *Labour*) GOD denies the sight of *Truth*. For such a *Man* is constituted in perpetual *Labour*, beset with all *Misfortune* and *Infelicity*, loseth the *Consolation*, *Joy*, and *Delight* of his whole *Time*, and consumes his Life in Grief without *Profit*. Likewise, the *Artist*, when he shall be in his *Work*, should study to impress in his *Mind*, all *Signs* that appear in every *Decoction*, and to search out their *Causes*.

These are the *Things* necessary for an *Artificer* fit for our *Art*; but if any of these We have declared be wanting in him, he should not approach to our *Art*.

CHAPTER VIII

Of Sol, *or* Gold.

We have already given you, in a *General Chapter*, the *Sum* of the *Intention* of *Metals*; and here we now intend to make a special *Declaration* of each one. And first of *Gold*. We say, *Gold* is a *Metallick Body*, *Citrine*, ponderous, mute, fulgid, equally digested in the *Bowels* of the *Earth*, and very long washed with *Mineral Water*; under the *Hammer* extensible, fusible, and sustaining the Tryal of the *Cupel*, and *Cement*. According to this Definition, you may conclude, that nothing is true *Gold*, unless it hath all the *Causes* and *Differencies* of the Definition of *Gold*. Yet, whatsoever *Metal* is radically Citrine, and brings to *Equality*, and cleanseth, it makes *Gold* of every kind of *Metals*. Therefore, we consider by the *Work* of *Nature*, and discern, that *Copper* may be changed into *Gold* by *Artifice*. For we see in *Copper Mines*, a certain *Water* which flows out, and carries with it thin *Scales* of *Copper*, which (by a continual and long continued Course) it washeth and cleanseth. But after such *Water* ceaseth to flow, we find these thin *Scales* with the dry *Sand*, in three years time to be digested with the *Heat* of the *Sun*; and among these *Scales* the purest *Gold* is found. Therefore, We judg, those *Scales* were cleansed by the benefit of the *Water*, but were equally digested by heat of the *Sun*, in the *Dryness* of the *Sand*, and so brought to *Equality*. Wherefore, imitating *Nature*, as far as can, we likewise alter; yet in this we cannot follow *Nature*.

offen den rouch vß zelaſſen/alſo dz dz blech
wol vſtrichē ſy mit leymē. vñ vff dem blech
werd d offen gehöcht mit ſteynē eyns halbē
ſteyns dick mit vier hülen/vñ in der mittē
des offens ein loch gelaſſen / alſo das ouch

des rouchloch werd gemacht ein zapffen dz
füer domit zů regieren groß od clein nach di
nem gefallen/vñ d offen ſoll gehitziget wer
den mit kolen od ſeg ſpen oder loße klötz vō
eym rot gerber vñ kein holtz. des form alſo.

Ji ſollicher maſſen magſtu ouch eyn
i offen machē dz du mit holtz dar i brē
neſt/alſo dz d offen läg iſt/vñ von d
höche des roſts biß zů dem blech ſoll ſin ey/
ner eſſen hoch/vñd für die blech ſo werd ge

fens ſy vff einer ſiten in d wyte ein halb elle
vñ in d höße.iii. viertel eyner eſſen der offen
hab ouch zwei groß rouchlöcher.ſolliche offē
magſtu machē mit wie vil helmē du wilt
oder beßeren du biſt nach dinem gefallen.

A distillation furnace used by alchemists. From Hieronymus Brun-
schwig's *Das Buch der Rechten Kunst zu Distillieren*, Strasbourg, 1500.
(Courtesy of the Burndy Library.)

Also *Gold* is of *Metals* the most precious, and it is the *Tincture* of *Redness*; because it tingeth and transforms every *Body*. It is calcined and dissolved without profit, and is a *Medicine* rejoycing, and conserving the *Body* in *Youth*. It is most easily broken with *Mercury*, and by the *Odour* of *Lead*. There is not any *Body* that in act more agrees with it in *Substance* than *Jupiter* and *Luna*; but in *Weight, Deafeness,* and *Putrescibility,* *Saturn*, in *Colour Venus*; in *Potency* indeed *Venus* is more next *Luna* than *Jupiter*, and then *Saturn*: but lastly *Mars*. And this one of the *Secrets* of *Nature*. Likewise *Spirits* are commixed with it, and by it fixed, but not without very great *Ingenuity*, which comes not to an *Artificer* of a stiff neck.

CHAPTER IX

Of Luna, *or* Silver

Having premised the *Chapter* of *Sol*, We come now to speak of *Luna*, by a common name called *Silver*. Therefore, We say, *Silver* is a *Metallick Body,* White with pure Whiteness, Clean, Hard, Sounding, very durable in the *Cupel*, extensible under the *Hammer*, and fusible. And it is the *Tincture* of *Whiteness*, and hardens *Tin* by *Artifice*, and converts it to it self; and it is mixed with *Sol*, and breaks not; but in the *Examination* it perseveres not without *Artifice*. He who knows how more to subtiliate it, and after subtiliation, to inspissate and fix it associated with *Gold*; it remains with it in the *Test*, and will in no wise forsake it. Being put over the fume of acute Things, as of *Vinegar, Salarmoniac,* etc. it will be of a wonderful *Celestine Colour*. And it is a noble *Body*, but wants of the *Nobility* of *Gold*; and its *Minera* is found determinate: but it often hath a *Minera* confused with other *Bodies*, and that *Silver* is not so noble. It is likewise dissolved, and calcined with great *Labour*, and no *Profit*.

CHAPTER X

Of Saturn, *or* Lead.

Of *Lead* we likewise treat, and say, *Lead* is a *Metallick Body*, livid, earthy, ponderous, mute, partaking of a little *Whiteness*, with much paleness, refusing the *Cineritium* and *Cement*, easily in all its dimensions with small *Compression extensible*, and readily fusible, without *Ignition*. Yet some foolish Men conceit, and say, that *Lead* in its own *Nature* is much approximated to *Gold*. But because they are stiffnecked, and void of all *Reason*, they cannot conceive of the *Truth* of Things most subtile, as it is in it self, but judg of them according to sense. And because they see it ponderous, and mute, and not to putrifie, they believe it to be much nigh in *Property* to *Sol*; but this is wholly erroneous, as by the following shall be by us manifestly proved at large. Also *Lead* hath much of an *Earthy Substance*, therefore it is washed, and by a *Lavament* turned into *Tin*. Hence it is manifest that *Tin* is more assimilated to the *Perfect*. *Lead* is in like manner burnt, and made *Minium*; and it is put over the *Vapours* of Vinegar, and made *Ceruss*. And although it is not much approximate to *Perfection*, yet of it, by our *Artifice*, we easily make *Silver*; and it keeps not its proper weight in *Transmutation*, but is changed into a new weight: All this it acquires in our *Magistery*. *Lead* also is the *Tryal* of *Silver* in the *Cupel*, the *Causes* of which We give.

CHAPTER XI

Of Jupiter, *or* Tin.

Therefore, not omitting to discourse of *Jupiter,* We signifie to the *Sons* of *Learning*, that *Tin* is a *Metallick Body*, white, not pure, livid, and sounding little, partaking of little *Earthiness*; possessing in its *Root Harshness*, *Softness*, and swiftness of *Liquefaction*, without *Ignition*, and not abiding the *Cupel*, or *Cement,* but Extensible under the *Hammer*. Therefore, *Jupiter*, among *Bodies* diminished from *Perfection*, is in the *Radix* of its Nature of Affinity to the more Perfect, *viz.* to *Sol* and *Luna*; more to *Luna*, but less to *Sol*, as shall be clearly declared in the following. *Jupiter*, because it receives much *Whiteness* from the *Radix* of its *Generation*, therefore it whitens all *Bodies* not White; yet its vice is, that it breaks every *Body*, but *Saturn*, and most pure *Sol*. And *Jupiter* adheres much to *Sol* and *Luna*, and therefore doth not easily recede from them, by *Examen* (or *Tryal* of *Cupel*.) In the *Magistery* of this *Art*, it receives a *Tincture* of *Redness*, and that shines in it with inestimable *Brightness*. It is hardened and cleansed more easily than *Saturn*. And he who knows how to take away its *Vice* of breaking, will suddenly reap the fruit of his Labour with joy. For it agrees with *Sol* and *Luna*, and will never be separated from them.

*"For a miner must have the greatest skill in
his work that he may know first of all what mountain or hill,
what valley or plain, can be prospected most profitably
or what he should leave alone; moreover, he
must understand the veins,.stringers
and seams in the rocks."*

Agricola
(Georg Bauer)
1490 – 1555

THE FORMATION OF METALS IN THE
EARTH IS DISCUSSED

In contrast to the alchemists, such men as Biringuccio
(*fl.* 1540) and Agricola were forerunners of a new period in
chemical investigation; abandoning the dark mysteries of transmutation, they studied and described natural (and especially geological) phenomena, the preparation of metals from ores, and
the various mechanical procedures available in their times. Agricola, whose writings are chosen to represent this new phase, was
a Latin scholar and a physician. Under the name of Georg Bauer
(George the Farmer), he lived in mining towns in Bohemia and
Saxony, where he observed the mining of the ores of gold, silver,
iron, copper, tin, and lead and described the various methods of
separation of the ore, of smelting, and of the transformation of
raw materials into usable products. He demonstrated, also, how
gold and silver were separated from base metals.

The beauty of Agricola's work lies in his use of illustrations.
The woodcuts are clear enough to enable a modern builder to
recreate models of the machines Agricola describes; thus we

have, for the first time, a definite picture of metallurgical art in the early days of the Renaissance.

This kind of observation, which brought out much information about chemical processes, was a prelude to a new period in the history of chemistry. The mystical assumptions of the alchemists were supplanted by accurate observation—a method which was to be ably demonstrated later by Robert Boyle and his contemporaries.

Agricola's theories of the origins of metals described in the present selection show the influence of Aristotle, who had posited that the elements of earth and water were combined into a juice and solidified by cold into a metal.

This selection was taken from the H. C. Hoover and L. H. Hoover translation of *De Re Metallica,* published in 1928 and now available in a Dover Press reprint.

HOW METALS ARE PRODUCED

I now come to the canales in the earth. These are veins, veinlets, and what are called "seams in the rocks." These serve as vessels or receptacles for the material from which minerals are formed. The term vena is most frequently given to what is contained in the canales, but likewise the same name is applied to the canales themselves. The term vein is borrowed from that used for animals, for just as their veins are distributed through all parts of the body, and just as by means of the veins blood is diffused from the liver throughout the whole body, so also the veins traverse the whole globe, and more particularly the mountainous districts; and water runs and flows through them. With regard to veinlets or stringers and "seams in the rocks," which are the thinnest stringers, the following is the mode of their arrangement. Veins in the earth, just like the veins of an animal, have certain veinlets of their own, but in a contrary way. For the larger veins of animals pour blood into the veinlets, while in the earth the humours (fluids) are usually poured from the veinlets into the larger veins, and rarely flow from the larger into the smaller ones. As for the seams in the rocks we consider that they are produced by two methods: by the first, which is peculiar to themselves, they are formed at the same time as the rocks, for the heat bakes the refractory material into stone and the non-refractory material similarly heated exhales its humours and is made into "earth" generally friable. The other method is common also to veins and veinlets, when water is collected into one place it softens the rock by its liquid nature, and by its weight and pressure breaks and divides it. Now, if the rock is hard, it makes seams in the rocks and veinlets, and if it is not too hard it makes veins. However, if the rocks are not hard, seams and veinlets are created as well as veins. If these do not carry a very large quantity of water, or if they are pressed by a great volume of it, they soon discharge themselves into the nearest veins. . . .

I must explain what it really is from which metals are produced. The best proof that there is water in their materials is the fact that they flow when melted, whereas they are again solidified by the cold of air or water. This, however, must be understood in the sense that there is more water in them and less "earth"; for it is not simply water that is their substance but water mixed with "earth." And such a proportion of "earth" is in the mixture as may obscure the transparency of the water, but not remove the brilliance which is frequently in unpolished things. Again, the purer the mixture, the more precious the metal which is made from it, and the greater its resistance to fire. But what proportion of "earth" is in each liquid from which a metal is made no mortal can ever ascertain, or still less explain, but the one God has known it, Who has given certain sure and fixed laws to nature for mixing and blending things together. It is a juice then, from which metals are formed; and this juice is created by various operations. Of these operations the first is a flow of water which softens the "earth" or carries the "earth" along with it, thus there is a mixture of "earth" and water, then the power of heat works upon the mixtures so as to produce that kind of a juice.

We have spoken of the substance of metals; we must now speak of their efficient cause. . . . We do not deny the statement of Albertus Magnus that the mixture of "earth" and water is baked by subterranean heat to a certain denseness, but it is our opinion that the juice so obtained is after-ward solidified by a cold so as to become a metal. . . . This view of Aristotle is the true one. For metals melt through the heat and somehow become softened; but those which have become softened through heat are again solidified by the influence of cold, and, on the contrary, those which become softened by moisture are solidified by heat.

CONSTRUCTION AND DESTRUCTION OF MOUNTAINS

Hills and mountains are produced by two forces, one of which is the power of water, and the other the strength of the wind. There are three forces which loosen and demolish the mountains, for in this case, to the power of the water and the strength of the wind we must add the fire in the interior of the earth. Now we can plainly see that a great abundance of water produces mountains, for the torrents first of all, wash out the soft earth, next carry away the harder earth, and then roll down the rocks, and thus in a few years they excavate the plains or slopes to a considerable depth; this may be noticed in mountainous regions even by unskilled observers. By such excavation to a great depth through many ages, there rises an immense eminence on each side. When an eminence has thus arisen, the earth rolls down, loosened by constant rain and split away by frost, and the rocks, unless they are exceedingly firm, since their seams are similarly softened by the damp, roll down into the excavations below. This continues until the steep eminence is changed into a slope. Each side of the excavation is said to be a mountain, just as the bottom is called a valley. Moreover, streams, and to a far greater extent rivers, effect the same results by their rushing and washing; for this reason they are frequently seen flowing either between very high mountains which they have created, or close by the shore which borders them. . . .

Nor did the hollow places which now contain the seas all formerly exist, nor yet the mountains which check and break their advance, but in many parts there was a level plain, until the force of winds let loose upon it a tumultuous sea and a scathing tide. By a similar process the impact of water entirely overthrows and flattens out hills and mountains. But these changes of local conditions, numerous and important as they are, are not noticed by the common people to be taking place at the very moment when they are happening, because, through their antiquity, the time, place, and manner in which they began is far prior to human memory.

The wind produces hills and mountains in two ways: either when set loose and free from bonds, it violently moves and agitates the sand; or else when, after having been driven into the hidden recesses of the earth by cold, as into a prison, it struggles with a great effort to burst out. For hills and mountains are created in hot countries, whether they are situated by the sea coasts or in districts remote from the sea, by the force of winds; these no longer held in check by the valleys, but set free, heap up the sand and dust, which they gather from all sides, to one spot, and a mass arises and grows together. If time and space allow, it grows together and hardens, but if it be not allowed (and in truth this is more often the case), the same force again scatters the sand far and wide. . . .

Then, on the other hand, an earthquake either rends and tears away part of a mountain, or engulfs and devours the whole mountain in some fearful chasm. In this way it is recorded the Cybotus was destroyed, and it is believed that within the memory of man an island under the rule of Denmark disappeared. Historians tell us that Taygetus suffered a loss in this way, and that Therasia was swallowed up with the island of Thera. Thus it is clear that water and the powerful winds produce mountains, and also scatter and destroy them. Fire only consumes them, and does not produce at all, for part of the mountains—usually the inner part—takes fire.

"But I have learned by this handicraft-operation
that all vegetables do immediately and materially proceed
out of the Element of water only."

Johann Baptista
van Helmont

1577 – 1644

THE ROLE OF WATER IN THE GROWTH OF
PLANTS IS SHOWN BY EXPERIMENT

Another stage in the gradual move toward the development
of a true science of chemistry is represented by Johann Baptista
van Helmont, a Flemish chemist. This stage, generally referred
to as "iatrochemistry," was based upon a concept that chemistry
and mechanics had complete control over the human system—
a new form of the dogmatic approach of the Schoolmen. Van
Helmont sought the explanation of nature in chemistry and developed a natural philosophy in which he recognized only two
elements, air and water. The experiment described in the reading
demonstrated that water had been transmuted into solid wood by
the action of the "Seedes" in the tree—"Seede" meaning a kind
of ferment.

Although van Helmont introduced the word "gas," he
used it in a sense very different from that of our modern concept
of a "completely elastic fluid not liquid or solid at ordinary tem-
peratures." For him, "gas" was a form of water. He observed
various kinds of "fumes," but he apparently did not find any
explanation for them other than that—in his terms—they were

a stage in the process of converting water into substance and back to water. Thus van Helmont made no contribution of great importance to modern chemistry, which began only when the chemist came to understand the nature of gases. He had some influence, however, in other areas of practical chemistry.

This selection is taken from the collected works titled *Ortus Medicine,* translated by John Chandler in 1662.

IS WOOD MADE OF WATER?

All earth, clay, and every body that may be touched, is truly and materially the offspring of water onely, and is reduced again into water, by nature and art. . . . Water alwayes remains whole as it is; or without any dividing of the three beginnings, it is transformed and goes into fruits whither the Seedes do call and withdraw it.

For an Element should cease to be a simple body if it is to be separated into anything before or more simple than itself. But nothing in corporeall things is granted to be before, or more simple than an element.

But I have learned by this handicraft-operation, that all Vegetables do immediately and materially proceed out of the Element of water onely. For I took an Earthen vessel in which I put two hundred pounds of Earth that had been dried in a Furnace, which I moystened with Rainwater, and I implanted therein the Trunk or Stem, of a Willow Tree, weighing five pounds; and at length, five years being finished, the Tree sprung from thence did weigh one hundred and sixty-nine pounds, and about three ounces: But I moystened the Earthen vessel with Rainwater, or distilled water (alwayes when there was need) . . . and lest the dust should be co-mingled with the Earth, I covered the lip or mouth of the Vessel, with an Iron Plate covered with Tin, and easily passable with many holes, I computed not the weight of the leaves that fell off, in the four Autumnes. At length, I again dried the Earth of the Vessel, and there were found the same two hundred pound, wanting about two ounces. Therefore one hundred and sixty-four pounds of Wood, Barks, and Roots arose out of water onely. . . . Fire indeed destroyeth simple but it generates nothing. . . . Therefore Wood, since it is wholly of water, the ashes . . . shall be of water.

*"The Balenae [whales] are animals of prodigious size,
and they get their name from blowing or spouting waters. They
puff the water higher than other beasts of the sea.
In Greek, 'ballein' means 'to throw out.' "*

The Book of Beasts
Twelfth-Century Latin Bestiary

SOME FABULOUS ANIMALS ARE DESCRIBED
ALONG WITH SOME FACTS AND
MISCONCEPTIONS ABOUT
REAL ANIMALS

Science depends on observation as well as experiment; and
the progress of science depends heavily on the proper recording
of observational data. We have noted the fondness of the Greeks
and, especially, of the Romans for compiling encyclopedias of
existing knowledge. In some fields, such as anatomy or astronomy, it was reasonably easy for the facts, as reported in such
works, to be verified by personal observation of the reader; but
where the compilation included travelers' tales of things they
had seen in far countries, doubt could not be eliminated. In this
way, legends become established as realities, to survive generally for many centuries until other explorers brought back
new and sometimes equally fantastic tales.

This was specially true of zoology. As we have seen, Pliny
the Elder indiscriminately accepted the fabulous along with the
real, and his descriptions of the characteristics of animals provided material for the medieval compilers. Toward the end of
the second century, the scholars of Alexandria accepted these

201

and other descriptions and, combining them with Christian teachings, produced a series of allegorical tales (the *Physiologos*) which became as popular as science fiction is today and was translated from the Greek into many languages.

The selection included below is enough to indicate the attractions of the theme for the artists of the early Christian period, some of whose interpretations remain in use today in the form of heraldic devices. The unicorn and the griffin are as much a part of modern life as they were in the Middle Ages. A hypocrite still sheds "crocodile tears." We may laugh at the crudities of the bestiaries, but we must be careful not to overlook the fact that they contain much that was scientific. Unverified report and theological analogy were combined with the data of active observation. Perhaps the scientific aspects would have survived with more effect if the unknown had not overstimulated the artists' imaginations.

It has been suggested by H. T. Pledge (*Science since 1500*) that the first difficulty in connection with zoological studies was that of preserving specimens (other than the skin). The corrective to the bestiaries came when increasing wealth and expanded travel permitted the collection of live specimens and the establishment of zoological gardens, so that personal observation could finally winnow fact from fiction about the giraffe or the elephant.

TIGRIS THE TIGER gets his name from his speedy pace; for the Persians, Greeks and Medes used to call an arrow "tygris."

The beast can be distinguished by his manifold specklings, by his courage and by his wonderful velocity. And from him the River Tigris is named, because it is the most rapid of all rivers.

Hyrcania is his principal home.

Now the Tigress, when she finds the empty lair of one of her cubs that

Cocodrillus acroco colore dictus. gignit in nilo flumi
ne. animal quadrupes. intra 7 aquales. longitudine
plerumqʒ uiginti cubitoꝛ. dentiu 7 unguium inmanitate
armatus. Tantaqʒ cutis duricia. ut quinus fortiu icʒ lapi
dum tergo repariat non nocet. nocte in aquis. die in hu
mo qʒescit. Oua intra fouet. masculus 7 femina uices suant.
hunc pisces qdam serratam hntes cristam. tenera uent
um desecantes intimunt. Sol autem ɓomnibʒ animali
bʒ supiora mouet. inferiora u inmota tenet. Sterʒ eˀ fit un
guentu. unde uetule 7 rugose meretces faciet suas pungunt.
fiuntqʒ pulchre donec sudor defluens lauet. Cui figuram
portant hypocte siue luxuriosi atqʒ auari. qʒquuius uitco
supbie inflentˀ. tabo luxurie maculentˀ. auariae moꝛbo ob

A manuscript page from *The Book of Beasts*. The text was recorded by
several scribes, to whom it was dictated. In this way a number of copies
could be made at the same time. The drawings were usually filled in
by a limner.

has been stolen, instantly presses along the tracks of the thief. But this person who has stolen the cub, seeing that even though carried by a swiftly galloping horse he is on the point of being destroyed by the speed of the tigress, and seeing that no safety can be expected from flight, cunningly invents the following ruse. When he perceives that the mother is close, he throws down a glass ball, and she, taken in by her own reflection, assumes that the image of herself in the glass is her little one. She pulls up, hoping to collect the infant. But after she had been delayed by the hollow mockery, she again throws herself with all her might into the pursuit of the horseman, and, goaded by rage, quickly threatens to catch up with the fugitive. Again he delays the pursuer by throwing down a second ball, nor does the memory of his former trick prevent the mother's tender care. She curls herself round the vain reflection and lies down as if to suckle the cub. And so, deceived by the zeal of her own dutifulness, she loses both her revenge and her baby.

A STAG is called 'Cervus' from its habit of snuffing up the Cerastes— which are horned snakes—or else from being 'horn-bearing', for horns are called 'cerata' in Greek.

These creatures are enemies to serpents. When they feel themselves to be weighed down by illness, they suck snakes from their holes with a snort of the nostrils and, the danger of their venom having been survived, the stags are restored to health by a meal of them.

The plant called Dittany offers them the same sort of medical food, for, when they have fed on it, they can shake off any arrows which they may have received.

Stags listen admiringly to the music of rustic pipes. With their ears pricked, they hear acutely; with the ears lowered, not at all.

Also these animals have the following peculiarity: that when they change their feeding grounds for love of a foreign pasture, and browse along on the way there, if by any chance they have to cross huge rivers or seas, each rests his head on the haunches of the one in front, and, since the one behind does the same thing for him in turn, they suffer no trouble from the weight. And, when they have mounted their heads upon those parts, they hurry across with the greatest possible speed for fear of getting befouled.

Stags have another feature too, for, after a dinner of snake, they shed their coats and all their old age with them.

THIS IS CALLED A COCODRYLLUS from its crocus or saffron colour. It breeds in the River Nile: an animal with four feet, amphibious, generally about thirty feet long, armed with horrible teeth and claws. So great is the hardness of its skin that no blow can hurt a crocodile, not even if hefty stones are bounced on its back. It lies in the water by night, on land by day.

It incubates its eggs in the earth. The male and female take turns. Certain fishes which have a saw-like dorsal fin destroy it, ripping up the tender parts of its belly. Moreover, alone among animals, it moves its upper jaw, keeping the lower one quite motionless. Its dung provides an ointment with which old and wrinkled whores anoint their figures and are made beautiful, until the flowing sweat of their efforts washes it away.

Hypocritical, dissolute and avaricious people have the same nature as this brute—also any people who are puffed up with the vice of pride, dirtied with the corruption of luxury, or haunted with the disease of avarice—even if they do make a show of falling in with the justifications of the Law, pretending in the sight of men to be upright and indeed very saintly.

Crocodiles lie by night in the water, by day on land, because hypocrites, however luxuriously they live by night, delight to be said to live holily and justly by day. Conscious of their wickedness in doing so, they beat their breasts: yes, but with use, habit always brings to light the things which they have done.

The monster moves his upper jaws because these people hold up the higher examples of the Fathers and an abundance of precepts in speech to others, while they show in their lower selves all too little of what they say.

An ointment is made of its evil dung because bad people are often admired and praised by the inexperienced for the evil they have done, and extolled by the plaudits of this world, as if beautified by an ointment. But when the Judgement, sweated out by the evils perpetrated, moves its anger to the striking, then all that elegance of flattery vanishes like a smoke.

THIS IS CALLED A GRIFFIN because it is a winged quadruped. This kind of wild animal is born in Hyperborean parts, or in mountains. All its bodily members are like a lion's but its wings and mask are like an eagle's.

It is vehemently hostile to horses. But it will also tear to pieces any human beings which it happens to come across.

The Griffin as pictured in *The Book of Beasts*. It has the body parts of a lion and the wings and beak of an eagle.

A BEAST gets born in India called the LEUCROTA, and it exceeds in velocity all the wild animals there are. It has the size of a donkey, the haunches of a stag, the breast and shins of a lion, the head of a horse, a cloven hoof, and a mouth opening as far as its ears. Instead of teeth, there is one continuous bone: but this is only as to shape, for in voice it comes near to the sounds of people talking.

"Universal chemistry is the Art of resolving mixt, compound or aggregate Bodies into their Principles; and of composing such bodies from those Principles."

Georg Ernst Stahl

1660 – 1734

BURNING IS EXPLAINED AS THE RESULT OF THE PRESENCE OF A COMBUSTIBLE PRINCIPLE, PHLOGISTON

Stahl's doctrine of "phlogiston" reminds us of the extent to which the Scholastic approach influenced the study of chemistry, long after astronomy and physics had shaken free of its limitations. The persistence with which men adhered to explanations of chemical phenomena in terms of basic "principles" contrasts strangely with the lively experimentalism that, while Stahl was still a young man, had brought Newton's great synthesis into being. Yet Stahl's ideas managed to survive to affect the views of such men as Joseph Priestley (1733-1804), who, almost a hundred years after Stahl's death, used "phlogistian" terms. Even stranger is the fact that the doctrine was defined at a time when the chemical significance of gases was beginning to be realized, if not fully explained, by such men as Robert Boyle (1627-1691).

First suggested by Becher (1635-1682), later confirmed and developed by his pupil Stahl, the phlogiston theory made possible the explanation of a wide range of experimental facts and seemed adequate to explain new facts as they were discovered. According to the phlogiston theory, all combustile substances and metals which are reduced to ashes by calcination (strong heating in air) contain a common combustible material called phlogiston, which is released into the air when the substance is burned. The combustible substance thus consists of two parts: the calx, or ash, and phlogiston. In burning, the phlogiston escapes and the calx remains. Different substances had different calx, but the phlogiston was the same. Since phlogiston left the substance when it burned, the primary ingredient which remained weighed less than the original substance. Air was capable of absorbing a certain amount of phlogiston; when completely "phlogisticated," it would no longer sustain combustion or support animal life.

Long before the full development of the phlogiston theory, Jean Rey (in 1630) showed that tin and lead actually gained weight when calcined. The phlogistonists countered this apparent contradiction with the hypothesis of levity—that is, that phlogiston imparted a kind of negative gravity which made the metal lighter than it was when it was freed of its phlogiston.

The phlogiston theory demonstrates the result of the failure to develop methods of weighing and measuring, a technical failure dealt with later by Lavoisier. In spite of its ambiguities and obscurities and of the objections to it which experimental data made necessary, the phlogiston theory was held and utilized by many outstanding chemists for a century after Stahl, even by four of the five chemists most responsible for its final, complete rejection (Black, Priestley, Scheele, and Cavendish). This does not reduce its importance but rather highlights its significance as a step in the development of modern chemical ideas. After all, it did deal more or less successfully with a number of experimental observations. It ultimately failed because it was used to explain too wide a range of chemical events without quantitative methods.

The reading that follows has been taken from a translation by H. M. Leicester and H. S. Klickstein, in *A Source Book in Chemistry* (Harvard, 1952), of *Zymotechnia Fundamentalis,* first published in 1697.

DEFINITION OF PHLOGISTON

The same thing works very well with sulfur, when certainly two parts, or better, three parts of alkali salt and one of pulverized sulfur are successively poured into and fused in a crucible. There is formed liver of sulfur. This, in the space of a quarter of an hour more or less, by fire alone, without any addition, can be converted to such a salt as is obtained from oil of sulfur *per campanum* [H_2SO_4] and salt of tartar, that which is commonly called *vitriolated tartar*. There is no more trace of sulfur or alkali salt, and in place of the red color of the liver, this salt is most white; in place of the very evil taste of the liver, this salt is very bitter; in place of the easy solution, nay, the spontaneous deliquescence of the liver, by reason of its alkali salt, this salt is the most difficult of all salts except tartar of wine to be dissolved; in place of the impossibility of crystallizing the liver, this is very prone to form almost octahedral crystals; in place of the fusibility of the liver, this is devoid of all fusion.

If this new salt, from the acid of sulfur and alkaline salt formed as stated above when the phlogiston has been used up, is treated with charcoal, in the space of a quarter of an hour the original liver of sulfur reappears, and this can be so converted a hundred times. . . .

I can indeed show by various other experiments how phlogiston from fatty substances and charcoal enters very promptly into metals themselves and regenerates them from the burned calx into their own *fusible, malleable,* and *amalgamable* state.

* * *

Now the first thing to consider concerning the principle of sulfur is its properties, as follows:

1. Behavior toward fire
2. Display of colors
3. Subtle and intimate mixing with other metal substances
4. Behavior toward water and humidity
5. Its own great and wonderful subtlety
6. Its own form in the dry or fluid state
7. Where it can be found or occurs

According to these conditions and intentions, I now have demonstrable grounds to say, first,

Toward fire, this sulfur principle behaves in such a manner that it is not only suitable for the movement of fire but is also one and the same being, yes, even created and designed for it.

But also, according to a reasonable manner of speaking, it is the corporeal fire, the essential fire material, the true basis of fire movement in all inflammable compounds.

However, except in compounds, no fire at all occurs, but it dissipates and volatilizes in invisible particles, or at least, develops and forms a finely divided and invisible fire, namely, heat.

On the other hand, it is very important to note that this fire material, of and by itself and apart from other things, especially air and water, is not found united and active, either as a liquid or in an attenuated state. But if once by the movement of fire, with the addition of free air, it is attenuated and volatilized, then by this in all such conditions it is lost through unrecognizable subtlety and immeasurable attenuation, so that from this point on no science known to man, no human art, can collect it together or bring it into narrow limits, especially if this occurred rapidly and in quantity.

But how enormously attenuated and subtle material becomes through the movement of fire is shown by experience, which furnishes a field for thought and which also delights us.

From all these various conditions, therefore, I have believed that it should be given a name, as the first, unique, basic, inflammable principle. But since it cannot, until this hour, be found by itself, outside of all compounds and unions with other materials, and so there are no grounds or basis for giving a descriptive name based on properties, I have felt that it is most fitting to name it from its general action, which it customarily shows in all its compounds. And therefore I have chosen the Greek name phlogiston, in German, *Brennlich* [inflammable]. . . .

The seventh and last consideration was where it could be found or occurred. The answer to this is now also in part easy to give from the discussion already presented, and from consideration that all corporeal compounded things have more or less of this substance, in all the so-called "kingdoms": vegetable, animal, and mineral. As then in the first two kingdoms there is contained a great amount of this principle, and all their parts are intimately penetrated and combined with it (except the watery parts which occur in them, but which still are not entirely free from it as long as they are in the body), then it is chiefly found in the fatty materials of both kingdoms.

In the mineral kingdom there is nothing but water, common salt, pure vitriolic salts, and light sand and stones in which the substance is little or not at all found. On the other hand, coal and bitumen are full of it; sulfur, not indeed in weight, but in the number of its finest particles, is completely possessed with it. Not less is it found in all inflammable, incomplete, and so-called "unripe" metals.

V

The Scientific Revolution

*"Therefore, what the founders of modern science,
among them Galileo, had to do, was not to criticize and to combat
certain faulty theories, and to correct or to reduce them
by better ones. They had to do something quite
different. They had to destroy one world
and replace it by another."*

—Alexandre Koyré

DISCOVERY OF THE
INFINITELY LARGE

The readings that follow must be considered in the light of the status of astronomical science and the conception of the universe at the opening of the sixteenth century. We have had a number of opportunities to observe, in earlier pages, the effect of the combination of philosophy with scientific observation that characterized the first fifteen hundred years of the Christian era; and nowhere was this more evident than in the attempts to explain the relationship of the earth to the sun, the stars, and the planets. The work of Copernicus, Brahe, Galileo, Kepler, and Newton inaugurated a new approach. What were the foundations on which they built? What was wrong with the explanations of Aristotle and Ptolemy, which had sufficed for so long? What were the influences that called for a new approach?

Among the Greeks, the work of Aristotle, Hipparchus, and Ptolemy most directly laid the foundations of medieval astronomy. Aristotle and Ptolemy were the theorists; Hipparchus was the observer. Aristotle conceived of a universe centered not only

213

on the earth but on man himself as the supreme achievement of creation. It was this point of view that was to attract the interest of the medieval Schoolmen. For them, scientific observation was subordinate to the authority of the divinely inspired scriptures; and there was little in Aristotle's geocentric universe that conflicted with the Church's teachings. The universe was finite and complete as constructed by the Creator during the six days of labor described in the book of *Genesis*. The stationary earth was the center about which the heavenly spheres revolved. Being perfect spheres, their movement was perfectly regular. To the outermost sphere, which set the limits to the universe, were attached the fixed stars. The inner spheres, which were transparent in order to allow the passage of light, were occupied by the planets. To account for the movements that he and others had observed, Aristotle had to use a total of fifty-five spheres.

To this simple, physical explanation, Hipparchus (*c.* 190-120 B.C.) added refinements based on observations. Because his writings have been lost, it is not easy to separate his contributions from those of Ptolemy, who three hundred years later assembled all the available knowledge on the subject. Ptolemy's *Almagest* was, as we have already seen, the authoritative text on the subject until 1543. Hipparchus and Ptolemy between them expanded Aristotle's concentric spheres into a more sophisticated array which explained the movements of the planets in such a way that the mathematicians and geometricians could establish tables that were used for prediction of these movements.

The Hipparchian-Ptolemaic system continued to assume that the earth was the center of the universe and the center of the movements of the stars and the planets, even though it was observed that the velocities of the sun and the planets were not uniform. But this paradox was resolved by assuming that the circular paths did not have their centers directly at the center of the earth.

The retrograde movements of the planets as they circled the earth were explained by hypothesizing that the planet rotated in an epicycle, a secondary, smaller circle, which, in turn, revolved in a primary circle around the earth.

The epicycle was an invention necessary to make the observed phenomena fit the Ptolemaic system; and those who, in Ptolemy's time and later, were able to prepare tables from which the position of the planets could be determined for any period by reference to the fixed stars undoubtedly deserve our respect. The test of these tables came, of course, when their predictions could be compared against observable facts. The equinox, the instant of time at which the sun in its apparent annual movement crosses the celestial equator, was the date chosen for the spring and autumn festivals, both religious and pagan. Over the centuries the error involved in the predictions accumulated, until, by the year 1500, it was more than evident that the equinox occurred in fact at a different time from that predicted for the celebration—a matter disturbing to the faithful. Moreover, the general effect on the calendar of the resulting accumulation of minute annual errors eventually again drew attention to the discrepancy between fact and prediction.

We have on record, however, an interesting tribute to the effectiveness of the Ptolemaic system. The Julian calendar, which was introduced by Julius Caesar in 45 B.C., could be inaugurated only by extending the year 46 B.C. to a length of 445 days in order to bring the date of the spring equinox into line with the sun's passage. After that, the Julian calendar was used for more than five hundred years among churchmen and for seven hundred years in Britain. When, in 1752, Britain finally adopted the Gregorian calendar we now use, the observed error had accumulated to only eleven days, which had to be dropped out of the calendar. The Ptolemaic assumptions had indeed been heroic.

These very significant accomplishments of the classical astronomers were made, too, without benefit of any instruments other than the astrolabe. This was, in effect, a projection onto a plane surface of the spherical design of the planetary system. It facilitated observation but it was no substitute for the telescope for determining the relative sizes of the stars or for detecting new stars; in reading the selections that follow, it must be remembered that the telescope did not exist until the time of Galileo.

Clearly, the impetus to re-examination of the Ptolemaic

doctrines came less from new scientific observations than from the need to correct the mathematical tables whose errors had become so apparent by the time of Copernicus. The epicycles had been introduced to provide a mathematical—or rather, geometrical—support for the Aristotelian model and to make the phenomena fit the theory of the spheres. The job of the sixteenth century was to examine the situation to see if the "phenomena could be saved" again.

This, as we shall see in the first selection, is what Copernicus attempted.

*"In the midst of all,
the sun reposes, unmoving."*

Copernicus

1473 − 1543

THE MOTIONS OF THE PLANETS AROUND
THE SUN IN CIRCULAR ORBITS
ARE DEMONSTRATED

The revolution wrought by Copernicus is symbolic of the
transition from the medieval to the modern world. It is more
important for what it made possible than for what it actually was,
for it involved not a new idea or a great discovery but, rather,
a new way of looking at things. It set in motion the monumental
achievements of Galileo, Kepler, and Newton, which completed
the overthrow of the medieval world view.

Niklas Koppernigk (called, in Latin, Copernicus), born in
Thorn, in Poland, student at Cracow, Bologna, Ferrara, and
Padua and, thereafter and until his death, canon of the Cathedral at Frauenburg, was a splendid example of the medieval
scholar. His genius was universal, and his reading ranged from
economics and medicine to mathematics and astronomy. Such
breadth of interest reflected a high intelligence and imaginative
instructors. One of the latter, Domenico Novaro, Professor of
Mathematics and Astronomy at Bologna, was a Pythagorean in
that he believed in the essential simplicity and harmony of the
universe, and he criticized the complexities of the Ptolemaic
system. Copernicus was thus encouraged to study the classics in
order to discover the objections to the concept that the earth was

fixed and immovable and the center of the universe. He found that Hicetas, for example, who lived in the fifth century before the Christian era, had taught that the earth rotated on its own axis in twenty-four hours. Aristarchus, two hundred years after Hicetas, taught the same idea and added that the sun was the center of an immeasurably great universe. These views had been discussed by Bishop Oresme (1320?-1382) and others whose works were included in Copernicus's curriculum.

Copernicus's alternative to Ptolemaic astronomy took many years of preparation, and his conclusions were reached largely by the use of mathematics, logic, and observation. By setting the heavenly bodies in relation to the sun at the center, and considering the earth as one of the planets, Copernicus found that he could account for all their movements. He demonstrated the rotation of the earth on its axis, as well as its movement around the sun, and analyzed the significance of that movement in relation to that of the other planets.

Copernicus's system was, in the main, a reconstruction of Ptolemy's, which by the end of the fifteenth century had grown extremely complex and cumbersome, consisting of more than eighty spheres but still inadequate to explain celestial movements. Copernicus was able to simplify the celestial model by reducing the number of spheres to thirty-four. By assuming that the earth moved and that the sun was at the center of the universe, he was able, in some thirty years of effort, to devise a new scheme of the universe which was much simpler and explained more. He recalculated the tables which had been developed out of the Ptolemaic system, but in doing this he had to rely on the basic observations made by his predecessors, even those of Ptolemy himself. He represented the symmetry and order of the sun-centered system by a combination of a few uniform circular paths, retaining a few of the epicycles of Ptolemy to "save the phenomena" and account for observed details of motion.

Copernicus was an eminently modest and gentle man, not overeager to publicize the results of his work. There is no evidence that he himself feared the reactions of the Church to his assertion that the earth moved; he was more concerned with the possibility of ridicule and once said, "The contempt which I had to fear because of the novelty and apparent absurdity of my view nearly induced me to abandon utterly the work I had begun." Three years before Copernicus's death, one Rheticus published a summary of his book under the title *De Libris Revolutionum Narratio Prima,* apparently with the permission of Church officials who had read some of Copernicus's drafts during the long period of its preparation. His definitive work, *De Revolutionibus Orbium Caelestium,* was published shortly before he died. The book contained a preface, afterwards found to have been written by a Lutheran minister named Osiander, intended to placate the Protestants and describing the work as a mathematical exercise rather than an astronomical treatise. This preface may have been the reason why the Copernican ideas failed to have an immediate revolutionary effect; in fact, the Ptolemaic system and the new Copernican model were taught as alternative explanations until the eighteenth century, even at Harvard and Yale.

The Church took no positive action against the Copernican view until the teachings of Giordano Bruno (*c.* 1548?-1600) drew attention to its consequences on Church doctrine. Thus, almost a century after Copernicus's death, his work, by undermining the unity of the medieval system of thought, became the center of a violent intellectual controversy. Bruno accepted the Copernican scheme and went one step further by denying the necessity for a finite universe. If the Deity were infinite, why should His creations be finite? The effect was to abolish the idea of that final sphere which, Ptolemy and his followers held, contained the fixed stars. Since the Church had located Heaven beyond this last sphere and Bruno had now removed the boundaries of the physical universe, the way was open to the idea that creation might extend beyond the world described in the book of *Genesis.* Bruno was burned at the stake for thus upsetting the Church's teaching that man was God's principal concern. Copernicus's work was banned and remained in the Church's disfavor until 1822.

The full effect of Copernicus's work was, therefore, not felt until after Galileo's telescope had produced experimental support for some of his most revolutionary opinions and Newton gave them that scientific explanation which was the crowning achievement of the scientific revolution.

The following reading, taken from *A Source Book in Astronomy* (edited by H. Shapley and H. E. Howarth and published by McGraw-Hill Book Company in 1929), was translated by Martha B. Shapley.

CHAPTER I

That the Universe Is Spherical

First of all we assert that the universe is spherical; partly because this form, being a complete whole, needing no joints, is the most perfect of all; partly because it constitutes the most spacious form, which is thus best suited to contain and retain all things; or also because all discrete parts of the world, I mean the sun, the moon and the planets, appear as spheres; or because all things tend to assume the spherical shape, a fact which appears in a drop of water and in other fluid bodies when they seek of their own accord to limit themselves. Therefore no one will doubt that this form is natural for the heavenly bodies.

CHAPTER II

That the Earth Is Likewise Spherical

That the earth is likewise spherical is beyond doubt, because it presses from all sides to its center. Although a perfect sphere is not immediately recognized because of the great height of the mountains and the depression of the valleys, yet this in no wise invalidates the general spherical form of the earth. This becomes clear in the following manner: To people who travel from any place to the North, the north pole of the daily revolution rises gradually, while the south pole sinks a like amount. Most of the stars in the neighborhood of the Great Bear appear not to set, and in the South some stars appear no longer to rise. Thus Italy does not see Canopus, which is visible to the Egyptians. And Italy sees the outermost star of the River, which is unknown to us of a colder zone. On the other hand, to people who travel toward the South, these stars rise higher in the heavens, while those stars which are higher to us become lower. Therefore, it is plain that the earth is included between the poles and is spherical. Let us add that the inhabitants of the East do not see the solar and lunar eclipses that occur in the evening, and people who live in the West do not see eclipses that occur in the morning, while those living in between see the former later, and the latter earlier.

That even the water has the same shape is observed on ships, in that the land which can not be seen from the ships can be spied from the tip of the mast. And, conversely, when a light is put on the tip of the mast, it appears to observers on land gradually to drop as the ship recedes until the light disappears, seeming to sink in the water. It is clear that the water, too, in accordance with its fluid nature, is drawn downwards, just as is the earth, and its level at the shore is no higher than its convexity allows. The land therefore projects everywhere only as far above the ocean as the land accidentally happens to be higher. . . .

CHAPTER IV

That the Motions of the Heavenly Bodies are Uniform, Circular, Uninterrupted, or Are Made Up of Combined Circular Motions

Hereupon, we note that the motions of the heavenly bodies are circular. When a sphere is in motion it rotates, expressing, through this activity, its form as that of the simplest of bodies, in which there is to be found neither a beginning nor an end; nor can the beginning be distinguished from the end, as the sphere achieves, through the same intermediate points, its original position. Because of the multiplicity of circles there are, however, numerous possible motions. The best known of all is the daily revolution which the Greeks call Nychthemeron, i.e., the period of day and night. To achieve this motion, it is believed the whole universe with the exception of the earth, turns from east to west. It is recognized as the common measure of all motions, since time itself is measured chiefly by the number of days. In addition, we see progressing other revolutions which are apparently retrograde, i.e., from west to east; namely those of the sun, the moon, and the five planets.

By means of this motion the sun measures for us the year, the moon the month, as the most common units of time. And thus each of the other five planets completes its orbit. Yet they are peculiar in many ways. First, in that they do not revolve about the same poles around which the first motion takes place, progressing instead in the oblique path of the Zodiac; second, in that they do not seem to move uniformly in their own orbits, for the sun and the moon are discovered moving now with a slower, now a faster motion. The remaining five planets, moreover, we also see at times going backward and, in the transition, standing still. And while the sun moves along always in its direct path, the planets wander in various ways, roaming, now to the South, now to the North. Wherefore they are designated "planets." They have the added peculiarity that they at times come nearer to the earth, where they are called at perigee, then again they recede from it, where they are called at apogee. Nevertheless, it must be admitted that the motions are circular, or are built up of many circles; for thus such irregularities would occur according to a reliable law and a fixed period, which could not be the case if they were not circular. For the circle alone can bring back the past, as the sun, so to speak, brings back to us, through its motion made up of circles, the irregularities of the days and nights and the four seasons; in which several motions are recognized because it cannot happen that the simple heavenly bodies move irregularly in a single circle. For this would either have to be caused by an inconstancy in the nature of the moving force—whether the inconstancy be brought about by a cause from without or within—or would have to originate in an irregularity of the moving body. But as reason rebels against both, and as it is unworthy to assume such a thing concerning that which is arranged in the best of order, so one must admit that the regular motions seem irregular to us, either because the various circles have different poles, or because the earth is not situated in the center of the circles in which the planets move; and that to us who observe the motions of the stars from the earth, the planets, because of the varying distances, appear larger when near us than when they are in paths more remote; that can be proved in optics. In this way the motions which take place in equal times through equal arcs, seem to us unequal due to different distances. Therefore, I consider it above all things necessary that we investigate carefully what relation the earth has to the heavens, so that we, when we wish to investigate the most noble things in nature, do not leave out of consideration the nearest, and erroneously attribute to the heavenly bodies what belongs to the earth.

CHAPTER V

Whether the Earth Has a Circular Motion, And Concerning the Location of the Earth

Since it has already been proved that the earth has the shape of a sphere, I insist that we must investigate whether from its form can be deduced a motion, and what place the earth occupies in the universe. Without this knowledge no certain computation can be made for the phenomena occurring in the heavens. To be sure, the great majority of writers agree that the earth is at rest in the center of the universe, so that they consider it unbelievable and even ridiculous to suppose the contrary. Yet, when one weighs the matter carefully, he will see that this question is not yet disposed of, and for that reason is by no means to be considered unimportant. Every change of position which is observed is due either to the motion of the observed object or of the observer, or to motions, naturally in different directions, of both; for when the observed object and the observer move in the same manner and in the same direction, then no motion is observed. Now the earth is the place from which we observe the revolution of the heavens and where it is displayed to our eyes. Therefore, if the earth should possess any motion, the latter would be noticeable in everything that is situated outside of it, but in the opposite direction, just as if everything were traveling past the earth. And of this nature is, above all, the daily revolution. For this motion seems to embrace the whole world, in fact, everything that is outside of the earth, with the single exception of the earth itself. But if one should admit that the heavens possess none of this motion, but that the earth rotates from west to east; and if one should consider this seriously with respect to the seeming rising and setting of the sun, of the moon and stars; then one would find that it is actually true. Since the heavens which contain and retain all things are the common home of all things, it is not at once comprehensible why a motion is not rather ascribed to the thing contained than to the containing, to the located rather than to the locating. This opinion was actually held by the Pythagoreans Heraklid and Ekphantus and the Syracusean Nicetas (as told by Cicero), in that they assumed the earth to be rotating in the center of the universe. They were indeed of the opinion that the stars set due to the intervening of the earth, and rose due to its receding.

From this assumption follows the other not less important doubt concerning the position of the earth, though it is assumed and believed by almost everyone that the earth occupies the center of the universe. If, therefore, one should maintain that the earth is not in the center of the universe, but that the discrepancy between the two is not great enough to be measurable on the sphere of the fixed stars, but on the other hand noticeable and recognizable in the orbits of the sun and the planets; and if further he were of the opinion that the motions of the latter for this reason appear irregular, just as if they were oriented with respect to another center than that of the earth—such a person might, perhaps, have assigned the true reason for the apparently irregular motions. For since the planets appear now nearer, now more distant from the earth, this betrays necessarily that the center of the earth is not the center of those circular orbits. And yet it is not determined whether the earth decreases and increases its distance from them or they their distance from the earth.

It would thus not be strange if someone should ascribe to the earth, in addition to its daily rotation, also another motion. However, it is said that the Pythagorean Philolaus, a not ordinary mathematician, believed that the earth rotates, that it moves along in space with various motions, and that it belongs to the planets; wherefore, Plato did not delay journeying to Italy to interview him, as is told by those who have described Plato's life. Many, on the other hand, believed that it could be proved by mathematical calculation that the earth is situated in the center of the universe, and since, compared with the enormous size of the heavens, it can be considered as a point, it occupies the central point and is for this reason immovable; because if the universe moves, its central point must remain motionless, and that which is nearest the central point must move most slowly.

CHAPTER VII

Why the Ancients Believed that the Earth Rests in the Middle of the Universe, as Its Central Point

Thus for certain other reasons the ancient philosophers sought to prove that the earth is in the center of the universe. As chief cause, however, they cite weight and imponderability. The element earth is, to be sure, the heaviest of all, and everything ponderable tends to move, governed by its impulse, toward the innermost center of the earth. Now since the earth is spherical—the earth, onto the surface of which heavy bodies from all sides fall perpendicularly, due to their own nature—the falling bodies would meet at its center if they were not held back on the surface; because, indeed, a straight line which is perpendicular to the tangent plane at its point of tangency leads to the center. As to those bodies which move toward the center, it seems to follow that they would come to rest at the center. All the more would the whole earth be at rest in the center, and no matter what it might accumulate in the way of falling bodies, it would remain motionless due to its own weight.

In a similar manner the ancients support their proofs with the cause of motion and its nature. Aristotle says, for example, that a simple body has a simple motion; of possible simple motions, however, one is motion in a straight line, the other is circular motion. Of simple motions in a straight line, one is upwards, and the other is downwards. Therefore, every simple motion would be either toward the center, i.e. downward, or away from the center, i.e., upwards, or around the center, and this would be the circular motion or revolution. Only the earth and the water, which are considered heavy, move downwards, that is, tend to move towards the center. Air, however, and fire, which are endowed with imponderability, move upwards and away from the center. It seems clear that one must admit motion in a straight line for these four elements; as regards the heavenly bodies, however, one must admit motion in a circle around the center. Thus says Aristotle. "If, therefore," says the Alexandrian Ptolemy, "the earth turns, at least in daily rotation, the opposite of all that is said above must take place; that is to say the motion which traverses throughout the whole circumference of the earth in twenty-four hours would have to be the most violent of all and its velocity would have to be transcendent. But matter which is set in violent rotation does not seem at all fit to be massed together, but rather to be dispersed, if the component parts are not held together with some firmness. And long before now," he says, "the disintegrated earth would have been dissipated over the heavens themselves, which is very ridiculous; and much less would the living beings and other separated masses in any way have remained unannihilated. But also the bodies falling in straight lines would not arrive on the places destined for them, as these spots would in the meantime have moved from under which such great velocity. We would also see the clouds and whatever else is floating in the air always moving toward the west."

CHAPTER VIII

Refutation of the Arguments, and Their Insufficiency

From these and similar reasons it is claimed that the earth is at rest in the center of the universe and that this is undoubtedly true. But one who believes that the earth rotates will also certainly be of the opinion that this motion is natural and not violent. Whatever is in accordance with nature produces effects which are the opposite of what happens through violence. Things upon which violence or an external force is exerted must become annihilated and cannot long exist. But whatever happens in the course of nature remains in good condition and in its best arrangement. Without cause, therefore, Ptolemy feared that the earth and all earthly things if set in rotation would be dissolved by the action of nature, for the functioning of nature is something entirely different from artifice, or from that which could be contrived by the human mind. But why did he not fear the same, and indeed in much higher degree, for the universe, whose motion would have to be as much more rapid as the heavens are larger than the earth? Or have the heavens become infinite just because they have been removed from the center by the inexpressible force of the motion; while otherwise, if they were at rest, they would collapse? Certainly if this argument were true the extent of the heavens would become infinite. For the more they were driven aloft by the outward impulse of the motion, the more rapid would the motion become because of the ever increasing circle which it would have to describe in the space of 24 hours; and, conversely, if the motion increased, the immensity of the heavens would also increase. Thus velocity would augment size into infinity, and size, velocity. But according to the physical law that the infinite can neither be traversed, nor can it for any reason have motion, the heavens would, however, of necessity be at rest.

But it is said that outside of the heavens there is no body, nor place, nor empty space, in fact, that nothing at all exists, and that, therefore, there is no space in which the heavens could expand; then it is really strange that something could be enclosed by nothing. If, however, the heavens

net, in quo terram cum orbe lunari tanquam epicyclo contineri diximus. Quinto loco Venus nono menſe reducitur. Sextum deniꝗ locum Mercurius tenet, octuaginta dierum ſpacio circū currens. In medio uero omnium reſidet Sol. Quis enim in hoc

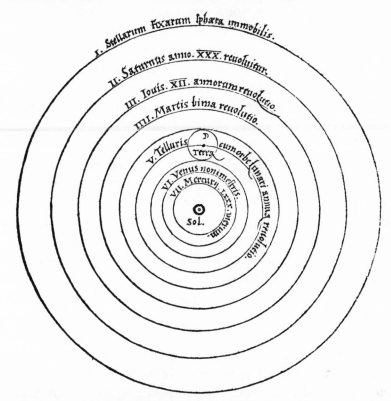

pulcherimo templo lampadem hanc in alio uel meliori loco po neret, quàm unde totum ſimul poſsit illuminare? Siquidem non inepte quidam lucernam mundi, alij mentem, alij rectorem uo= cant. Trimegiſtus uiſibilem Deum, Sophoclis Electra intuentē omnia. Ita profecto tanquam in ſolio re gali Sol reſidens circum agentem gubernat Aſtrorum familiam. Tellus quoꝗ minime fraudatur lunari miniſterio, ſed ut Ariſtoteles de animalibus ait, maximā Luna cū terra cognationē habet. Concipit interea à Sole terra, & impregnatur annuo partu. Inuenimus igitur ſub hac

Representation of the solar system by Copernicus in which he places the sun at the center. From *De Revolutionibus Orbium Coelestium,* Nuremberg, 1543. (Courtesy of the Burndy Library.)

were infinite and were bounded only by their inner concavity, then we have, perhaps, even better confirmation that there is nothing outside of the heavens, because everything, whatever its size, is within them; but then the heavens would remain motionless. The most important argument, on which depends the proof of the finiteness of the universe, is motion. Now, whether the world is finite or infinite, we will leave to the quarrels of the natural philosophers; for us remains the certainty that the earth, contained between poles, is bounded by a spherical surface. Why should we hesitate to grant it a motion, natural and corresponding to its form; rather than assume that the whole world, whose boundary is not known and cannot be known, moves? And why are we not willing to acknowledge that the appearance of a daily revolution belongs to the heavens, its actuality to the earth? The relation is similar to that of which Virgil's Aeneas says: "We sail out of the harbor, and the countries and cities recede." For when a ship is sailing along quietly, everything which is outside of it will appear to those on board to have a motion corresponding to the movement of the ship, and the voyagers are of the erroneous opinion that they with all that they have with them are at rest. This can without doubt also apply to the motion of the earth, and it may appear as if the whole universe were revolving.

Now what shall we say about the clouds and whatever else is somehow floating, falling or rising in the air? Except that not only does the earth move with its attached watery element, but it also carries with it no small part of the air and whatever else is thus joined with the earth. It may be that the air lying nearest the earth, mixed with earthy and watery material, obeys the same nature as the earth; it may be that the motion has been communicated to the air, the atmosphere partaking of this motion because of the contact with the earth and the resistance during the constant rotation. Again, an equally astonishing claim, namely, that the highest region of the air obeys the heavenly motion, is said to be supported by those suddenly-appearing stellar objects which are called by the Greeks comets or bearded stars, the origin of which one assigns to just that region, and which, like other constellations, rise and set. It may be said that that part of the air, due to its great remoteness from the earth, has remained immune from the earthly motion. Therefore, the air which lies nearest the earth will appear at rest, as well as those objects floating in it, when they are not driven hither and yon by the wind or by some other external force, as may happen by chance; for what is the wind in the air other than the waves in the sea? We must admit that the motion of falling and rising objects is, with respect to the universe, a double one, compounded always of rectilinear and circular motions. Since that which, due to its weight, is attracted downwards is essentially earthy, there is no doubt that these parts obey the same law as their whole—namely, the earth; and for the same reason such objects as belong to the fire class are drawn aloft with violence. Earthly fire is fed principally with earthy materials, and it is said that a flame is only burning smoke. The peculiarity of fire, however, consists in expanding that which it has taken hold of; and it achieves this with such violence that it can be hindered by no method or machine from breaking down the barriers and fulfilling its work. But the expanding motion is directed from the center to the periphery. Therefore, when anything composed of earthy parts is ignited, it moves from the center upwards.

Thus, as has been claimed, a simple body has a simple motion and this proves to be preferably a circular motion as long as the simple body remains in its natural position and retains its unity. In this position its motion is merely the circular motion which, being entirely within the body, makes it seem to be at rest. Rectilinear motion, however, attacks bodies which have left or have been displaced. Nothing militates so against the order and form of the whole world as "being-out-of-its-place." Thus motion in a straight line enters only when things are not in their proper relations and are not completely as they should be, having been separated from their whole and having lost their unity. Moreover, such bodies which are driven upwards or downwards, disregarding the circular motion, do not describe simple uniform and constant motion, for they cannot orient themselves by their lightness or the pressure of their weight; and if at the beginning of their plunge they have a slower motion, they increase their velocity in falling. While on the other hand we see that earthly fire (and we know of no other kind) when driven aloft at once becomes inert, as if it showed by this means the origin of the earthy materials. Circular motion, on the other hand, is always uniform because it has a cause that does not slacken. The other motions, however, diminish during their progress, when the bodies have reached their natural position they cease to be either imponderable or heavy, and, therefore, their motion ceases. If, therefore, the universe possesses circular motion and its parts possess also rectilinear motion, then we might say that circular motion is compatible with rectilinear motion, just as the animal with disease. If Aristotle divided simple motions into three kinds, away from the center, toward the center, and around the center, that seems to be only an intellectual exercise, just as we distinguish between a line, a point, and a surface, even though one of these cannot exist without the others, and none of them without matter. Moreover, the condition of rest is considered as nobler and more divine than that of change and inconstancy, so the latter would, therefore, be more suited to the earth than to the universe. And I add to this that it seems irrational to ascribe a motion to that which contains and locates and not to that which is contained and is located, namely the earth. Finally, since the planets clearly are now nearer, now farther from the earth, the motion of one and the same body about the center (which is said to be the center of the earth), is also directed away from and toward this center. It is, therefore, necessary to have a more general conception of motion about a center, and it should be sufficient if each single motion has its own center. It is clear, therefore, from all this, that motion of the earth is more probable than rest, especially in relation to the daily rotation, which is most characteristic of the earth.

CHAPTER IX

Whether the Earth Can Be Assigned Several Motions; and Concerning the Center of the Universe

Since nothing stands in the way of the movability of the earth, I believe we must now investigate whether it also has several motions, so that it can be considered one of the planets. That it is not the center of all the revolutions is proved by the irregular motions of the planets, and their varying distances from the earth, which cannot be explained as concentric circles with the earth at the center. Therefore, since there are several central points, no one will without cause be uncertain whether the center of the universe is the center of gravity of the earth or some other central point. I, at least, am of the opinion that gravity is nothing else than a natural force planted by the divine providence of the Master of the World into its parts, by means of which they, assuming a spherical shape, form a unity and a whole. And it is to be assumed that the impulse is also inherent in the sun and the moon and the other planets, and that by the operation of this force they remain in the spherical shape in which they appear; while they, nevertheless, complete their revolutions in diverse ways. If then the earth, too, possesses other motions besides that around its center, then they must be of such a character as to become apparent in many ways and in appropriate manners; and among such possible effects we recognize the yearly revolution. If one admits the motionlessness of the sun, and transfers the annual revolution from the sun to the earth, there would result, in the same manner as actually observed, the rising and setting of the constellations and the fixed stars, by means of which they become morning and evening stars; and it will thus become apparent that also the haltings and the backward and forward motion of the planets are not motions of these but of the earth, which lends them the appearance of being actual planetary motions. Finally, one will be convinced that the sun itself occupies the center of the universe. And all this is taught us by the law of sequence in which things follow one upon another and the harmony of the universe; that is, if we only (so to speak) look at the matter with both eyes.

"May I not seem to have lived in vain."

Tycho Brahe

1546 – 1601

A NEW STAR IS REPORTED

Copernicus, the contemplative scholar, was first opposed by an aggressive, practical astronomer, Tycho Brahe. Brahe—a Dane who had studied mathematics and astronomy in German and Swiss universities—came to the conclusion that Copernicus's assumption that the earth moved in space defied the Scriptures and violated the principles of physics; and so he set out to rehabilitate Ptolemaic astronomy. Brahe succeeded in restating Ptolemy's system by showing that the sun revolved around the earth and the planets turned around the sun in epicycles. He made no great effort, however, to promote his theories, finding himself much more interested in making observations of the stars.

With the encouragement of royal patrons, Brahe worked at Uraniborg (near Hamlet's Elsinore) in Denmark until 1597 and then, for the few years until his death, at Prague. With instruments based mainly on the astrolabe but improved and enlarged by him, Brahe attained an accuracy that could hardly be improved upon without lenses. Moreover, he refined the methods of his predecessors, who had relied on what they believed to be the best possible observations. With a group of assistants, Brahe maintained systematic series of observations of the planets and stars, averaging the results so as to minimize errors. His data were regularly recorded, and his catalogue of the stars—listing 777 when he published it in 1592—became a standard reference, especially as enlarged by his pupil Kepler. Brahe's detailed records provided data that upset the long-held proposition that the heavenly orbits were perfectly circular.

Brahe's instruments merely guided his naked eye; they did not supplement its powers. Yet he was able to record measurements of stellar positions with an error of less than one-sixtieth of a degree of arc—an achievement that testifies to the persistence as well as the accuracy of his researches. His data long retained their value, establishing Brahe as one of the most successful astronomical observers of all time. His return to Ptolemaic theory was, perhaps, the result of his cantankerousness; he was a natural objector to other people's ideas who nevertheless served science by expanding its horizons and adding to its store of accumulated verified fact.

Brahe's observation of a new star in 1572, recorded in the following selection, was a direct challenge to the Aristolelian concept that the universe was confined by a sphere containing an unalterable number of stars.

The reading that follows has been taken from the J. H. Walden translation of *De Nova Stella* in *A Source Book in Astronomy* (Harvard, 1929).

ON A NEW STAR, NOT PREVIOUSLY SEEN WITHIN THE MEMORY OF ANY AGE SINCE THE BEGINNING OF THE WORLD

Its First Appearance in 1572.—Last year (1572), in the month of November, on the eleventh day of that month, in the evening, after sunset, when, according to my habit, I was contemplating the stars in a clear sky, I noticed that a new and unusual star, surpassing the others stars in brilliancy, was shining almost directly above my head; and since I had, almost from boyhood, known all the stars of the heavens perfectly (there is no great difficulty in attaining that knowledge), it was quite evident to me that there had never before been any star in that place in the sky, even the smallest, to say nothing of a star so conspicuously bright as this. I was so astonished at this sight that I was not ashamed to doubt the trustworthiness of my own eyes. But when I observed that others, too, on having the place pointed out to them, could see that there was really a star there, I had no further doubts. A miracle indeed, either the greatest of all that have occurred in the whole range of nature since the beginning of the world, or one certainly that is to be classed with those attested by the Holy Oracles, the staying of the Sun in its course in answer to the prayers of Joshua, and the darkening of the Sun's face at the time of the Crucifixion. For all philosophers agree, and facts clearly prove it to be the case, that in the ethereal region of the celestial world no change, in the way either of gen-ration or of corruption, takes place; but that the heavens and the celestial bodies in the heavens are without increase or diminution, and that they undergo no alteration, either in number or in size or in light or in any other respect; that they always remain the same, like unto themselves in all respects, no years wearing them away. Furthermore, the observations of all founders of the science, made some thousands of years ago, testify that all the stars have always retained the same number, position, order, motion, and size as they are found, by careful observation on the part of those who take delight in heavenly phenomena, to preserve even in our own day. Nor do we read that it was ever before noted by any one of the founders that a new star had appeared in the celestial world, except only by Hipparchus, if we are to believe Pliny. For Hipparchus, according to Pliny (Book II of his Natural History), noticed a star different from all others previously seen, one born in his own age. . . .

   Its Position with Reference to the Diameter of the World and its Distance from the Earth, the Center of the Universe.—It is a difficult matter, and one that requires a subtle mind, to try to determine the distances of the stars from us, because they are so incredibly far removed from the earth; nor can it be done in any way more conveniently and with greater certainty than by the measure of the parallax (diurnal), if a star have one. For if a star that is near the horizon is seen in a different place than when it is at its highest point and near the vertex, it is necessarily found in some orbit with respect to which the Earth has a sensible size. How far distant the said orbit is, the size of the parallax compared with the semi-diameter of the Earth will make clear. If, however, a (circumpolar) star, that is as near to the horizon (at lower culmination) as to the vertex (at upper culmination), is seen at the same point of the Primum Mobile, there is no doubt that it is situated either in the eighth sphere or not far below it, in an orbit with respect to which the whole Earth is as a point.

In order, therefore, that I might find out in this way whether this star was in the region of the Element or among the celestial orbits, and what its distance was from the Earth itself, I tried to determine whether it had a parallax, and, if so, how great a one; and this I did in the following way: I observed the distance between this star and Schedir of Cassiopeia (for the latter and the new star were both nearly on the meridian), when the star was at its nearest point to the vertex, being only 6 degrees removed from the zenith itself (and for that reason, though it were near the Earth, would produce no parallax in that place, the visual position of the star and the real position then uniting in one point, since the line from the center of the Earth and that from the surface nearly coincide). I made the same observation when the star was farthest from the zenith and at its nearest point to the horizon, and in each case I found that the distance from the above-mentioned fixed star was exactly the same, without the variation of a minute: namely 7 degrees and 55 minutes. Then I went through the same process, making numerous observations with other stars. Whence I conclude that this new star has no diversity of aspect, even when it is near the horizon. For otherwise in its least altitude it would have been farther away from the above-mentioned star in the breast of Cassiopeia than when in its greatest altitude. Therefore, we shall find it necessary to place this star, not in the region of the Element, below the moon, but far above, in an orbit with respect to which the Earth has no sensible size. For if it were in the highest region of the air, below the hollow region of the Lunar sphere, it would, when nearest the horizon, have produced on the circle a sensible variation of altitude from that which it held when near the vertex.

To make the proof clearer, let a circle be drawn representing the meridian, or some other vertical circle of the Primum Mobile, in which the places of all the stars are held to be, and let this circle be CBDE, with its center A. Let the diameter BE indicate the vertex, and CD the horizon. Furthermore, let there be described with the same center a circle MKL, which shall indicate the circumference of the Earth. Between these let there be drawn another circle GHFI, to represent the lowest circle of the Lunar sphere and the one nearest the Earth, in which we are to imagine this star to be. And let it first be in its greatest altitude, near the point G: it is clear that it is entirely without diversity of aspect; for the two lines, one drawn from the center of the Earth, and the other drawn from the eye placed on the surface of the Earth, unite in one and the same point of the circle of the Primum Mobile CBDE, that is, in the point B, or near it if the star is not exactly at G. For this star is removed 6 degrees from the vertex, when it is for us at its highest point; which distance, however, produces no sensible variation from the vertex itself. But let this star be placed in the same circle GHFI at its lowest altitude, which is the point O, and, if the eye is placed at K on the surface of the Earth, the star will necessarily be seen in another place on the outermost circle from what it will if the eye is at A, the center of the earth. For, if lines are drawn from K on the surface, and A, the center of the Earth, through O, which is the position of the star, to the outermost orbit BDEC, the line from A through O will fall in P, while the line from K through the same point O will fall in Q. PQ, therefore, is the arc of the Primum Mobile showing the diversity of aspect of the star.

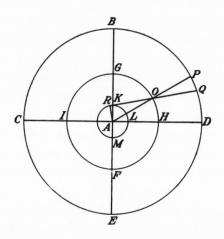

I will try to determine, therefore, the length of the arc PQ, so that we may learn how great is the diversity of aspect which this star has when it is at its nearest point to the horizon, if it is placed in the circle IGHF, immediately below the orbit of the Moon, at the point O. That this may be done more conveniently, let the line QOK be produced until another line drawn from the center A meets perpendicularly, and let the point of meeting be R. Since the angle BKO is known by observation—for it is the complement of the least altitude of the star itself, namely 62 degrees, 5 minutes—its vertical angle RKA will be known, being its equal. Furthermore, the angle KRA is by hypothesis a right angle; and the side KA is known by some measurement or other, for it is the semidiameter of the Earth itself. AR will be found by Proposition 29 of Regiomontanus concerning plane triangle ROA, two sides of which, RA and AO, are known. For AO is the distance from the center of the Earth to the lowest surface of the orbit of the Moon, which distance, with Copernicus, I have set at 5,200,000 of the same units in which the semidiameter of the Earth, AK, was reckoned at 100,000 (for I find it best to make use of larger numbers in this computation, that the calculation may be carried on more conveniently and the result be given more exactly); and since in the aforementioned triangle the angle ORA is by hypothesis a right angle, the angle ROA will be found by the 27th Proposition of Regiomontanus on plane triangles. For by multiplying the side AR in to the whole sine, we get 8,863,300,000, which number, being divided by the side AO, gives 1699 units, the sine, namely, of the angle ROA, whose arc is 0 degrees, 58½ minutes; and this number determines the size of the required angle. To this angle, ROA, the angle POQ is equal, since it is its vertical angle, as is manifest from the principles of geometry. Therefore, the arc PQ, which is the measure of this angle (for, owing to the immense distance between the Lunar sphere and Primum Mobile, the arc PQ does not differ sensibly from the arc of the circle intercepted by the same lines at the distance OP) and indicates the parallax of the star, will be 58½ minutes, which was what we had to find. So great, therefore, would have been the diversity of aspect of this star in the position O, as between that place which it held near the vertex and that in which it was seen when nearest the horizon. But after making many careful observations, as I said above, with a most delicate and accurate instrument, I found that this was not the case. Whence I conclude that this star which has recently become visible is not in the circle IGHF, in the uppermost region, that is, of the air, immediately below the orbit of the Moon, nor in any place yet nearer the Earth—for in the latter case the arc PQ would have produced a greater length, and the diversity of aspect would be greater—but that it is situated far above the Lunar sphere, in the heaven itself, and in fact in some orbit so far removed from the Earth that the line KA, the semidiameter of the Earth, has no sensible size in respect to it, but that the whole Earth, when compared to it, is observed to be no more than a point; and this has been found by the founders of the science to be in the eighth sphere or not far from it, in the higher orbits of three superior planets. Whence this star will be placed in the heavens themselves, either in the eighth orbit with the other fixed stars or in that of any one of the other planets, is clear from this fact: after the lapse of six months it had not advanced by its own motion a single minute from that place in which I first saw it; and this it must have done if it were in some planetary orbit. For, unlike the Primum Mobile, it would be moved by the peculiar motion of the orbit itself, unless it were at rest at one or the other pole of the orbits of the Secundum Mobile; from which, however, as I have shown above, it is removed 28 degrees. For the entire orbits, revolving on their own poles, carry along their own stars, or (as I see Pliny and some others hold) are carried along by them; unless, indeed, one would deny the belief accepted by philosophers and mathematicians, and assert (what is absurd) that the stars alone revolve, while the orbits are fixed. Therefore, if this star were placed in some one of the orbits of the seven wandering stars, it would necessarily be carried around with the orbit itself to which it were affixed, in the opposite direction to the daily revolution. And, furthermore, this motion, even in the case of the orbit which moves the slowest, that of Saturn, would, after such a length of time, be noticed, though one were to make his observation without any instrument at all.

Therefore, this new star is neither in the region of the Element, below the Moon, nor among the orbits of the seven wandering stars, but it is in the eighth sphere, among the other fixed stars, which was what we had to prove. Hence it follows that it is not some peculiar kind of comet or some other kind of fiery meteor become visible. For none of these are generated in the heavens themselves, but they are below the Moon, in the upper region of the air, as all philosophers testify; unless one would believe with Albategnius that comets are produced, not in the air, but in the heavens. For he believes that he has observed a comet above the Moon, in the sphere of Venus. That this can be the case, is not yet clear to me. But, please God, sometime, if a comet shows itself in our age, I will investigate the truth of the matter. Even should we assume that it can happen (which I, in company with other philosophers, can hardly admit), still it does not follow that this star is a kind of comet; first, by reason of its very form, which is the same as the form of the real stars and different from the form of all the comets hitherto seen, and then because, in such a length of time, it advances neither latitudinally nor longitudinally by any motion of its own, as comets have been observed to do. For, although these sometimes seem to remain in one place several days, still, when the observation is made carefully by exact instruments, they are seen not to keep the same position for so very long or so very exactly. I conclude, therefore, that this star is not some kind of comet or a fiery meteor, whether these be generated beneath the Moon or above the Moon, but that it is a star shining in the firmament itself—one that has never previously been seen before our time, in any age since the beginning of the world.

*"Methinks that in the discussion of
natural problems we ought not to begin with the
authority of passages from Scriptures, but with sensible
experiments and necessary demonstrations. . . . Nature being
inexorable, acting only through immutable laws which
she never transgresses, and caring nothing whether
her reasons and methods of operating be or
be not understandable by men. . . ."*

Galileo Galilei

1564 – 1642

THE CONSTRUCTION OF A TELESCOPE AND OBSERVATIONS OF THE MOON, SOME PLANETS, AND SOME STARS ARE DESCRIBED. THE PTOLEMAIC AND COPERNICAN SYSTEMS ARE COMPARED

According to Alfred North Whitehead, "the worship of God . . . is an adventure of the spirit, a flight after the unattainable." Most people today probably accept this statement as the basis for a working distinction between religion and science: the latter, by definition, can examine only the attainable. Yet this distinction, which to us seems obvious, was established neither quickly nor easily, and the experience of Galileo is an almost legendary example of the struggle to obtain recognition of science's more limited objectives.

Galileo's life covered precisely the period between the death of Michelangelo and the birth of Newton, a coincidence that dramatizes the shift of scientific leadership from Italy to countries further north. Galileo's reference to "transalpine diligence," in the second of the two readings that follow, suggests his awareness of this transition. This "diligence" had, no doubt, been brought to his attention not only by the work of Kepler, with whom he was in correspondence in 1597, but also by the death of Giordano Bruno, who was burned at the stake in 1600 for the heresy of his scientific ideas.

Galileo was born at Pisa and educated in a monastery, as was customary for a nobleman's son. His original interest was medicine, but an accidental encounter with geometry changed the course of his career. His mathematical studies led him, at the age of twenty-five, to a lectureship at the University of Pisa. Three years later he was appointed Professor of Mathematics at the University of Padua, then one of the intellectual meccas of Europe. For eighteen years, Galileo developed his studies of bodies in motion—inspired, it is said, by his observation of the swing of a lamp suspended from the roof of the Cathedral of Pisa. The study of the pendulum followed, leading to Galileo's suggestion for a clock regulated by a pendulum—actually accomplished, however, not by Galileo but by Huygens in 1617.

Galileo's discovery that bodies of unequal weight fall the same distance in the same period of time was developed through experiments with sloping, grooved boards. From this he was able to enunciate the "law of uniform acceleration" and, even more significant, the law of inertia—that a moving body, free from friction, will continue to move with "the motion that is natural to it, if it is not deflected by something else." These experimental demonstrations of movement were of profound importance in the study of mechanics; Newton, for example, used them as the starting point for his whole system of dynamics. The ideas of velocity and force provided a new basis for thinking about the larger problems of the movements of the heavenly bodies.

Galileo remained an avowed Copernican. His development in 1609 of the telescope, from ideas about lenses reported from the Netherlands, opened up a new world of observation. Protuberances in the sun, the mountains of the moon, new stars, and the Milky Way were now revealed. Galileo's descriptions of these discoveries—and exposure of his Copernican views—brought about his conflict with the theologians, who apparently then for the first time realized the effect on religious teaching of the view that the earth was not the center of the universe. Galileo was reprimanded but allowed, in effect, to continue his studies provided that he treated the Copernican thesis of a daily revolution of the earth not as an absolute truth but as a hypothesis to facilitate mathematical calculations. This was in 1613. From then until 1632, when he published his *Dialogue on the Two Chief Systems of the World* (from which the second extract is taken), Galileo worked without much opposition from the Church; but the *Dialogue* (which, like all his works, was written in Italian and was thus available to any reader) brought him once more before the Inquisition. Galileo and the whole Copernican doctrine were condemned and he was compelled to sign a recognition of the Church's authority in these matters. Though Galileo kept himself out of controversy from this time on, others did not: the march of science continued at a rapidly accelerating speed.

The characters in the *Dialogue* are the Copernican, Salviati, whose propositions are stimulated by the questions of Sagredo, in the role of the intelligent layman. The objections of the anti-Copernicans are put forward by Simplicius, who is sometimes presented as a stupid person and sometimes as representative of those who were honestly convinced of the soundness of Ptolemy and the Aristotelian philosophy. The dialogue form was adopted to meet the conditions imposed on his continued work—that Galileo present the views of the Church.

Of the two readings that follow, the first, on the construction of the telescope, is taken from *The Sidereal Messenger* of 1610, translated by E. S. Carlos in 1880; the second, the comparison of the Ptolemaic with the Copernican system, is taken from *Dialogue on the Two Chief World Systems,* translated by Stillman Drake in 1953 (University of California Press).

THE FOUNDATION OF
TELESCOPIC ASTRONOMY

Introduction.—In the present small treatise I set forth some matters of great interest for all observers of natural phenomena to look at and consider. They are of great interest, I think, first, from their intrinsic excellence; secondly, from their absolute novelty; and lastly, also on account of the instrument by the aid of which they have been presented to my apprehension.

The number of the Fixed Stars which observers have been able to see without artificial powers of sight up to this day can be counted. It is therefore decidedly a great feat to add to their number, and to set distinctly before the eyes other stars in myriads, which have never been seen before, and which surpass the old, previously known, stars in number more than ten times.

Again, it is a most beautiful and delightful sight to behold the body of the Moon, which is distant from us nearly sixty semidiameters of the Earth, as near as if it was at distance of only two of the same measures; so that the diameter of this same Moon appears about thirty times larger, its surface about nine hundred times, and its solid mass nearly 27,000 times larger than when it is viewed only with the naked eye: and consequently any one may know with the certainty that is due to the use of our sense, that the Moon certainly does not possess a smooth and polished surface, but one rough and uneven, and, just like the face of the Earth itself, is everywhere full of vast protuberances, deep chasms, and sinuosities.

Then to have got rid of disputes about the Galaxy or Milky Way, and to have made its nature clear to the very senses, not to say to the understanding, seems by no means a matter which ought to be considered of slight importance. In addition to this, to point out, as with one's finger, the nature of those stars which every one of the astronomers up to this time has called nebulous, and to demonstrate that it is very different from what has hitherto been believed, will be pleasant, and very fine. But that which will excite the greatest astonishment by far, and which indeed especially moved me to call the attention of all astronomers and philosophers, is this, namely, that I have discovered four planets, neither known nor observed by any one of the astronomers before my time, which have their orbits round a certain bright star, one of those previously known like Venus and Mercury round the Sun, and are sometimes in front of it, sometimes behind it, though they never depart from it beyond certain limits. All which facts were discovered and observed a few days ago by the help of a telescope devised by me, through God's grace first enlightening my mind.

Perchance, other discoveries still more excellent will be made from time to time by me or by other observers, with assistance of a similar instrument, so I will first briefly record its shape and preparation, as well as the occasion of its being devised, and then I will give an account of the observations made by me.

The Telescope.—About ten months ago a report reached my ears that a Dutchman had constructed a telescope, by the aid of which visible objects, although at a great distance from the eye of the observer, were seen distinctly as if near; and some proofs of its most wonderful performances were reported, which some gave credence to, but others contradicted. A few days after, I received confirmation of the report in a letter written from Paris by a noble Frenchman, Jaques Badovere, which finally determined me to give myself up first to inquire into the principle of the telescope, and then to consider the means by which I might compass the invention of a similar instrument, which after a little while I succeeded in doing, through deep study of the theory of Refraction; and I prepared a tube, at first of lead, in the ends of which I fitted two glass lenses, both plane on one side, but on the other side one spherically convex, and the other concave. Then bringing my eye to the concave lens I saw objects satisfactorily large and near, for they appeared one-third of the distance off and nine times larger than when they are seen with the natural eye alone. I shortly afterwards constructed another telescope with more nicety, which magnified objects more than sixty times. At length, by sparing neither labour nor expense, I succeeded in constructing for myself an instrument so superior that objects seen through it appear magnified nearly a thousand times and more than thirty times nearer than if viewed by the natural powers of sight alone.

First Telescopic Observations.—It would be altogether a waste of time to enumerate the number and importance of the benefits which this instrument may be expected to confer, when used by land or sea. But without paying attention to its use for terrestrial objects, I betook myself to observations of the heavenly bodies; and first of all, I viewed the Moon as near as if it was scarcely two semidiameters of the Earth distant. After the Moon, I frequently observed other heavenly bodies, both fixed stars and planets, with incredible delight; and, when I saw their very great number, I began to consider about a method by which I might be able to measure their distances apart, and at length I found one. And here it is fitting that all who intend to turn their attention to observations of this kind should receive certain cautions. For, in the first place, it is absolutely necessary for them to prepare a most perfect telescope, one which will show very bright objects distinct and free from any mistiness, and will magnify them at least 400 times, for then it will show them as if only one-twentieth of their distance off. For, unless the instrument be of such power, it will be in vain to attempt to view all the things which have been seen by me in the heavens, or which will be enumerated hereafter.

Observations of Lunar Mountains and Valleys.—Let me first speak of the surface of the Moon, which is turned towards us. For the sake of being understood more easily, I distinguish two parts in it, which I call respectively the brighter and the darker. The brighter part, like a sort of cloud, discolours the Moon's surface and makes it appear covered with spots. Now these spots, as they are somewhat dark and of considerable size, are plain to every one, and every age has seen them, wherefore I shall call them great or ancient spots to distinguish them from other spots, smaller in size, but so thickly scattered that they sprinkle the whole surface of the Moon, but especially the brighter portion of it. These spots have never been observed by any one before me; and from my observations of them, often repeated, I have been led to that opinion which I have expressed, namely, that I feel sure that the surface of the Moon is not perfectly smooth, free from inequalities and exactly spherical, as a large school of philosophers considers with regard to the Moon and the other heavenly bodies, but that, on the contrary, it is full of inequalities, uneven, full of hollows and protuberances, just like the surface of the Earth itself, which is varied everywhere by lofty mountains and deep valleys.

The appearances from which we may gather these conclusions are of the following nature: On the fourth or fifth day after new-moon, when the Moon presents itself to us with bright horns, the boundary which divides the part in shadow from the enlightened part does not extend continuously in an ellipse, as would happen in the case of a perfectly spherical body, but it is marked out by an irregular, uneven, and very wavy line . . . for several bright excrescences, as they may be called, extend beyond the boundary of light and shadow into the dark part, and on the other hand pieces of shadow encroach upon the light—nay, even a great quantity of small blackish spots, altogether separated from the dark part, sprinkle everywhere almost the whole space which is at the time flooded with the Sun's light, with the exception of that part alone which is occupied by the great and ancient spots. I have noticed that the small spots just mentioned have this common characteristic always and in every case, that they have the dark part towards the Sun's position, and on the side away from the Sun they have brighter boundaries, as if they were crowned with shining summits. Now we have an appearance quite similar on the Earth about sunrise, when we behold the valleys, not yet flooded with light, but the mountains surrounding them on the side opposite to the Sun already ablaze with the splendour of his beams; and just as the shadows in the hollows of the Earth diminish in size as the Sun rises higher, so also these spots on the Moon lose their blackness as the illuminated part grows larger and larger. Again, not only are the boundaries of light and shadow in the Moon seen to be uneven and sinuous, but—and this produces still greater astonishment—there appear very many bright points within the darkened portion of the Moon, altogether divided and broken off from the illuminated tract, and separated from it by no inconsiderable interval, which, after a little while, gradually increase in size and brightness, and after an hour or two become joined on to the rest of the main portion, now become somewhat larger; but in the meantime others, one here and another there, shooting up as if growing, are lighted up within the shaded portion, increase in size, and at last are linked on to the same luminous surface, now still more extended. . . . Now, is it not the case on the Earth before sunrise, that while the level plain is still in shadow, the peaks of the most lofty mountains are illuminated by the Sun's rays? After a little while does not the light spread further, while the middle and larger parts of those mountains are becoming illuminated; and at length, when the Sun has risen, do not the illuminated parts of the plains and hills join together? The grandeur, however, of such prominences and depressions in the Moon seems to surpass both in magnitude and extent the ruggedness of the Earth's surface, as I shall hereafter show. . . .

Appearance of Stars in the Telescope.—Hitherto I have spoken of the observations which I have made concerning the Moon's body; now I will briefly announce the phenomena which have been, as yet, seen by me with reference to the Fixed Stars. And first of all the following fact is worthy of consideration: The stars, fixed as well as erratic, when seen with a telescope, by no means appear to be increased in magnitude in the same proportion as other objects, and the Moon herself, gain increase of size; but in the case of the stars such an increase appears much less, so that you may consider that a telescope, which (for the sake of illustration) is powerful enough to magnify other objects a hundred times, will scarcely render the stars magnified four or five times. But the reason of this is as follows: When stars are viewed with our natural eyesight they do not present themselves to us of their bare, real size, but beaming with a certain vividness, and fringed with sparkling rays, especially when the night is far advanced; and from this circumstance they appear much larger than they would if they were stripped of those adventitious fringes, for the angle which they subtend at the eye is determined not by the primary disc of the star, but by the brightness which so widely surrounds it. . . . A telescope . . . removes from the stars their adventitious and accidental splendours before it enlarges their true discs (if indeed they are of that shape), and so they seem less magnified than other objects, for a star of the fifth or sixth magnitude seen through a telescope is shown as of the first magnitude only.

The difference between the appearance of the planets and the fixed stars seems also deserving of notice. The planets present their discs round, just as if described with a pair of compasses, and appear as so many little moons, completely illuminated and of a globular shape; but the fixed stars do not look to the naked eye bounded by a circular circumference, but rather like blazes of light, shooting out beams on all sides and very sparkling, and with a telescope they appear of the same shape as when they are viewed by simply looking at them, but so much larger that a star of the fifth or sixth magnitude seems to equal Sirius, the largest of all the fixed stars.

The Infinite Multitude of Telescopic Stars.—But beyond the stars of the sixth magnitude you will behold through the telescope a host of other stars, which escape the unassisted sight, so numerous as to be almost beyond belief, for you may see more than six other differences of magnitude, and the largest of these, which I may call stars of the seventh magnitude, or of the first magnitude of invisible stars, appear with the aid of the telescope larger and brighter than stars of the second magnitude seen with the unassisted sight. But in order that you may see one or two proofs of the inconceivable manner in which they are crowded together, I have determined to make out a case against two star-clusters that from them as a specimen you may decide about the rest.

As my first example, I had determined to depict the entire constellation of Orion, but I was overwhelmed by the vast quantity of stars and by want of time, and so I have deferred attempting this to another occasion, for there are adjacent to, or scattered among, the old stars more than five hundred new stars within the limits of one or two degrees. For this reason I have selected the three stars in Orion's Belt and the six in his Sword, which have been long well-known groups, and I have added eighty other stars recently discovered in their vicinity, and I have preserved as exactly as possible the intervals between them. The well-known or old stars, for the sake of distinction, I have depicted of larger size, and I have outlined them with a double line; the others, invisible to the naked eye, I have marked smaller and with one line only. I have also preserved the differences of magnitude as much as I could. As a second example, I have depicted the six stars of the constellation Taurus, called the Pleiades (I say six intentionally, since the seventh is scarcely ever visible), a group of stars which is enclosed in the heavens within very narrow precincts. Near these there lie more than forty others invisible to the naked eye, no one of which is more than half a degree off any of the aforesaid six; of these I have noticed only thirty-six in my diagram. I have preserved their intervals, magnitudes, and the distinction between the old and the new stars, just as in the case of the constellation Orion.

Telescopic Appearance of Milky Way.—The next object which I have observed is the essence or substance of the Milky Way. By the aid of a telescope any one may behold this in a manner which so distinctly appeals to the senses that all the disputes which have tormented philosophers through so many ages are exploded at once by the irrefragable evidence of our eyes, and we are freed from wordy disputes upon this subject, for the Galaxy is nothing else but a mass of innumerable stars planted together in clusters. Upon whatever part of it you direct the telescope straightway a vast crowd of stars presents itself to view; many of them are tolerably large and extremely bright, but the number of small ones is quite beyond determination. . . .

Discovery of Jupiter's Satellites.—I have now finished my brief ac-

count of the observations which I have thus far made with regard to the
Moon, the Fixed Stars, and the Galaxy. There remains the matter, which
seems to me to deserve to be considered the most important in this work,
namely, that I should disclose and publish to the world the occasion of discovering and observing four Planets, never seen from the very beginning
of the world up to our own times, their positions, and the observations
made during the last two months about their movements and their changes
of magnitude; and I summon all astronomers to apply themselves to
examine and determine their periodic times, which it has not been permitted me to achieve up to this day, owing to the restriction of my time.
I give them warning, however, again, so that they may not approach such
an inquiry to no purpose, that they will want a very accurate telescope,
and such as I have described in the beginning of this account.

On the 7th day of January in the present year, 1610, in the first hour
of the following night, when I was viewing the constellations of the
heavens through a telescope, the planet Jupiter presented itself to my
view, and as I had prepared for myself a very excellent instrument, I
noticed a circumstance which I had never been able to notice before, owing
to want of power in my other telescope, namely, that three little stars, small
but very bright, were near the planet; and although I believed them to
belong to the number of the fixed stars, yet they made me somewhat
wonder, because they seemed to be arranged exactly in a straight line,
parallel to the ecliptic, and to be brighter than the rest of the stars, equal
to them in magnitude. The position of them with reference to one another
and to Jupiter was as follows:

Ori.   *   *   O   *   Occ.

On the east side there were two stars, and a single one towards the
west. The star which was furthest towards the east, and the western star,
appeared rather larger than the third.

I scarcely troubled at all about the distance between them and Jupiter,
for, as I have already said, at first I believed them to be fixed stars; but when
on January 8th, led by some fatality, I turned again to look at the same
part of the heavens, I found a very different state of things, for there were
three little stars all west of Jupiter, and nearer together than on the

previous night, and they were separated from one another by equal intervals, as the accompanying figure shows.

Ori.   O * * *   Occ.

At this point, although I had not turned my thoughts at all upon the approximation of the stars to one another, yet my surprise began to be excited, how Jupiter could one day be found to the east of all the aforesaid fixed stars when the day before it had been west of two of them; and forthwith I became afraid lest the planet might have moved differently from the calculation of astronomers, and so had passed those stars by its own proper motion. I, therefore, waited for the next night with the most intense longing, but I was disappointed of my hope, for the sky was covered with clouds in every direction.

But on January 10th the stars appeared in the following position with regard to Jupiter, the third, as I thought, being

Ori.   *   * O   Occ.

hidden by the planet. They were situated just as before, exactly in the same straight line with Jupiter, and along the Zodiac. . . .

When I had seen these phenomena, as I knew that corresponding changes of position could not by any means belong to Jupiter, and as, moreover, I perceived that the stars which I saw had always been the same, for there were no others either in front or behind, within a great distance, along the Zodiac—at length, changing from doubt into surprise, I discovered that the interchange of position which I saw belonged not to Jupiter, but to the stars to which my attention had been drawn, and I thought therefore that they ought to be observed henceforward with more attention and precision.

Accordingly, on January 11th I saw an arrangement of the following kind:

Ori.   * * O   Occ.

namely, only two stars to the east of Jupiter, the nearer of which was distant from Jupiter three times as far as from the star further to the east; and the star furthest to the east was nearly twice as large as the other one; whereas on the previous night they had appeared nearly of equal magnitude. I, therefore, concluded, and decided unhesitatingly, that there are three stars in the heavens moving about Jupiter, as Venus and Mercury round the Sun; which at length was established as clear as daylight by numerous other subsequent observations. These observations also established that there are not only three, but four, erratic sidereal bodies performing their revolutions round Jupiter. . . .

These are my observations upon the four Medicean planets, recently discovered for the first time by me; and although it is not yet permitted me to deduce by calculation from these observations the orbits of these bodies, yet I may be allowed to make some statements, based upon them, well worthy of attention.

Orbits and Periods of Jupiter's Satellites.—And, in the first place, since they are sometimes behind, sometimes before Jupiter, at like distances, and withdraw from this planet towards the east and towards the west only within very narrow limits of divergence, and since they accompany this planet alike when its motion is retrograde and direct, it can be a matter of doubt to no one that they perform their revolutions about this planet, while at the same time they all accomplish together orbits of twelve years' length about the centre of the world. Moreover, they revolve in unequal circles, which is evidently the conclusion to be drawn from the fact that I have never been permitted to see two satellites in conjunction when their distance from Jupiter was great, whereas near Jupiter two, three, and sometimes all four, have been found closely packed together. Moreover, it may be detected that the revolutions of the satellites which describe the smallest circles round Jupiter are the most rapid, for the satellites nearest to Jupiter are often to be seen in the east, when the day before they have appeared in the west, and contrariwise. Also, the satellite moving in the greatest orbit seems to me, after carefully weighing the occasions of its returning to positions previously noticed, to have a periodic time of half a month. Besides, we have a notable and splendid argument to remove the scruples of those who can tolerate the revolution of the planets round the Sun in the Copernican system, yet are so disturbed by the motion of one Moon about the Earth, while both accomplish an orbit of a year's length about the Sun, that they consider that this theory of the universe must be upset as impossible: for now we have not one planet only revolving about another, while both traverse a vast orbit about the Sun, but our sense of sight presents to us four satellites circling about Jupiter, like the Moon about the Earth, while the whole system travels over a mighty orbit about the Sun in the space of twelve years.

TO THE DISCERNING READER

SEVERAL YEARS AGO *there was published in Rome a salutary edict which, in order to obviate the dangerous tendencies of our present age, imposed a seasonable silence upon the Pythagorean opinion that the earth moves. There were those who impudently asserted that this decree had its origin not in judicious inquiry, but in passion none too well informed. Complaints were to be heard that advisers who were totally unskilled at astronomical observations ought not to clip the wings of reflective intellects by means of rash prohibitions.*

Upon hearing such carping insolence, my zeal could not be contained. Being thoroughly informed about that prudent determination, I decided to appear openly in the theater of the world as a witness of the sober truth. I was at that time in Rome; I was not only received by the most eminent prelates of that Court, but had their applause; indeed, this decree was not published without some previous notice of it having been given to me. Therefore I propose in the present work to show to foreign nations that as much is understood of this matter in Italy, and particularly in Rome, as transalpine diligence can ever have imagined. Collecting all the reflections that properly concern the Copernican system, I shall make it known that everything was brought before the attention of the Roman censorship, and that there proceed from this clime not only dogmas for the welfare of the soul, but ingenious discoveries for the delight of the mind as well.

To this end I have taken the Copernican side in the discourse, proceeding as with a pure mathematical hypothesis and striving by every artifice to represent it as superior to supposing the earth motionless—not, indeed, absolutely, but as against the arguments of some professed Peripatetics. These men indeed deserve not even that name, for they do not walk about; they are content to adore the shadows, philosophizing not with due circumspection but merely from having memorized a few ill-understood principles.

Three principal headings are treated. First, I shall try to show that all experiments practicable upon the earth are insufficient measures for prov-

ing its mobility, since they are indifferently adaptable to an earth in motion or at rest. I hope in so doing to reveal many observations unknown to the ancients. Secondly, the celestial phenomena will be examined, strengthening the Copernican hypothesis until it might seem that this must triumph absolutely. Here new reflections are adjoined which might be used in order to simplify astronomy, though not because of any necessity imposed by nature. In the third place, I shall propose an ingenious speculation. It happens that long ago I said that the unsolved problem of the ocean tides might receive some light from assuming the motion of the earth. This assertion of mine, passing by word of mouth, found loving fathers who adopted it as a child of their own ingenuity. Now, so that no stranger may ever appear who, arming himself with our weapons, shall charge us with want of attention to such an important matter, I have thought it good to reveal those probabilities which might render this plausible, given that the earth moves.

I hope that from these considerations the world will come to know that if other nations have navigated more, we have not theorized less. It is not from failing to take count of what others have thought that we have yielded to asserting that the earth is motionless, and holding the contrary to be a mere mathematical caprice, but (if for nothing else) for those reasons that are supplied by piety, religion, the knowledge of Divine Omnipotence, and a consciousness of the limitations of the human mind.

I have thought it most appropriate to explain these concepts in the form of dialogues, which not being restricted to the rigorous observance of mathematical laws, make room also for digressions which are sometimes no less interesting than the principal argument.

Many years ago I was often to be found in the marvelous city of Venice, in discussions with Signore Giovanni Francesco Sagredo, a man of noble extraction and trenchant wit. From Florence came Signore Filippo Salviati, the least of whose glories were the eminence of his blood and the magnificence of his fortune. His was a sublime intellect which fed no more hungrily upon any pleasure than it did upon fine meditations. I often talked with these two of such matters in the presence of a certain Peripatetic philosopher whose greatest obstacle in apprehending the truth seemed to be the reputation he had acquired by his interpretations of Aristotle.

Now, since bitter death has deprived Venice and Florence of those two great luminaries in the very meridian of their years, I have resolved to make their fame live on in these pages, so far as my poor abilities will permit, by introducing them as interlocutors in the present argument. (Nor shall the good Peripatetic lack a place; because of his excessive affection toward the Commentaries of Simplicius, I have though fit to leave him under the name of the author he so much revered, without mentioning his own.) May it please those two great souls, ever venerable to my heart, to accept this public monument of my undying love. And may the memory of their eloquence assist me in delivering to posterity the promised reflections.

It happened that several discussions had taken place casually at various times among these gentlemen, and had rather whetted than satisfied their thirst for learning. Hence very wisely they resolved to meet together on certain days during which, setting aside all other business, they might apply themselves more methodically to the contemplation of the wonders of God in the heavens and upon the earth. They met in the palace of the illustrious Sagredo; and, after the customary but brief exchange of compliments, Salviati commenced as follows.

*   *   *

SALV. Then let the beginning of our reflections be the consideration that whatever motion comes to be attributed to the earth must necessarily remain imperceptible to us and as if nonexistent, so long as we look only at terrestrial objects; for as inhabitants of the earth, we consequently participate in the same motion. But on the other hand it is indeed just as necessary that it display itself very generally in all other visible bodies and objects which, being separated from the earth, do not take part in this movement. So the true method of investigating whether any motion can be attributed to the earth, and if so what it may be, is to observe and consider whether bodies separated from the earth exhibit some appearance of motion which belongs equally to all. For a motion which is perceived only, for example, in the moon, and which does not affect Venus or Jupiter or the other stars, cannot in any way be the earth's or anything but the moon's.

Now there is one motion which is most general and supreme over all, and it is that by which the sun, moon, and all other planets and fixed stars—in a word, the whole universe, the earth alone excepted—appear to be moved as a unit from east to west in the space of twenty-four hours. This, in so far as first appearances are concerned, may just as logically belong to the earth alone as to the rest of the universe, since the same

Frontispiece from Galileo's *Dialogue Concerning the Two Chief World Systems,* Florence, 1632. The three figures are Aristotle, Ptolemy, and Copernicus. (Courtesy of the Burndy Library.)

appearances would prevail as much in the one situation as in the other. Thus it is that Aristotle and Ptolemy, who thoroughly understood this consideration, in their attempt to prove the earth immovable do not argue against any other motion than this diurnal one, though Aristotle does drop a hint against another motion ascribed to it by an ancient writer, of which we shall speak in the proper place.

SAGR. I am quite convinced of the force of your argument, but it raises a question for me from which I do not know how to free myself, and it is this: Copernicus attributed to the earth another motion than the diurnal. By the rule just affirmed, this ought to remain imperceptible to all observations on the earth, but be visible in the rest of the universe. It seems to me that one may deduce as a necessary consequence either that he was grossly mistaken in assigning to the earth a motion corresponding to no appearance in the heavens generally, or that if the correspondent motion does exist, then Ptolemy was equally at fault in not explaining it away, as he explained away the other.

SALV. This is very reasonably questioned, and when we come to treat of the other movement you will see how greatly Copernicus surpassed Ptolemy in acuteness and penetration of mind by seeing what the latter did not—I mean the wonderful correspondence with which such a movement is reflected in all the other heavenly bodies. But let us postpone this for the present and return to the first consideration, with respect to which I shall set forth, commencing with the most general things, those reasons which seem to favor the earth's motion, so that we may then hear their refutation from Simplicio.

First, let us consider only the immense bulk of the starry sphere in contrast with the smallness of the terrestrial globe, which is contained in the former so many millions of times. Now if we think of the velocity of motion required to make a complete rotation in a single day and night, I cannot persuade myself that anyone could be found who would think it the more reasonable and credible thing that it was the celestial sphere which did the turning, and the terrestrial globe which remained fixed.

SAGR. If, throughout the whole variety of effects that could exist in nature as dependent upon these motions, all the same consequences followed indifferently to a hairsbreadth from both positions, still my first general impression of them would be this: I should think that anyone who considered it more reasonable for the whole universe to move in order to let the earth remain fixed would be more irrational than one who should climb to the top of your cupola just to get a view of the city and its environs, and then demand that the whole countryside should revolve around him so that he would not have to take the trouble to turn his head. Doubtless there are many and great advantages to be drawn from the new theory and not from the previous one (which to my mind is comparable with or even surpasses the above in absurdity), making the former more credible than the latter. But perhaps Aristotle, Ptolemy, and Simplicio ought to marshal their advantages against us and set them forth, too, if such there are; otherwise it will be clear to me that there are none and cannot be any.

SALV. Despite much thinking about it, I have not been able to find any difference, so it seems to me I have found that there can be no difference; hence I think it vain to seek one further. For consider: Motion, in so far as it is and acts as motion, to that extent exists relatively to things that lack it; and among things which all share equally in any motion, it does not act, and is as if it did not exist. Thus the goods with which a ship is laden leaving Venice, pass by Corfu, by Crete, by Cypus and go to Aleppo. Venice, Corfu, Crete, etc. stand still and do not move with the ship; but as to the sacks, boxes, and bundles with which the boat is laden and with respect to the ship itself, the motion from Venice to Syria is as nothing, and in no way alters their relation among themselves. This is so because it is common to all of them and all share equally in it. If, from the cargo in the ship, a sack were shifted from a chest one single inch, this alone would be more of a movement for it than the two-thousand-mile journey made by all of them together.

SIMP. This is good, sound doctrine, and entirely Peripatetic.

SALV. I should have thought it somewhat older. And I question whether Aristotle entirely understood it when selecting it from some good school of thought, and whether he has not, by altering it in his writings, made it a source of confusion among those who wish to maintain everything he said. When he wrote that everything which is moved is moved upon something immovable, I think he only made equivocal the saying that whatever moves, moves with respect to something motionless. This proposition suffers no difficulties at all, whereas the other has many.

SAGR. Please do not break the thread, but continue with the argument already begun.

SALV. It is obvious, then, that motion which is common to many moving things is idle and inconsequential to the relation of these movables among themselves, nothing being changed among them, and that it is operative only in the relation that they have with other bodies lacking that motion, among which their location is changed. Now, having divided the universe into two parts, one of which is necessarily movable and the other motionless, it is the same thing to make the earth alone move, and to move all the rest of the universe, so far as concerns any result which may depend upon such movement. For the action of such a movement is only in the relation between the celestial bodies and the earth, which relation alone is changed. Now if precisely the same effect follows whether the earth is made to move and the rest of the universe stay still, or the earth alone remains fixed while the whole universe shares one motion, who is going to believe that nature (which by general agreement does not act by means of many things when it can do so by means of few) has chosen to make an immense number of extremely large bodies move with inconceivable velocities, to achieve what could have been done by a moderate movement of one single body around its own center?

Simp. I do not quite understand how this very great motion is as nothing for the sun, the moon, the other planets, and the innumerable host of the fixed stars. Why do you say it is nothing for the sun to pass from one meridian to the other, rise above this horizon and sink beneath that, causing now the day and now the night; and for the moon, the other planets, and the fixed stars to vary similarly?

Salv. Every one of these variations which you recite to me is nothing except in relation to the earth. To see that this is true, remove the earth; nothing remains in the universe of rising and setting of the sun and moon, nor of horizons and meridians, nor day and night, and in a word from this movement there will never originate any changes in the moon or sun or any stars you please, fixed or moving. All these changes are in relation to the earth, all of them meaning nothing except that the sun shows itself now over China, then to Persia, afterward to Egypt, to Greece, to France, to Spain, to America, etc. And the same holds for the moon and the rest of the heavenly bodies, this effect taking place in exactly the same way if, without embroiling the biggest part of the universe, the terrestrial globe is made to revolve upon itself.

And let us redouble the difficulty with another very great one, which is this. If this great motion is attributed to the heavens, it has to be made in the opposite direction from the specific motion of all the planetary orbs, of which each one incontrovertibly has its own motion from west to east, this being very gentle and moderate, and must then be made to rush the other way; that is, from east to west, with this very rapid diurnal motion. Whereas by making the earth itself move, the contrariety of motions is removed, and the single motion from west to east accommodates all the observations and satisfies them all completely.

* * *

SAGR. O Nicholas Copernicus, what a pleasure it would have been for you to see this part of your system confirmed by so clear an experiment!

SALV. Yes, but how much less would his sublime intellect be celebrated among the learned! For as I said before, we may see that with reason as his guide he resolutely continued to affirm what sensible experience seemed to contradict. I cannot get over my amazement that he was constantly willing to persist in saying that Venus might go around the sun and be more than six times as far from us at one time as at another, and still look always equal, when it should have appeared forty times larger.

SAGR. I believe then that in Jupiter, Saturn, and Mercury one ought also to see differences of size corresponding exactly to their varying distances.

SALV. In the two outer planets I have observed this with precision in almost every one of the past twenty-two years. In Mercury no observations of importance can be made, since it does not allow itself to be seen except at its maximum angles with the sun, in which the inequalities of its distances from the earth are imperceptible. Hence such differences are unobservable, and so are its changes of shape, which must certainly take place as in Venus. But when we do see it, it would necessarily show itself to us in the shape of a semicircle, just as Venus does at its maximum angles, though its disc is so small and its brilliance so lively that the power of the telescope is not sufficient to strip off its hair so that it may appear completely shorn.

It remains for us to remove what would seem to be a great objection to the motion of the earth. This is that though all the planets turn about the sun, the earth alone is not solitary like the others, but goes together in the company of the moon and the whole elemental sphere around the sun in one year, while at the same time the moon moves around the earth every month. Here one must once more exclaim over and exalt the admirable perspicacity of Copernicus, and simultaneously regret his misfortune at not being alive in our day. For now Jupiter removes this apparent anomaly of the earth and moon moving conjointly. We see Jupiter, like another earth, going around the sun in twelve years accompanied not by one but by four moons, together with everything that may be contained within the orbits of its four satellites.

SAGR. And what is the reason for your calling the four Jovian planets "moons"?

SALV. That is what they would appear to be to anyone who saw them from Jupiter. For they are dark in themselves, and receive their light from the sun; this is obvious from their being eclipsed when they enter into the cone of Jupiter's shadow. And since only that hemisphere of theirs is illuminated which faces the sun, they always look entirely illuminated to us who are outside their orbits and closer to the sun; but to anyone on Jupiter they would look completely lighted only when they were at the highest points of their circles. In the lowest part—that is, when between Jupiter and the sun—they would appear horned from Jupiter. In a word, they would make for Jovians the same changes of shape which the moon makes for us Terrestrials.

Now you see how admirably these three notes harmonize with the Copernican system, when at first they seemed so discordant with it. From this, Simplicio will be much better able to see with what great probability one may conclude that not the earth, but the sun, is the center of rotation of the planets. And since this amounts to placing the earth among the world bodies which indubitably move about the sun (above Mercury and Venus but beneath Saturn, Jupiter, and Mars), why will it not likewise be probable, or perhaps even necessary, to admit that it also goes around?

SIMP. These events are so large and so conspicuous that it is impossible for Ptolemy and his followers not to have had knowledge of them. And having had, they must also have found a way to give reasons sufficient to account for such sensible appearances; congruous and probable reasons, since they have been accepted for so long by so many people.

SALV. You argue well, but you must know that the principal activity of pure astronomers is to give reasons just for the appearances of celestial bodies, and to fit to these and to the motions of the stars such a structure and arrangement of circles that the resulting calculated motions correspond with those same appearances. They are not much worried about admitting anomalies which might in fact be troublesome in other respects. Copernicus himself writes, in his first studies, of having rectified astronomical science upon the old Ptolemaic assumptions, and corrected the motions of the planets in such a way that the computations corresponded much better with the appearances, and vice versa. But this was still taking them separately, planet by planet. He goes on to say that when he wanted to put together the whole fabric from all individual constructions, there resulted a monstrous chimera composed of mutually disproportionate members, incompatible as a whole. Thus however well the astronomer might be satisfied merely as a calculator, there was no satisfaction and peace for the astronomer as a scientist. And since he very well understood that although the celestial appearances might be saved by means of assumptions essentially false in nature, it would be very much better if he could derive them from true suppositions, he set himself to inquiring diligently whether any one among the famous men of antiquity had attributed to the universe a different structure from that of Ptolemy's which is commonly accepted. Finding that some of the Pythagoreans had in particular attributed the diurnal rotation to the earth, and others the annual revolution as well, he began to examine under these two new suppositions the appearances and peculiarities of the planetary motions, all of which he had readily at hand. And seeing that the whole then corresponded to its parts with wonderful simplicity, he embraced this new arrangement, and in it he found peace of mind.

SIMP. But what anomalies are there in the Ptolemaic arrangement which are not matched by greater ones in the Copernican?

SALV. The illnesses are in Ptolemy, and the cures for them in Copernicus. First of all, do not all philosophical schools hold it to be a great impropriety for a body having a natural circular movement to move irregularly with respect to its own center and regularly around another point? Yet Ptolemy's structure is composed of such uneven movements, while in the Copernican system each movement is equable around its own center. With Ptolemy it is necessary to assign to the celestial bodies contrary movements, and make everything move from east to west and at the same time from west to east, whereas with Copernicus all celestial revolutions are in one direction, from west to east. And what are we to say of the apparent movement of a planet, so uneven that it not only goes fast at one time and slow at another, but sometimes stops entirely and even goes backward a long way after doing so? To save these appearances, Ptolemy introduces vast epicycles, adapting them one by one to each planet, with certain rules about incongruous motions—all of which can be done away with by one very simple motion of the earth. Do you not think it extremely absurd, Simplicio, that in Ptolemy's construction where all planets are assigned their own orbits, one above another, it should be necessary to say that Mars, placed above the sun's sphere, often falls so far that it breaks through the sun's orb, descends below this and gets closer to the earth than the body of the sun is, and then a little later soars immeasurably above it? Yet these and other anomalies are cured by a single and simple annual movement of the earth.

SAGR. I should like to arrive at a better understanding of how these stoppings, retrograde motions, and advances, which have always seemed to me highly improbable, come about in the Copernican system.

SALV. Sagredo, you will see them come about in such a way that the theory of this alone ought to be enough to gain assent for the rest of the doctrine from anyone who is neither stubborn nor unteachable. I tell you, then, that no change occurs in the movement of Saturn in thirty years, in that of Jupiter in twelve, that of Mars in two, Venus in nine months, or in that of Mercury in about eighty days. The annual movement of the earth alone, between Mars and Venus, causes all the apparent irregularities of the five stars named. For an easy and full understanding of this, I wish to draw you a picture of it. Now suppose the sun to be located in the center O, around which we shall designate the orbit described by the earth with its annual movement, BGM. The circle described by Jupiter (for example) in 12 years will be *BGM* here, and in the stellar sphere we shall take the circle of the zodiac to be *PUA*. In addition, in the earth's annual orbit we shall take a few equal arcs, BC, CD, DE, EF, FG, GH, HI, IK, KL, and LM, and in the circle of Jupiter we shall indicate these other arcs passed over in the same times in which the earth is passing through these. These are *BC, CD, DE, EF, FG, GH, HI, IK, KL,* and *LM,* which will be proportionately smaller than those noted on the earth's orbit, as the motion of Jupiter through the zodiac is slower than the annual celestial motion.

Now suppose that when the earth is at B, Jupiter is at *B;* then it will appear to us as being in the zodiac at *P,* along the straight line BB*P*. Next let the earth move from B to C and Jupiter from *B* to *C* in the same time; to us, Jupiter will appear to have arrived at *Q* in the zodiac, having advanced in the order of the signs from *P* to *Q.* The earth then passing to D and Jupiter to *D,* it will be seen in the zodiac at *R;* and from E, Jupiter

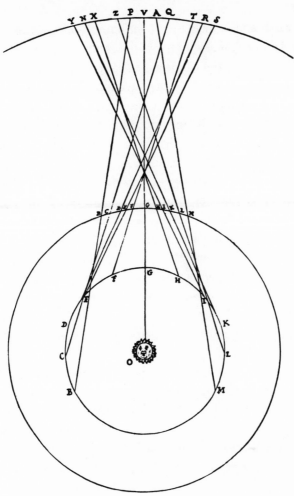

being at *E,* it will appear in the zodiac at *S,* still advancing. But now when the earth begins to get directly between Jupiter and the sun (having arrived at F and Jupiter at *F*), to us Jupiter will appear to be ready to commence returning backward through the zodiac, for during the time in which the earth will have passed through the arc EF, Jupiter will have been slowed down between the points *S* and *T,* will look to us almost stationary. Later the earth coming to G, Jupiter at *G* (in opposition to the sun) will be seen in the zodiac at *U,* turned far back through the whole arc *TU* in the zodiac; but in reality, following always its uniform course, it has advanced not only in its own circle but in the zodiac too, with respect to the center of the zodiac and to the sun which is located there.

The earth and Jupiter then continuing their movements, when the earth is at H and Jupiter is at *H*, it will be seen as having returned far back through the zodiac by the whole arc *UX;* but the earth having arrived at I and Jupiter at *I*, it will apparently have moved in the zodiac by only the small space *XY*, and will there appear stationary. Then when the earth shall have progressed to K and Jupiter to *K*, Jupiter will have advanced through the arc *YN*, in the zodiac; and, continuing its course, from L the earth will see Jupiter at *L* in the point *Z*. Finally, Jupiter at *M* will be seen from the earth at M to have passed to *A*, still advancing. And its whole apparent retrograde motion in the zodiac will be as much as the arc *TX*, made by Jupiter while it is passing in its own circle through the arc *FH*, the earth going through FH in its orbit.

Now what is said here of Jupiter is to be understood of Saturn and Mars also. In Saturn these retrogressions are somewhat more frequent than in Jupiter, because its motion is slower than Jupiter's, so that the earth overtakes it in a shorter time. In Mars they are rarer, its motion being faster than that of Jupiter, so that the earth spends more time in catching up with it.

Next, as to Venus and Mercury, whose circles are included within that of the earth, stoppings and retrograde motions appear in them also, due not to any motion that really exists in them, but to the annual motion of the earth. This is acutely demonstrated by Copernicus, enlisting the aid of Apollonius of Perga, in chapter 35 of Book V in his *Revolutions*.

You see, gentlemen, with what ease and simplicity the annual motion—if made by the earth—lends itself to supplying reasons for the apparent anomalies which are observed in the movements of the five planets, Saturn, Jupiter, Mars, Venus, and Mercury. It removes them all and reduces these movements to equable and regular motions; and it was Nicholas Copernicus who first clarified for us the reasons for this marvelous effect.

"My first error was to take the planet's path
as a perfect circle, and this mistake robbed me of the more time,
as it was taught on the authority of all philosophers,
and consistent in itself, with Metaphysics."

Johann Kepler

1571 — 1630

IT IS ANNOUNCED THAT THE PLANETS
MOVE IN ELLIPTICAL ORBITS AND
THAT THE UNIVERSE IS AN
ORDERLY ONE

Shortly before his death, Tycho Brahe appointed as his assistant a young German, Johann Kepler—a protegé of the Holy Roman Emperor and already a convinced follower of Copernicus. Kepler took over Brahe's records and edited and extended them by his own observations, adding another 228 stars to Brahe's catalogue. He did more than this; he established, inductively, laws of the planetary orbits which were later to serve as the foundation of Newton's astronomy.

Before joining Brahe in Prague, Kepler had published, in 1596, his *Mysterium Cosmographicum,* in which he had defended Copernicus and, at the same time, presented his own ideas as to the shape of the universe. This concept, based on his preoccupation with the mysticism of numbers, involved the use of various polygons as well as spheres and resulted in a model whose attributes appeared to be verifiable against observation. Brahe's attempt to prove Copernican doctrines with the use of his observed data left him with certain errors. Kepler, in investigating these errors, found himself obliged to question a fundamental assumption—that heavenly movements were limited to the circular or to curves derived from a circle. Basing his work on the observation of Mars, he came to the conclusion that the shape of the planetary orbit was elliptical. From this hypothesis, Kepler established his three laws of planetary motion. Although it has since been shown that Kepler's laws are not absolutely precise, they stood the test of observation for two hundred years before any error was detected.

Kepler succeeded in presenting a workable explanation of the movement of the planets, but he left a gap to be filled by others. Since the old, spherical conception assumed the circle as the divinely perfect form, the question of what kept the planets moving in their orbits had been taken for granted. Now a new kind of orbit was suggested—but why an ellipse and not some other curve? Kepler's explanations were not satisfactory, relying on a vague application of the ideas of magnetism, just then receiving the attention of the scientists, and of a motive force emanating from the sun.

It is perhaps one of the accidents of the history of science that Kepler and Galileo did not collaborate with each other. It was to be the task of Newton to synthesize the work of these two great contemporaries.

The following reading from *The Laws of Planetary Motion* has been taken from the J. H. Walden translation in *A Source Book in Astronomy*.

THE DISCOVERY OF THE LAWS OF PLANETARY MOTION

Chief Points of Astronomical Learning, Necessary for the Contemplation of the Celestial Harmonies

In the beginning let my readers understand this: that the old astronomical hypotheses of Ptolemy, as they are set forth in the Theoriae of

Purbach and the writings of the other epitomizers, are to be kept far from the present enquiry and banished wholly from the mind; for they fail to give a true account either of the arrangement of the heavenly bodies or of the laws governing their motions.

In their place I cannot do otherwise than substitute simply Copernicus's theory of the universe, and (were it possible) convince all men of its truth; but, since among the mass of students the idea is still unfamiliar, and the theory that the Earth is one of the planets and moves among the stars about the Sun, which is stationary, sounds to the most of them quite absurd, let those who are offended by the strangeness of this doctrine know that these harmonic speculations hold a place even among the hypotheses of Tycho Brahe. While that author agrees with Copernicus in regard to everything else which concerns the arrangement of the heavenly bodies and the laws governing their motions, the annual motion of the Earth alone, as held by Copernicus, he transfers to the whole system of the planetary orbits and to the Sun, which, according to both authors, is the center of the system. For from this transference, motion results just the same, so that, if not in that utterly vast and immense space of the sphere of the fixed stars, at least in the system of the planetary world, the Earth holds at any one time the same place according to Brahe as is given to it by Copernicus. Furthermore, just as he who draws a circle on paper moves the writing foot of the compass around, while he who fastens the paper or a board to a revolving wheel keeps the foot of the compass or the style stationary and draws the same circle on the moving board, so also in the present case; for Copernicus, the Earth measures out its orbit, between the outer circle of Mars and the inner circle of Venus, by the real motion of its own body, while for Tycho Brahe the whole planetary system (in which among the other orbits are also those of Mars and Venus) turns around like the board on the wheel and brings to the stationary Earth, as to the style of the turner, the space between the orbits of Mars and Venus; and from this motion of the system it results that the Earth, itself remaining stationary, marks on space the same course around the Sun, between Mars and Venus, which, according to Copernicus, it marks by the real motion of its own body with the system at rest. Since, then, the harmonic speculation considers the eccentric motions of the planets, as seen from the Sun, one can easily understand that, if an observer were on the Sun, however great the Sun's motion; the Earth, although it were at rest (to grant this for the moment to Brahe),

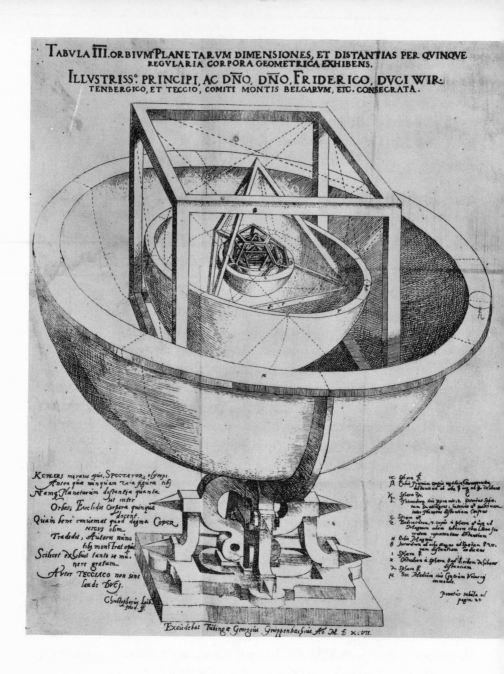

Kepler's model of a planetary system in which the five regular solids—a cube, tetrahedron, octahedron, dodecahedron, and icosahedron—are shown inscribed in and circumscribed by spheres. The spheres are shown in proportion to the distances of the planets from the sun. From Kepler's, *Harmonices Mundi Libri V*, Lincii, 1619. (Courtesy of the Burndy Library.)

would, nevertheless, seem to him to run its annual course in the space between the planets, and also in a time between the planet's times. Although,
therefore, a man may be weak in faith and so unable to conceive of the
motion of the Earth among the stars, he may still find it possible to take
pleasure in the exalted contemplation of this most divine mechanism; he
needs but to apply whatever he hears about the daily motions of the Earth
in its eccentric to the appearance of those motions on the Sun, as even
Tycho Brahe presents it with the Earth at rest.

The true followers of the Samian philosophy, however, have no just
cause for envying such men this participation in a most delightful speculation, for if they accept also the immovability of the Sun and the motion of
the Earth, their pleasure will be more exquisite in many ways, since it will
be derived from the very consummated perfection of contemplation.

In the first place, therefore, let my readers understand that at the
present day among all astronomers it is held to be a well-established fact
that all the planets except the Moon, which alone has the Earth as its
center, revolve around the Sun; the Moon's orbit of course, be it said, is not
large enough to enable it to be drawn on this chart in proper relation to
the other orbits. To the other five planets, therefore, is added the Earth as
sixth, which either by its own motion, with the Sun stationary, or, itself
being at rest while the whole planetary system is in revolution, describes,
it too, its orbit, the sixth, about the Sun.

Secondly, the following fact is also established: that all the planets
revolve in eccentric orbits; that is, they alter their distances from the Sun,
so that in one part of the orbit they are very remote from the Sun, while in
the opposite part they come very near the Sun. In the appended scheme
there have been made for each planet three circles, no one of which indicates the real eccentric path of the planet; the middle one, however, as,
for instance, in the case of Mars, BE, has a diameter equal to the longer
diameter of the eccentric orbit; the orbit itself, as AD, touches AF, the
highest of the three, in the one quarter, A, and CD the lowest, in the other
quarter, D.

The orbit GH, represented by points and drawn through the center
of the Sun, indicates the path of the Sun according to Tycho Brache. If the
Sun travels this path, every point of the planetary system here depicted
advances in a like path, each in its own; and if one point of it, that is the
center of the Sun, stands in one part of its orbit, as here in the lowest part,

all parts of the system will stand, each in the lowest part of its own orbit. Owing to the narrowness of the space, the three circles of Venus have run into one, contrary to my intention.

Thirdly, let the reader recall from my "Mysterium Cosmographicum," which I published twenty-two years ago, that the number of the planets, or orbits about the Sun, was derived by the most wise Creator from the five solid figures, about which Euclid so many centuries ago wrote the book which, since it is made up of a series of propositions, is called "Elementa." That there cannot be more regular bodies, that regular plane figures, that is, cannot unite into a solid in more than five ways, was made clear in the second book of the present work.

Fourthly, as regards the relations of the planetary orbits, the relation between two neighboring orbits is always such that, as will easily be seen, each one of the orbits approximates one of the terms of the ratio which exists between the orbits of one of the five solid bodies; the ratio, that is, of the orbit circumscribed about the figure to the orbit inscribed. For when, following the observations of Brahe, I had completed the demonstration of the distances, I discovered this fact: if the angles of the cube are applied to the innermost circle of Saturn, the centers of the planes nearly touch the middle circle of Jupiter, and if the angles of the tetrahedron rest on the innermost circle of Jupiter, the centers of the planes of the tetrahedron nearly touch the outermost circle of Mars; also, if the angles of the octa-hedron rise from any one of the circles of Venus (for all three are reduced to a very narrow space), the centers of the planes of the octahedron enter and descend below the outermost circle of Mercury; finally, coming to the ratios which exist between the orbits of the dodecahedron and the orbits of the icosahedron, which ratios are equal to each other, we find that the nearest of all to these are the ratios or distances between the circles of Mars and the Earth and between those of the Earth and Venus, and these ratios also, if we reckon from the innermost circle of Mars to the middle circle of the Earth and from the middle circle of the Earth to the middle circle of Venus, are similarly equal to each other; for the middle distance of the Earth is the mean proportional between the smallest distance of Mars and the middle distance of Venus; but these two ratios between the circles of the planets are still larger than are the ratios of those two sets of orbits in the figures, so that the centers of the planes of the dodecahedron do not touch the outermost circle of the Earth, nor do the centers of the planes of the

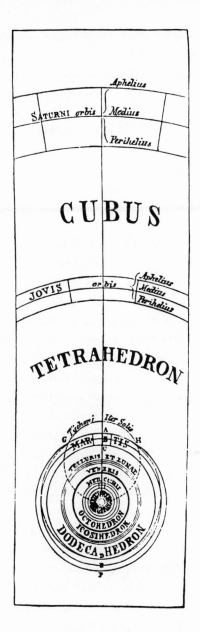

icosahedron touch the outermost circle of Venus; and this hiatus is not filled up by the semidiameter of the orbit of the Moon, added to the greatest distance of the Earth and taken away from the smallest distance. But there is a certain other relation connected with a figure that I notice: if an enlarged dodecahedron to which I have given the name echinus (hedgehog) as being formed of twelve five-cornered stars and thereby being very near to the five regular bodies, if, I say, this dodecahedron should place its twelve points on the innermost circle of Mars, then the sides of the pentagons, which are, respectively, the bases of the different radii or points, touch the middle circle of Venus.

Briefly: the cube and the octahedron enter somewhat their conjugate planetary orbits, the dodecahedron and the icosahedron do not quite reach their conjugate orbits, the tetrahedron just touches both orbits; in the first case there is a deficiency, in the second case an excess, in the last case an equality, in the distances of the planets.

From these considerations it is apparent that the exact relations of the planetary distances were not derived from the regular figures alone; for the Creator, the very fountain head of geometry, who, as Plato says, practises geometry eternally, does not deviate from his archetype. And indeed this fact might be gathered from the consideration that all the planets change their distances through definite periods of time; so that each one has two notable distances from the Sun, the maximum and minimum; and there may be made between every two planets a fourfold comparison of their distances from the Sun, comparisons of their mutually opposed distances, those that are farthest apart and those that are nearest together; thus, of all the combinations of two neighboring planets, the comparisons are twenty in number, while on the other hand the solid figures are but five. It is reasonable to believe, however, that the Creator, if he paid attention to the relation of the orbits in their general aspect, paid attention also to the relation of the varying distances of the individual orbits in detail, and that these acts of attention were the same in both cases and were connected with each other. When we duly consider this fact, we shall certainly arrive at the conclusion that for establishing the diameters and the eccentricities of the orbits there are required several principles in combination, besides the principle of the five regular bodies.

Fifthly, to come to the motions, among which are established the harmonies, I again impress upon the reader the fact that it has been shown by me in my Commentaries on Mars, from the exceedingly accurate observations of Brahe, that equal diurnal arcs on one and the same eccentric are not traversed with equal velocities, but that these different times in equal parts of the eccentric are to each other as the distances from the Sun, the source of the motion; and, on the other hand, that, the times being supposed equal, as, for instance, one natural day in each case, the true diurnal arcs corresponding to them in a single eccentric orbit are inversely proportional to the two distances from the Sun. It has likewise been shown by me that the orbit of a planet is elliptical, and the Sun, the source of motion, is in one of the foci of this ellipse, and so it results that the planet, when it has completed a quarter of the entire circuit, beginning at the aphelion, is at a distance from the Sun exactly half way between the maximum distance in aphelion and the minimum distance in perihelion. From these two axioms it results that the mean diurnal motion of the planet in its eccentric is the same as the real diurnal arc of that eccentric at the moments at which the planet is at the end of the quarter eccentric reckoned from the aphelion, although that true quadrant as yet appears smaller than the exact quadrant. It follows, further, that any two perfectly exact diurnal arcs of the eccentric, at exactly the same distance, the one from the aphelion, the other from the perihelion, are together equal to two median diurnal arcs; and consequently, that, since circumferences are to each other as diameters, one mean diurnal arc is to the sum of all the mean arcs, which are equal to each other, as many as there are in the whole circumference, as one mean diurnal arc is to the sum of all the real eccentric arcs, the same in number but unequal to each other. And these truths concerning the real diurnal arcs of the eccentric and the real motions must be known beforehand, that now from these we may understand the apparent motions as they are when observed from the Sun.

Sixthly, as regards the apparent arcs as seen from the Sun, it is known even from the ancient astronomy that of real motions, even when they are equal to each other, that which is farther from the center of the universe (as one that is in aphelion) appears to the eye looking at it from that center to be less, and that which is nearer (as one that is in perihelion) seems to be greater. Since, therefore, in addition, the real diurnal arcs which are in proximity are greater still on account of the greater velocity, and the real arcs in the remote aphelion are smaller still on account of the retardation, it results, as I have shown in my Commentaries on Mars, that the apparent diurnal arcs of one eccentric are almost exactly inversely proportional to the square of their distances from the Sun. As, for instance, if a planet in one of its days when it is in aphelion is distant from the Sun 10 units, in any measure whatsoever, and in its opposite day, when it is in perihelion, is distant 9 units of exactly the same kind, it is certain that, as seen from the Sun, its apparent progress in aphelion will be to its apparent progress in perihelion as 81 is to 100.

Now this is true with these reservations; first, that the arcs of the eccentric be not large, that they may not have different distances varying greatly, that is, that they may not cause a sensible variation in the distances of their ends from the apsides; secondly, that the eccentricity be not very great, for the greater the eccentricity, that is the greater the arc, the greater is the increase of the angle of that appearance in comparison with its own advance toward the Sun, according to Theorem 8 of the "Optics" of Euclid. But there is another reason why I give this warning. The arcs of the eccentric about the middle of the anomalies are observed obliquely from the center of the Sun, and this obliquity diminishes the size of their appearance, while, on the other hand, the arcs round the apsides are presented to the sight, which is supposed to be on the Sun, from directly in front. When, therefore, the eccentricity is very great, the relation of the motions is sensibly disarranged if we apply the mean diurnal motion without diminution to the mean distance, as if it appeared from the mean distance as large as it is; and this will appear below in the case of Mercury. All this matter is treated at greater length in "Epitome Astronomiæ Copernicæ," Book V, but it had to be given here because it concerns the very terms themselves of the celestial harmonies, when considered apart each by itself.

Seventhly, in case anyone chances to think of those diurnal motions that are apparent, not to the assumed observer on the Sun, but to the observer on the Earth, with regard to which motions Book VI of "Epitome Astronomiæ Copernicæ" deals, let him know that these do not come under consideration at all in the present enquiry; clearly they should not, since the Earth is not the source of their motion, nor can they, since these motions, being referred to a false appearance, change not only into absolute rest or apparent motionlessness, but even into retrograde motion; whereby all the infinity of relations is attributed to all the planets at one and the same time and equally. That we may determine, therefore, what the inherent relations are that are established by the diurnal motions of the true individual eccentric orbits (although as yet even they are apparent, being supposed to be seen from the Sun, the source of motion), we must first separate from these inherent motions this appearance of extrinsic annual motion common to all five planets, whether that motion is due, as Copernicus holds, to the motion of the Earth itself, or, as Tycho Brahe holds, to the annual motion of the whole system, and these motions peculiar to each planet must be presented to our view freed from what is extraneous.

Eighthly, thus far we have dealt with the various times of arcs of one and the same planet. Now we must deal also with the motions of the planets taken two at a time and compare these motions with each other. And here note the definition of the terms that we shall find it necessary to use. By the proximate apsides of two planets we shall mean the perihelion of the higher and the aphelion of the lower, notwithstanding the fact that they turn not toward the same quarter of the heavens, but toward different and possibly opposite quarters. Extreme motions, understand to be the slowest and the fastest of the entire planetary circuit; convergent extreme or converse, those that are in the nearest apsides of two orbits, that is, in the perihelion of the superior, and the aphelion of the inferior; divergent or diverse, those that are in opposite apsides, that is in the aphelion of the superior, and the perihelion of the inferior: Again, therefore, a part of my "Mysterium Cosmographicum," suspended twenty-two years ago, because I did not then see my way clear, must be completed and introduced here. For, after I had by unceasing toil through a long period of time, using the observations of Brahe, discovered the true distances of the orbits, at last, the true relation of the periodic times to the orbits and, if you ask for the exact time,

> . . . though late, yet looked upon me idle
> And after long time came;

conceived on the 8th of March of this year, 1618, but unsuccessfully brought to the test and for that reason rejected as false, but, finally returning on the 15th of May, by a new onset it overcame by storm the shadows of my mind, with such fullness of agreement between my seventeen-years' labor on the observations of Brahe and this present study of mine that I at first believed that I was dreaming and was assuming as an accepted principle what was still a subject of enquiry. But the principle is unquestionably true and quite exact: the periodic times of any two planets are to each other exactly as the cubes of the square roots of their median distances; this fact should be observed, however, that the arithmetic mean between the two diameters of the elliptical orbit is a little less than the longer diameter. And so, if one takes from the period, say, of the Earth, which is one year, and from Saturn's period of thirty years, the third part of the ratio, that is the cubic roots, and doubles this ratio by squaring the roots, one has in the resulting numbers the exact ratio of the median distances from the Sun of the Earth and Saturn. For the cubic root of 1 is 1 and the square of that is 1; and the cubic root of 30 is greater than 3, and the square of that, therefore, is greater than 9. And Saturn, when at its mean distance from the Sun, is a little higher than nine times the mean distance of the Earth from the Sun.

Ninthly, if now you wish to measure as by the same ten-foot rule the exact journeys made by each planet daily through the sky, you will have to combine two ratios, one of the real (not apparent) daily arcs of the eccentric, the other of the mean distance of each planet from the Sun, because this is likewise the ratio of the amplitudes of the orbits; that is, the real daily arc of each planet must be multiplied into the semidiameter of its own orbit. This done, there will result numbers suitable for use in ascertaining whether those journeys have harmonic relations.

Tenthly, that you may know how great the apparent length of any such daily journey is when the eye is supposed to be on the Sun—although this may be obtained directly from astronomical observation, still it will also result if you add to the ratio of the journeys the inverse ratio of the mean, not real, distances of any point of the eccentrics, the journey of the superior eccentric being multiplied into the distance from the Sun of the inferior, and, on the other hand, the journey of the inferior being multiplied into the distance from the Sun of the superior.

Eleventhly, furthermore, given the apparent motions, the aphelion of one and the perihelion of the other, or conversely, or alternately, there are elicited ratios of the distances, of the aphelion of one to the perihelion of the other; in which case, however, the mean motions must be known beforehand, that is the inverse ratio of the periodic times, from which is deduced the proportion relating to the orbits found in paragraph VIII. Then, taking the mean proportional between either apparent motion and its own mean, the result is that, as this mean proportional is to the semidiameter of its orbit (which is already given), so is the mean motion to the distance or interval sought. Let the periodic times of two planets be 27 and 8; then their mean diurnal motions are to each other as 8 is to 27. Therefore, the semidiameters of the orbits will be as 9 is to 4. For the cubic root of 27 is 3, and that of 8 is 2, and the squares of these roots, 3 and 2, are 9 and 4. Now let the apparent motions be, the aphelion of one 2, and the perihelion of the other 33⅓. The mean proportionals between the mean motions, 8 and 27, and these apparent motions will be 4 and 30. If, therefore, the mean 4 gives the mean distance of the planet 9, then the mean motion 8 gives the aphelion distance 18, corresponding to the apparent motion 2; and if the other mean 30 gives the mean distance of the other planet 4, then the mean motion of that planet 27 gives its perihelion distance 3⅗. I say, therefore, that the aphelion distance of the former planet is to the perihelion of this as 18 is to 3⅗. From which it is clear that, the harmonies between the extreme motions of two planets having been found, and the periodic times assigned to each, there must result the extreme and mean distances, and, therefore, also the eccentricities.

Twelfthly, it is given also, from different extreme motions of one and the same planet, to find the mean motion. For this is not exactly the arithmetical mean between the extreme motions, nor is it exactly the geometrical mean, but it is as much less than the geometrical mean as the geometrical mean is less than the (arithmetical) mean between the two. Let the two extreme motions be 8 and 10. The mean motion will be less than 9, less even than the root of 80 by a half of the difference between the two, 9 and the root of 80. So, if the aphelion is 20, and the perihelion 24, the mean motion will be less than 22, less even than the root of 480 by a half of the difference between this root and 22.

*"And to us it is enough that gravity does really
exist and act accordingly to the laws we have explained and
abundantly serves to account for all the motions
of the celestial bodies and of our sea."*

Isaac Newton

1642 – 1727

THE UNIVERSAL LAWS OF MOTION
ARE ESTABLISHED

The achievement of Newton demonstrates simultaneously
the value of contemplation and the importance of discussion.
Observation gave Newton the opportunity of evolving his basic
principle and laying out a program of study; but it was the discussion among the members of the Royal Society that caused his
great synthesis to be announced and its fruits to be made available to guide scientific thought substantially unchallenged until
Einstein, two hundred years later, produced his fundamental law
of relativity.

The country boy, who began as a poor scholar with a preference for playing at the work bench, reached Cambridge when
he was nineteen. Attracted by alchemy, he turned to Euclid to
study his geometry and so learned of Descartes's contributions
to mathematics. Then came the Great Plague of 1665-1666,
which devastated London and caused the students of Cambridge
to retreat to their homes. Working alone in the country for two
years, Newton evolved the binominal theorem and developed
the differential calculus. He began to think about gravity and,
using Kepler's law of the periodic times of the planets, he came

to conclusions as to the force which kept the planets in their orbits. This was the time when he was most preoccupied with mathematics and philosophy, for when he returned to Cambridge and became professor of mathematics there (1669-1696), he seems to have spent much time in the study of chemistry—or, rather, alchemy. It was nearly twenty years after the Plague that he was approached by Edmund Halley to discuss the validity of Kepler's theory of elliptical orbits. At that time he re-examined his earlier work and began to write his *Philosophiae Naturalis Principia Mathematica* (1687), from which this reading (translated by Andrew Motte in 1729) has been taken.

In this work Newton gave the world the application of his own axiom (see page 58 above), the first of his rules of reasoning in philosophy: "We are to admit no more causes of natural things than such as are both true and sufficient to explain their appearances"—in other words, to apply to the examination of the forces acting on celestial bodies what was known about the forces acting on terrestrial ones. Taking over Galileo's system, which became his Laws 1 and 2, he added his own third law— "To every action, there is always opposed an equal reaction."

The Newtonian synthesis gave the proper mathematical and physical setting to astrophysics by combining Galileo's law of falling bodies with Kepler's third law and thus established the validity of terrestrial mechanics in explaining the movements of the heavenly bodies. It also had an influence which transcended its unquestioned position as the crowning achievement of the scientific revolution. It was especially important as the basis for a mechanistic philosophy for explaining all natural phenomena in the form of mathematical terms as well as for the deistic theology, which pictured the universe as a mechanistic one operating according to universal law. The rational approach of Newtonian science was even more widely applied to other areas of knowledge and long served as a unifying principle of thought.

So the work of Galileo and Kepler, Copernicus, and Brahe was, in effect, synthesized and provided with the mathematics, developed by Newton, to permit the proof of the propositions. Newton had brought together ideas which had already been suggested, for example, by Hooke (1635-1703), who visualized a force of gravitation as necessary to account for the elliptical form of the path of a comet, and by Galileo in his studies of falling bodies.

There were controversies—with Hooke and, later, with Gottfried Leibniz (1646-1716)—in which Newton's originality was questioned. These disputes were, however, conducted with a certain dignity under the influence of the Royal Society, under whose wing science was beginning to make major advances in Britain. Scientific findings began to be published in learned journals and exposed immediately to the searching criticism of contemporaries. The modern era had opened.

THE MATHEMATICAL PRINCIPLES OF NATURAL PHILOSOPHY

DEFINITIONS

Definition 1. *The quantity of matter is the measure of the same, arising from its density and bulk conjunctly.*

Thus air of a double density, in a double space, is quadruple in quantity; in a triple space, sextuple in quantity. The same thing is to be understood of snow, and fine dust or powders, that are condensed by compression or liquefaction; and of all bodies that are by any causes whatever differently condensed. I have no regard in this place to a medium, if any such there is, that freely pervades the interstices between the parts of bodies. It is this quantity that I mean hereafter everywhere under the name of body or mass: And the same is known by the weight of each body; for it is proportional to the weight, as I have found by experiments on pendulums, very accurately made, which shall be shewn hereafter.

Definition 2. *The quantity of motion is the measure of the same, arising from the velocity and quantity of matter conjunctly.*

The motion of the whole is the sum of the motions of all the parts; and therefore in a body double in quantity, with equal velocity, the motion is double; with twice the velocity, it is quadruple.

Definition 3. *The* vis insita, *or innate force of matter, is a power of resisting, by which every body, as much as in it lies, endeavours to persevere in its present state, whether it be of rest, or of moving uniformly forward in a right line*

This force is ever proportional to the body whose force it is; and differs nothing from the inactivity of the mass, but in our manner of conceiving it. A body, from the inactivity of matter, is not without difficulty put out of its state of rest or motion. Upon which account, this *vis insita,* may, by a most significant name, be called *vis inertiæ,* or force of inactivity. But a body exerts this force only, when another force, impressed upon it, endeavours to change its condition; and the exercise of this force may be considered both as resistance and impulse; it is resistance, in so far as the body, for maintaining its present state, withstands the force impressed; it is impulse, in so far as the body, by not easily giving way to the impressed force of another, endeavours to change the state of that other. Resistance is usually ascribed to bodies at rest, and impulse to those in motion; but motion and rest, as commonly conceived, are only relatively distinguished; nor are those bodies always truly at rest, which commonly are taken to be so.

Definition 4. *An impressed force is an action exerted upon a body, in order to change its state, either of rest, or of moving uniformly forward in a right line.*

This force consists in the action only; and remains no longer in the body, when the action is over. For a body maintains every new state it acquires, by its *vis inertiæ* only. Impressed forces are of different origins; as from percussion, from pressure, from centripetal force.

Definition 5. *A centripetal force is that by which bodies are drawn or impelled, or any way tend, towards a point as to a centre.*

Of this sort is gravity, by which bodies tend to the centre of the earth's magnetism, by which iron tends to the load-stone; and that force, what ever it is, by which the planets are perpetually drawn aside from the rectilinear motions, which otherwise they would pursue, and made to revolve in curvilinear orbits. A stone, whirled about in a sling, endeavours to recede from the hand that turns it; and by that endeavour, distends the sling, and that with so much the greater force, as it is revolved with the greater velocity, and as soon as ever it is let go, flies away. That force which opposes itself to this endeavour, and by which the sling perpetually draws back the stone towards the hand and retains it in its orbit, because it is directed to the hand, as the centre of the orbit, I call the centripetal force. And the same thing is to be understood of all bodies, revolved in any orbits. They all endeavour to recede from the centres of their orbits; and were it not for the opposition of a contrary force which restrains them to, and detains them in their orbits, which I therefore call centripetal, would fly off in right lines, with an uniform motion. A projectile, if it was not for the force of gravity, would not deviate towards the earth, but would go off from it in a right line, and that with an uniform motion, if the resistance of the air was taken away. It is by its gravity that it is drawn aside perpetually from its rectilinear course, and made to deviate towards the earth, more or less, according to the force of its gravity, and the velocity of its motion. The less its gravity is, for the quantity of its matter, or the greater the velocity with which it is projected, the less will it deviate from a rectilinear course, and the farther it will go. If a leaden ball, projected from the top of a mountain by the force of gun- powder with a given velocity, and in a direction parallel to the horizon, is carried in a curved line to the distance of two miles before it falls to the ground; the same, if the resistance of the air were taken away, with a double or decuple velocity, would fly twice or ten times as far. And by increasing the velocity, we may at pleasure increase the distance to which it might be projected, and diminish the curvature of the line, which it might describe, till at last it should fall at the distance of 10, 30, or 90 degrees, or even might go quite round the whole earth before it falls; or lastly, so that it might never fall to the earth, but go forward into the celestial spaces, and proceed in its motion *in infinitum*. And after the same manner that a pro- jectile, by the force of gravity, may be made to revolve in an orbit, and go round the whole earth, the moon also, either by the force of gravity, if it is endued with gravity, or by any other force that impels it towards the earth, may be perpetually drawn aside towards the earth, out of the rectili- near way, which by its innate force it would pursue; and would be made so revolve in the orbit which it now described; nor could the moon without some such force, be retained in its orbit. If this force was too small, it would not sufficiently turn the moon out of a rectilinear course: if it was too great, it would turn it too much, and draw down the moon from its orbit towards the earth. It is necessary, that the force be of a just quantity, and it be- longs to the mathematicians to find the force, that may serve exactly to retain a body in a given orbit, which a given velocity; and *vice versa*, to determine the curvilinear way, into which a body projected from a given place, with a given velocity, may be made to deviate from its natural rectilinear way, by means of a given force.

The quantity of any centripetal force may be considered as of three kinds; absolute, accelerative, and motive.

Definition 6. *The absolute quantity of a centripetal force is the measure of the same proportional to the efficacy of the cause that propagates it from the centre, through the spaces round about.*

Thus the magnetic force is greater in one load-stone and less in another according to their sizes and strength of intensity.

Definition 7. *The accelerative quantity of a centripetal force is the measure of the same, proportional to the velocity which it generates in a given time.*

Thus the force of the same load-stone is greater at a less distance, and less at a greater: also the force of gravity is greater in valleys, less on tops of exceeding high mountains; and yet less (as shall hereafter be shown), at greater distances from the body of the earth; but at equal distances, it is the same everywhere; because (taking away, or allowing for, the resistance of the air), it equally accelerates all falling bodies, whether heavy or light, great or small.

Definition 8. *The motive quantity of a centripetal force, is the measure of the same, proportional to the motion which it generates in a given time.*

Thus the weight is greater in a greater body, less in a less body; and, in the same body, it is greater near to the earth, and less at remoter distances. This sort of quantity is the centripetency, or propension of the whole body towards the centre, or, as I may say, its weight; and it is always known by the quantity of an equal and contrary force just sufficient to hinder the descent of the body.

These quantities of forces, we may, for brevity's sake, call by the names of motive, accelerative, and absolute forces; and, for distinction's sake, consider them, with respect to the bodies that tend to the centre; to the places of those bodies; and to the centre of force towards which they tend; that is to say, I refer the motive force to the body as an endeavour and propensity of the whole towards a centre, arising from the propensities of the several parts taken together; the accelerative force to the place of the body, as a certain power or energy diffused from the centre to all places around to move the bodies that are in them; and the absolute force to the centre, as endued with some cause, without which those motive forces would not be propagated through the spaces round about; whether that cause be some central body (such as is the load-stone, in the centre of the magnetic force, or the earth in the centre of the gravitating force), or anything else that does not yet appear. For I here design only to give a mathematical notion of those forces, without considering their physical causes and seats.

Wherefore the accelerative force will stand in the same relation to the motive, as celerity does to motion. For the quantity of motion arises from the celerity drawn into the quantity of matter; and the motive force arises from the accelerative force drawn into the same quantity of matter. For the sum of the actions of the accelerative force, upon the several particles of the body, is the motive force of the whole. Hence it is, that near the surface of the earth, where the accelerative gravity, or force productive of gravity, in all bodies is the same, the motive gravity or the weight is as the body: but if we should ascend to higher regions, where the accelerative gravity is less, the weight would be equally diminished, and would always be as the product of the body, by the accelerative gravity. So in those regions, where the accelerative gravity is diminished into one half, the weight of a body two or three times less, will be four or six times less.

I likewise call attractions and impulses, in the same sense, accelerative, and motive; and use the words attraction, impulse or propensity of any sort towards a centre, promiscuously, and indifferently, one for another; considering those forces not physically, but mathematically: wherefore, the reader is not to imagine, that by those words, I anywhere take upon me to define the kind, or the manner of any action, the causes or the physical reason thereof, or that I attribute forces, in a true and physical sense, to certain centres (which are only mathematical points); when at any time I happen to speak of centres as attracting, or as endued with attractive powers.

Scholium. Hitherto I have laid down the definitions of such words as are less known, and explained the sense in which I would have them to be understood in the following discourse. I do not define time, space, place and motion, as being well known to all. Only I must observe, that the vulgar conceive those quantities under no other notions but from the relation they bear to sensible objects. And thence arise certain prejudices, for the removing of which, it will be convenient to distinguish them into absolute and relative, true and apparent, mathematical and common.

I. Absolute, true, and mathematical time, of itself, and from its own nature flows equably without regard to anything external, and by another name is called duration: relative, apparent, and common time, is some sensible and external (whether accurate or unequable) measure of duration by the means of motion, which is commonly used instead of true time; such as an hour, a day, a month, a year.

II. Absolute space, in its own nature, without regard to anything external, remains always similar and immovable. Relative space is some movable dimension or measure of the absolute spaces; which our senses determine by its position to bodies; and which is vulgarly taken for immovable space; such is the dimension of a subterraneous, an ærial, or celestial space, determined by its position in respect of the earth. Absolute and relative space, are the same in figure and magnitude; but they do not remain always numerically the same. For if the earth, for instance, moves, a space of our air, which relatively and in respect of the earth remains always the same, will at one time be one part of the absolute space into which the air passes; at another time it will be another part of the same, and so, absolutely understood, it will be perpetually mutable.

III. Place is a part of space which a body takes up, and is according to the space, either absolute or relative. I say, a part of space; not the situation, nor the external surface of the body. For the places of equal solids are always equal; but their superfices, by reason of their dissimilar figures, are often unequal. Positions properly have no quantity, nor are they so much the places themselves, as the properties of places. The motion of the whole is the same thing with the sum of the motions of the parts; that is, the translation of the whole, out of its place, is the same thing with the sum of the translations of the parts out of their places; and therefore the place of the whole is the same thing with the sum of the places of the parts, and for that reason, it is internal, and in the whole body.

IV. Absolute motion is the translation of a body from one absolute place into another; and relative motion, the translation from one relative place into another. Thus in a ship under sail, the relative place of a body is that part of the ship which the body possesses; or that part of its cavity which the body fills, and which therefore moves together with the ship: and relative rest is the continuance of the body in the same part of the ship, or of its cavity. But real, absolute rest, is the continuance of the body in the same part of that immovable space, in which the ship itself, its cavity, and all that it contains, is moved. Wherefore, if the earth is really at rest, the body, which relatively rests in the ship, will really and absolutely move with the same velocity which the ship has on the earth. But if the earth also moves, the true and absolute motion of the body will arise, partly from the true motion of the earth, in immovable space; partly from the relative motion of the ship on the earth; and if the body moves also relatively in the ship; its true motion will arise, partly from the true motion of the earth, in immovable space, and partly from the relative motions as well of the ship on the earth, as of the body in the ship; and from these relative motions will arise the relative motion of the body on the earth. As if that part of the earth, where the ship is, was truly moved toward the east, with a velocity of 10010 parts; while the ship itself, with a fresh gale, and full sails, is carried towards the west, with a velocity expressed by 10 of those parts; but a sailor walks in the ship towards the east, with 1 part of the said velocity; then the sailor will be moved truly in immovable space towards the east, with a velocity of 10001 parts, and relatively on the earth towards the west, with a velocity of 9 of those parts.

Absolute time, in astronomy, is distinguished from relative, by the equation or correction of the vulgar time. For the natural days are truly unequal, though they are commonly considered as equal, and used for a measure of time; astronomers correct this inequality for their more accurate deducing of the celestial motions. It may be, that there is no such thing as an equable motion, whereby time may be accurately measured. All motions may be accelerated and retarded, but the true, or equable, progress of absolute time is liable to no change. The duration or perseverance of the existence of things remains the same, whether the motions are swift or slow, or none at all: and therefore it ought to be distinguished from what are only sensible measures thereof; and out of which we collect it, by means of the astronomical equation. The necessity of which equation, for determing the times of a phænomenon, is evinced as well from the experiments of the pendulum clock, as by eclipses of the satellites of *Jupiter*.

As the order of the parts of time is immutable, so also is the order of the parts of space. Suppose those parts to be moved out of their places, and they will be moved (if the expression may be allowed) out of themselves. For times and spaces are, as it were, the places as well of themselves as of all other things. All things are placed in time as to order of succession; and in space as to order of situation. It is from their essence or nature that they are places; and that the primary places of things should be movable, is absurd. These are therefore the absolute places; and translations out of those places, are the only absolute motions.

But because the parts of space cannot be seen, or distinguished from one another by our senses, therefore in their stead we use sensible measures of them. For from the positions and distances of things from any body considered as immovable, we define all places; and then with respect to such places, we estimate all motions, considering bodies as transferred from some of those places into others. And so, instead of absolute places and motions, we use relative ones; and that without any inconvenience in common affairs; but in philosophical disquisitions, we ought to abstract from our senses, and consider things themselves, distinct from what are only sensible measures of them. For it may be that there is no body really at rest, to which the places and motions of others may be referred.

But we may distinguish rest and motion, absolute and relative, one from the other by their properties, causes and effects. It is a property of rest, that bodies really at rest do rest in respect to one another. And therefore as it is possible, that in the remote regions of the fixed stars, or perhaps far beyond them, there may be some body absolutely at rest; but impossible to know, from the position of bodies to one another in our regions whether any of these do keep the same position to that remote body; it follows that absolute rest cannot be determined from the position of bodies in our regions.

It is a property of motion, that the parts, which retain given positions to their wholes, do partake of the motions of those wholes. For all the parts of revolving bodies endeavour to recede from the axis of motion; and the impetus of bodies moving forward, arises from the joint impetus of all the parts. Therefore, if surrounding bodies are moved, those that are relatively at rest within them, will partake of their motion. Upon which account, the true and absolute motion of a body cannot be determined by the translation of it from those which only seem to rest; for the external bodies ought not only to appear at rest, but to be really at rest. For otherwise, all included bodies, beside their translation from near the surrounding ones, partake likewise of their true motions; and though that translation were not made they would not be really at rest, but only seem to be so. For the surrounding bodies stand in the like relation to the surrounded as the exterior part of a whole does to the interior, or as the shell does to the kernel; but, if the shell moves, the kernel will also move, as being part of the whole, without any removal from near the shell.

A property, near akin to the preceding, is this, that if a place is moved, whatever is placed therein moves along with it; and therefore a body, which is moved from a place in motion, partakes also of the motion of its place. Upon which account, all motions, from places in motion, are no other than parts of entire and absolute motions; and every entire motion is composed of the motion of the body out of its first place, and the motion of this place out of its place; and so on, until we come to some immovable place, as in the before-mentioned example of the sailor. Wherefore, entire and absolute motions can be no otherwise determined than by immovable places; and for that reason I did before refer those absolute motions to immovable places, but relative ones to movable places. Now no other places are immovable but those that, from infinity to infinity, do all retain the same given positon one to another; and upon this account must ever remain unmoved; and do thereby constitute immovable space.

The causes by which true and relative motions are distinguished, one from the other, are the forces impressed upon bodies to generate motion. True motion is neither generated nor altered, but by some force impressed upon the body moved; but relative motion may be generated or altered without any force impressed upon the body. For it is sufficient only to impress some force on other bodies with which the former is compared, that by their giving way, that relation may be changed, in which the relative rest or motion of this other body did consist. Again, true motion suffers always some change from any force impressed upon the moving body; but relative motion does not necessarily undergo any change by such forces. For if the same forces are likewise impressed on those other bodies, with which the comparison is made, that the relative positon may be preserved, then that condition will be preserved in which the relative motion consists. And therefore any relative motion may be changed when the true motion remains unaltered, and the relative may be preserved when the true suffers some change. Upon which accounts, true motion does by no means consist in such relations.

The effects which distinguish absolute from relative motion are, the forces of receding from the axis of circular motion. For there are no such forces in a circular motion purely relative, but in a true and absolute circular motion, they are greater or less, according to the quantity of the motion. If a vessel, hung by a long cord, is so often turned about that the cord is strongly twisted, then filled with water, and held at rest together with the water; after, by the sudden action of another force, it is whirled about the contrary way, and while the cord is untwisting itself, the vessel continues for some time in this motion; the surface of the water will at first be plain, as before the vessel began to move; but the vessel, by gradually communicating its motion to the water, will make it begin sensibly to revolve, and recede by little and little from the middle, and ascend to the sides of the vessel, forming itself into a concave figure (as I have experienced), and the swifter the motion becomes, the higher will the water rise, till at last, performing its revolutions in the same times with the vessel, it becomes relatively at rest in it. This ascent of the water shows its endeavour to recede from the axis of its motion; and the true and absolute circular motion of the water, which is here directly contrary to the relative, discovers itself, and may be measured by this endeavour. At first, when the relative motion of the water in the vessel was greatest, it produced no endeavour to recede from the axis; the water showed no tendency to the circumference, nor any ascent towards the sides of the vessel, but remained of a plain surface, and therefore its true circular motion had not yet begun. But afterwards, when the relative motion of the water had decreased, the ascent thereof towards the sides of the vessel proved its endeavour to recede from the axis; and this endeavour showed the real circular motion of the water perpetually increasing, till it had acquired its greatest quantity, when the water rested relatively in the vessel. And therefore this endeavour does not depend upon any translation of the water in respect of the ambient bodies, nor can true circular motion be defined by such translation. There is only one real circular motion of any one revolving body, corresponding to only one power of endeavouring to recede from its axis of motion, as its proper and adequate effect; but relative motions, in one and the same body, are innumerable, according to the various relations it bears to external bodies, and like other relations, are altogether destitute of any real effect, any otherwise than they may perhaps partake of that one only true motion. And therefore in their system who suppose that our heavens, revolving below the sphere of the fixed stars, carry the planets along with them; the several parts of those heavens, and the planets, which are indeed relatively at rest in their heavens, do yet really move. For they change their position one to another (which never happens to bodies truly at rest), and being carried together with their heavens, partake of their motions, and as parts of revolving wholes, endeavour to recede from the axis of their motions.

Wherefore relative quantities are not the quantities themselves, whose names they bear, but those sensible measures of them (either accurate or inaccurate), which are commonly used instead of the measured quantities themselves. And if the meaning of words is to be determined by their use, then by the names time, space, place and motion, their measures are properly to be understood; and the expression will be unusual, and purely mathematical, if the measured quantities themselves are meant. Upon which account, they do strain the sacred writings, who there interpret those words for the measured quantities. Nor do those less defile the purity of mathematical and philosophical truths, who confound real quantities themselves with their relations and vulgar measures.

It is indeed a matter of great difficulty to discover, and effectually to distinguish, the true motions of particular bodies from the apparent; because the parts of that immovable space, in which those motions are performed, do by no means come under the observation of our senses. Yet the thing is not altogether desperate; for we have some arguments to guide us, partly from the apparent motions, which are the differences of the true motions; partly from the forces, which are the causes and effects of the true motions. For instance, if two globes, kept at a given distance one from the other by means of a cord that connects them, were revolved about their common centre of gravity, we might, from the tension of the cord, discover the endeavour of the globes to recede from the axis of their motion, and from thence we might compute the quantity of their circular motions. And then if any equal forces should be impressed at once on the alternate faces of the globes to augment or diminish their circular motions, from the increase or decrease of the tension of the cord, we might infer the increment or decrement of their motions; and thence would be found on what faces those forces ought to be impressed, that the motions of the globes might be most augmented; that is, we might discover their hindermost faces, or those which, in the circular motion, do follow. But the faces which follow being known, and consequently the opposite ones that precede, we should likewise know the determination of their motions. And thus we might find both the quantity and the determination of this circular motion, even in an immense vacuum, where there was nothing external or sensible with which the globes could be compared. But now, if in that space some remote bodies were placed that kept always a given position one to another, as the fixed stars do in our regions, we could not indeed determine from the relative translation of the globes among those bodies, whether the motion did belong to the globes or to the bodies. But if we observed the cord, and found that its tension was that very tension which the motions of the globes required, we might conclude the motion to be in the globes, and the bodies to be at rest; and then, lastly, from the translation of the globes among the bodies, we should find the determination of their motions. But how we are to collect the true motions from their causes, effects, and apparent differences; and, *vice versa,* how from the motions, either true or apparent, we may come to the knowledge of their causes and effects, shall be explained more at large in the following tract. For to this end it was that I composed it.

AXIOMS, OR LAWS OF MOTION

Law 1. *Every body perseveres in its state of rest, or of uniform motion in a right line, unless it is compelled to change that state by forces impressed thereon.*

Projectiles persevere in their motions, so far as they are not retarded by the resistance of the air, or impelled downwards by the force of gravity. A top, whose parts by their cohesion are perpetually drawn aside from rectilinear motions, does not cease its rotation, otherwise than as it is retarded by the air. The greater bodies of the planets and comets, meeting with less resistance in more free spaces, preserve their motions both progressive and circular for a much longer time.

Law 2. *The alteration of motion is ever proportional to the motive force impressed; and is made in the direction of the right line in which that force is impressed.*

If any force generates a motion, a double force will generate double the motion, a triple force will generate triple the motion, whether that force be impressed altogether and at once, or gradually and successively. And this motion (being always directed the same way with the generating force), if the body moved before, is added to or subducted from the former motion, according as they directly conspire with or are directly contrary to each other; or obliquely joined, when they are oblique, so as to produce a new motion compounded from the determination of both.

Law 3. *To every action there is always opposed an equal reaction: or the mutual actions of two bodies upon each other are always equal, and directed to contrary parts.*

Whatever draws or presses another is as much drawn or pressed by that other. If you press a stone with your finger, the finger is also pressed by the stone. If a horse draws a stone tied to a rope, the horse (if I may so say) will be equally drawn back towards the stone: for the distended rope, by the same endeavour to relax or unbend itself, will draw the horse as much towards the stone, as it does the stone towards the horse, and will obstruct the progress of the one as much as it advances that of the other. If a body impinge upon another, and by its force change the motion of the other, that body also (because of the equality of the mutual pressure) will undergo an equal change, in its own motion, towards the contrary part. The changes made by these actions are equal, not in the velocities but in the motions of bodies; that is to say, if the bodies are not hindered by any other impediments. For, because the motions are equally changed, the changes of the velocities made towards contrary parts are reciprocally proportional to the bodies. This law takes place also in attractions, as will be proved in the next scholium.

Corollary 1. *A body by two forces conjoined will describe the diagonal of a parallelogram, in the same time that it would describe the sides, by those forces apart.*

If a body in a given time, by the force M impressed apart in the place A, should with an uniform motion be carried from A to B; and by the force N impressed apart in the same place, should be carried from A to C; complete the parallelogram ABCD, and, by both forces acting together, it will in the same time be carried in the diagonal from A to D. For since the force N acts in the direction of the line AC, parallel to BD, this force (by the second law) will not at all alter the velocity generated by the other force M, by which the body is carried towards the line BD. The body therefore will arrive at the line BD in the same time, whether the force N be impressed or not; and therefore at the end of that time it will be found somewhere in the line BD. By the same argument, at the end of the same time it will be found somewhere in the line CD. Therefore it will be found in the point D, where both lines meet. But it will move in a right line from A to D, by Law I.

Corollary 2. *And hence is explained the composition of any one direct force AD, out of any two oblique forces AC and CD; and, on the contrary, the resolution of any one direct force AD into two oblique forces AC and CD: which composition and resolution are abundantly confirmed from mechanics.*

As if the unequal radii OM and ON drawn from the centre O of any wheel, should sustain the weights A and P by the cords MA and NP; and the forces of those weights to move the wheel were required. Through the centre O draw the right line KOL, meeting the cords perpendicularly in K and L; and from the centre O, with OL the greater of the distances OK and OL, describe a circle, meeting the cord MA in D: and drawing OD, make AC parallel to DC perpendicular thereto. Now, it being indifferent whether the points K,L,D, of the cords be fixed to the plane of the wheel or not, the weights will have the same effect whether they are suspended from the points K and L, or from D and L. Let the whole force of the weight A be represented by the line AD, and let it be resolved into the forces AC and CD; of which the force AC, drawing the radius OD directly from the centre, will have no effect to move the wheel: but the other force

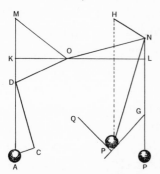

DC, drawing the radius DO perpendicularly, will have the same effect as if it drew perpendicularly the radius OL equal to OD; that is, it will have the same effect as the weight P, if that weight is to the weight A as the force DC is to the force DA; that is (because of the similar triangles ADC, DOK), as OK to OD or OL. Therefore the weights A and P, which are reciprocally as the radii OK and OL that lie in the same right line, will be equipollent, and so remain in equilibrio; which is the well known property of the balance, the lever, and the wheel. If either weight is greater than in this ratio, its force to move the wheel will be so much greater.

If the weight p, equal to the weight P, is partly suspended by the cord Np, partly sustained by the oblique plane pG; draw pH, NH, the former perpendicular to the horizon, the latter to the plane pG; and if the force of the weight p tending downwards is represented by the line pH, it may be resolved into the forces pN, HN. If there was any plane pQ, perpendicular to the cord pN, cutting the other plane pG in a line parallel to the horizon, and the weight p was supported only by those planes pQ, pG, it would press those planes perpendicularly with the forces pN, HN; to wit, the plane pQ with the force pN, and the plane pG with the force HN. And therefore if the plane pQ was taken away, so that the weight might stretch the cord, because the cord now sustaining the weight, supplies the place of the plane that was removed, it will be strained by the same force pN which pressed upon the plane before. Therefore, the tension of this oblique cord pN will be to that of the other perpendicular cord PN as pN to pH. And therefore if the weight p is to the weight A in a ratio compounded of the reciprocal ratio of the least distances of the cords PN, AM, from the centre of the wheel, and of the direct ratio of pH to pN, the weights will have the same effect towards moving the wheel, and will therefore sustain each other; as any one may find by experiment.

But the weight p pressing upon those two oblique planes, may be considered as a wedge between the two internal surfaces of a body split by it; and hence the forces of the wedge and the mallet may be determined; for because the force with which the weight p presses the plane pQ is to the force with which the same, whether by its own gravity, or by the blow of a mallet, is impelled in the direction of the line pH towards both the planes, as pN to pH; and to the force with which it presses the other plane pG, as pN to NH. And thus the force of the screw may be deduced from a like resolution of forces; it being no other than a wedge impelled with the force of a lever. Therefore the use of this Corollary spreads far and wide, and by that diffusive extent the truth thereof is farther confirmed. For on what has been said depends the whole doctrine of mechanics variously demonstrated by different authors. For from hence are easily deduced the forces of machines, which are compounded of wheels, pullies, levers, cords, and weights, ascending directly or obliquely, and other mechanical powers; as also the force of the tendons to move the bones of animals.

Corollary 3. *The quantity of motion, which is obtained by taking the sum of the motions directed towards the same parts, and the difference of those that are directed to contrary parts, suffers no change from the action of bodies among themselves.*

For action and its opposite re-action are equal, by Law III, and therefore, by Law II, they produce in the motions equal changes towards opposite parts. Therefore if the motions are directed towards the same parts, whatever is added to the motion of the preceding body will be subducted from the motion of that which follows; so that the sum will be the same as before. If the bodies meet, with contrary motions, there will be an equal deduction from the motions of both; and therefore the difference of the motions directed towards opposite parts will remain the same.

Thus if a spherical body A with two parts of velocity is triple of a spherical body B which follows in the same right line with ten parts of velocity, the motion of A will be to that of B as 6 to 10. Suppose, then, their motions to be of 6 parts and of 10 parts, and the sum will be 16 parts. Therefore, upon the meeting of the bodies, if A acquire 3, 4, or 5 parts of motion, B will lose as many; and therefore after reflexion A will proceed with 9, 10, or 11 parts, and B with 7, 6, or 5 parts; the sum remaining always of 16 parts as before. If the body A acquire 9, 10, 11, or 12 parts of motion, and therefore after meeting proceed with 15, 16, 17, or 18 parts, the body B, losing so many parts as A has got, will either proceed with 1 part, having lost 9, or stop and remain at rest, as having lost its whole progressive motion of 10 parts; or it will go back with 1 part, having not only lost its whole motion, but (if I may so say) one part more; or it will go back with 2 parts, because a progressive motion of 12 parts is taken off. And so the sums of the conspiring motions 15 + 1, or 16 + O, and the differences of the contrary motions 17 - 1 and 18 - 2, will always be equal to 16 parts, as they were before the meeting and reflexion of the bodies. But, the motions being known with which the bodies proceed after reflexion, the velocity of either will be also known, by taking the velocity after to the velocity before reflexion, as the motion after is to the motion before. As in the last case, where the motion of the body A was of 6 parts before reflexion and of 18 parts after, and the velocity was of 2 parts before reflexion, the velocity thereof after reflexion will be found to be of 6 parts; by saying, as the 6 parts of motion before to 18 parts after, so are 2 parts of velocity before reflexion to 6 parts after.

But if the bodies are either not spherical, or, moving in different right lines, impinge obliquely one upon the other, and their motions after reflexion are required, in those cases we are first to determine the position of the plane that touches the concurring bodies in the point of concourse; then the motion of each body (by Corol. 2) is to be resolved into two, one perpendicular to that plane, and the other parallel to it. This done, because the bodies act upon each other in the direction of a line perpendicular to this plane, the parallel motions are to be retained the same after reflexion as before; and to the perpendicular motions we are to assign equal changes towards the contrary parts; in such manner that the sum of the conspiring and the difference of the contrary motions may remain the same as before. From such kind of reflexions also sometimes arise the circular motions of bodies about their own centres. But these are cases which I do not consider in what follows, and it would be too tedious to demonstrate every particular that relates to this subject.

Corollary 4. *The common centre of gravity of two or more bodies does not alter its state of motion or rest by the actions of the bodies among themselves; and therefore the common centre of gravity of all bodies acting upon each other (excluding outward actions and impediments) is either at rest, or moves uniformly in a right line.*

For if two points proceed with an uniform motion in right lines, and their distance be divided in a given ratio, the dividing point will be either at rest, or proceed uniformly in a right line. This is demonstrated hereafter in Lem. XXIII and its Corol., when the points are moved in the same plane; and by a like way of arguing, it may be demonstrated when the points are not moved in the same plane. Therefore if any number of bodies move uniformly in right lines, the common centre of gravity of any two of them is either at rest, or proceeds uniformly in a right line; because the line which connects the centres of those two bodies so moving is divided at that common centre in a given ratio. In like manner the common centre of those two and that of a third body will be either at rest or moving uniformly in a right line; because at that centre the distance between the common centre of the two bodies, and the centre of this last, is divided in a given ratio. In like manner the common centre of these three, and of a fourth body, is either at rest, or moves uniformly in a right line; because the distance between the common centre of the three bodies, and the centre of the fourth is there also divided in a given ratio, and so on *in infinitum*. Therefore, in a system of bodies where there is neither any mutual action among themselves, nor any foreign force impressed upon them from without, and which consequently move uniformly in right lines, the common centre of gravity of them all is either at rest or moves uniformly forward in a right line.

Moreover, in a system of two bodies mutually acting upon each other, since the distances between their centres and the common centre of gravity of both are reciprocally as the bodies, the relative motions of those bodies, whether of approaching to or of receding from that centre, will be equal among themselves. Therefore since the changes which happen to motions are equal and directed to contrary parts, the common centre of those bodies, by their mutual action between themselves, is neither promoted nor retarded, nor suffers any change as to its state of motion or rest. But in a system of several bodies, because the common centre of gravity of any two acting mutually upon each other suffers no change in its state by that action; and much less the common centre of gravity of the others with which that action does not intervene; but the distance between those two centres is divided by the common centre of gravity of all the bodies into parts reciprocally proportional to the total sums of those bodies whose centres they are; and therefore while those two centres retain their state of motion or rest, the common centre of all does also retain its state: it is manifest that the common centre of all never suffers any change in the state of its motion or rest from the actions of any two bodies between themselves. But in such a system all the actions of the bodies among themselves either happen between two bodies, or are composed of action interchanged between some two bodies; and therefore they do never produce any alteration in the common centre of all as to its state of motion or rest. Wherefore since that centre, when the bodies do not act mutually one upon another, either is at rest or moves uniformly forward in some right line, it will, notwithstanding the mutual actions of the bodies among themselves, always persevere in its state, either of rest, or of proceeding uniformly in a right line, unless it is forced out of this state by the action of some power impressed from without upon the whole system. And therefore the same law takes place in a system consisting of many bodies as in one single body, with regard to their persevering in their state of motion or of rest. For the progressive motion, whether of one single body, or of a whole system of bodies, is always to be estimated from the motion of the centre of gravity.

Corollary 5. *The motions of bodies included in a given space are the same among themselves, whether that space is at rest, or moves uniformly forwards in a right line without any circular motion.*

For the differences of the motions tending towards the same parts, and the sums of those that tend towards contrary parts, are, at first (by supposition), in both cases the same; and it is from those sums and differences that the collisions and impulses do arise with which the bodies mutually impinge one upon another. Wherefore (by Law 2), the effects of those collisions will be equal in both cases; and therefore the mutual motions of the bodies among themselves in the one case will remain equal to the mutual motions of the bodies among themselves in the other. A clear proof of which we have from the experiment of a ship; where all motions happen after the same manner, whether the ship is at rest, or is carried uniformly forwards in a right line.

Corollary 6. If bodies, in any manner moved among themselves, are urged in the direction of parallel lines by equal accelerative forces, they will all continue to move among themselves, after the same manner as if they had been urged by those forces.

For these forces acting equally (with respect to the quantities of the bodies to be moved), and in the direction of parallel lines, will (by Law 2) move all the bodies equally (as to velocity), and therefore will never produce any change in the positions or motions of the bodies among themselves.

Scholium. Hitherto I have laid down such principles as have been received by mathematicians, and are confirmed by abundance of experiments. By the first two Laws and the first two Corollaries, Galileo discovered that the descent of bodies observed the duplicate ratio of the time, and that the motion of projectiles was in the curve of a parabola; experience agreeing with both, unless so far as these motions are a little retarded by the resistance of the air. When a body is falling, the uniform force of its gravity acting equally, impresses, in equal particles of time, equal forces upon that body, and therefore generates equal velocities; and in the whole time impresses a whole force, and generates a whole velocity proportional to the time. And the spaces described in proportional times are as the veloci-

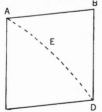

ties and the times conjunctly; that is, in a duplicate ratio of the times. And when a body is thrown upwards, its uniform gravity impresses forces and takes off velocities proportional to the times; and the times of ascending to the greatest heights are as the velocities to be taken off, and those heights are as the velocities and the times conjunctly, or in the duplicate ratio of the velocities. And if a body be projected in any direction, the motion arising from its projection is compounded with the motion arising from its gravity. Thus if the body A by its motion of projection alone could describe in a given time the right line AB, and with its motion of falling alone could describe in the same time the altitude AC; complete the paralellogram ABDC, and the body by that compounded motion will at the end of the time be found in the place D; and the curve line AED, which that body describes, will be a parabola, to which the right line AB will be a tangent in A; and whose ordinate BD will be as the square of the line AB. On the same Laws and Corollaries depend those things which have been demonstrated concerning the times of the vibration of pendulums, and are confirmed by the daily experiments of pendulum clocks. By the same, together with the third Law, Sir Christ. Wren, Dr. Wallis, and Mr. Huygens, the greatest geometers of our times, did severally determine the rules of the congress and reflexion of hard bodies, and much about the same time communicated their discoveries to the Royal Society, exactly agreeing among themselves as to those rules. Dr. Wallis, indeed, was something more early in the publication; then followed Sir Christopher Wren, and, lastly, Mr. Huygens. But Sir Christopher Wren confirmed the truth of the thing before the Royal Society by the experiment of pendulums, which Mr. Mariotte soon after thought fit to explain in a treatise entirely upon that subject. But to bring this experiment to an accurate agreement with the theory, we are to have a due regard as well to the resistance of the air as to the elastic force of the concurring bodies. Let the spherical bodies A, B be suspended by the parallel and equal strings AC, BD, from the centres C, D. About

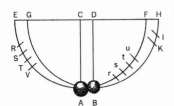

these centres, with those intervals, describe the semi-circles EAF, GBH, bisected by the radii CA, DB. Bring the body A to any point R of the arc EAF, and (withdrawing the body B) let it go from thence, and after one oscillation suppose it to return to the point V: then RV will be the retardation arising from the resistance of the air. Of this RV let ST be a fourth part, situated in the middle, to wit, so as RS and TV may be equal, and RS may be to ST as 3 to 2 then will ST represent very nearly the retardation during the descent from S to A. Restore the body B to its place: and, supposing the body A to be let fall from the point S, the velocity thereof in the place of reflexion A, without sensible error, will be the same as if it had descended *in vacuo* from the point T. Upon which account this velocity may be represented by the chord of the arc TA. For it is a proposition well known to geometers, that the velocity of a pendulous body in the lowest point is as the chord of the arc which it has described in its descent. After reflexion, suppose the body A comes to the place s, and the body B to the place k. Withdraw the body B, and find the place v, from which if the body A, being let go, should after one oscillation return to the place r, st may be a fourth part of rv, so placed in the middle thereof as to leave rs equal to tv, and let the chord of the arc tA represent the velocity which the body A had in the place A immediately after reflexion. For t will be the true and correct place to which the body A should have ascended, if the resistance of the air had been taken off. In the same way we are to correct the place k to which the body B ascends, by finding the place i to which it should have ascended *in vacuo*. And thus everything may be subjected to experiment, in the same manner as if we were really placed *in vacuo*. These things being done, we are to take the product (if I may so say) of the body A, by the chord of the arc TA (which represents its velocity), that we may have its motion in the place A immediately before reflexion; and then by the chord of the arc tA, that we may have its motion in the place A immediately after reflexion. And so we are to take the product of the body B by the chord of the arc Bi, that we may have the motion of the same immediately after reflexion. And in like manner, when two bodies are let go together from different places, we are to find the motion of each, as well before as after reflexion; and then we may compare the motions between themselves, and collect the effects of the reflexion. Thus trying the thing with pendulums of ten feet, in unequal as well as equal bodies, and making the bodies to concur after a descent through large spaces, as of 8, 12, or 16 feet, I found always, without an error of 3 inches, that when the bodies concurred together directly, equal changes towards the contrary parts were produced in their motions, and, of consequence, that the action and reaction were always equal. As if the body A impinged upon the body B at rest with 9 parts of motion, and losing 7, proceeded after reflexion with 2, the body B was carried backwards with those 7 parts. If the bodies concurred with contrary motions, A with twelve parts of motion, and B with six, then if A receded with 2, B receded with 8; to wit, with a deduction of 14 parts of motion on each side. For from the motion of A subducting twelve parts, nothing will remain; but subducting 2 parts more, a motion will be generated of 2 parts towards the contrary way; and so, from the motion of the body B of 6 parts, subducting 14 parts, a motion is generated of 8 parts towards the contrary way. But if the bodies were made both to move towards the same way, A, the swifter, with 14 parts of motion, B, the slower, with 5, and after reflexion A went on with 5, B likewise went on with 14 parts; 9 parts being transferred from A to B. And so in other cases. By the congress and collision of bodies, the quantity of motion, collected from the sum of the motions directed towards the same way, or from the difference of those that were directed towards contrary ways, was never changed. For the error of an inch or two in measures may be easily ascribed to the difficulty of executing everything with accuracy. It was not easy to let go the two pendulums so exactly together that the bodies should impinge one upon the other in the lowermost place AB; nor to mark the places s, and k, to which the bodies ascended after congress. Nay, and some errors, too, might have happened from the unequal density of the parts. of the pendulous bodies themselves, and from the irregularity of the texture proceeding from other causes.

But to prevent an objection that may perhaps be alleged against the rule, for the proof of which this experiment was made, as if this rule did suppose that the bodies were either absolutely hard, or at least perfectly elastic (whereas no such bodies are to be found in nature), I must add, that the experiments we have been describing, by no means depending upon that quality of hardness, do succeed as well in soft as in hard bodies. For if the rule is to be tried in bodies not perfectly hard, we are only to diminish the reflexion in such a certain proportion as the quantity of the elastic force requires. By the theory of Wren and Huygens, bodies absolutely hard return one from another with the same velocity with which they meet. But this may be affirmed with more certainty of bodies perfectly elastic. In bodies imperfectly elastic the· velocity of the return is to be diminished together with the elastic force; because that force (except when the parts of bodies are bruised by their congress, or suffer some such extension as happens under the strokes of a hammer) is (as far as I can perceive) certain and determined, and makes the bodies to return one from the other with a relative velocity, which is in a given ratio to that relative velocity with which they met. This I tried in balls of wool, made up tightly, and strongly compressed. For, first, by letting go the pendulous bodies, and measuring their reflexion, I determined the quantity of their elastic force:

and then, according to this force, estimated the reflexions that ought to happen in other cases of congress. And with this computation other experiments made afterwards did accordingly agree; the balls always receding one from the other with a relative velocity, which was to the relative velocity with which they met as about 5 to 9. Balls of steel returned with almost the same velocity: those of cork with a velocity something less; but in balls of glass the proportion was as about 15 to 16. And thus the third Law, so far as it regards percussions and reflexions, is proved by a theory exactly agreeing with experience.

In attractions, I briefly demonstrate the thing after this manner. Suppose an obstacle is interposed to hinder the congress of any two bodies A, B, mutually attracting one the other: then if either body, as A, is more attracted towards the other body B, than that other body B is towards the first body A, the obstacle will be more strongly urged by the pressure of the body A than by the pressure of the body B, and therefore will not remain in equilibrio: but the stronger pressure will prevail, and will make the system of the two bodies, together with the obstacle, to move directly towards the parts on which B lies; and in free spaces, to go forward *in infinitum* with a motion perpetually accelerated; which is absurd and contrary to the first Law. For, by the first Law, the system ought to persevere in its state of rest, or of moving uniformly forward in a right line; and therefore the bodies must equally press the obstacle, and be equally attracted one by the other. I made the experiment on the loadstone and iron. If these, placed apart in proper vessels, are made to float by one another in standing water, neither of them will propel the other; but, by being equally attracted, they will sustain each other's pressure, and rest at last in an equilibrium.

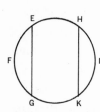

So the gravitation betwixt the earth and its parts is mutual. Let the earth FI be cut by any plane EG into two parts EGF and EGI, and their weights one towards the other will be mutually equal. For if by another plane HK, parallel to the former EG, the greater part EGI is cut into two parts EGKH and HKI, whereof HKI is equal to the part EFG, first cut off, it is evident that the middle part EGKH, will have no propension by its proper weight towards either side, but will hang as it were, and rest in an equilibrium betwixt both. But the one extreme part HKI will with its whole weight bear upon and press the middle part towards the other extreme part EGF; and therefore the force with which EGI, the sum of the parts HKI and EGKH, tends towards the third part EGF, is equal to the weight of the part HKI, that is, to the weight of the third part EGF. And therefore the weights of the two parts EGI and EGF, one towards the other, are equal, as I was to prove. And indeed if those weights were not equal, the whole earth floating in the non-resisting ether would give way to the greater weight, and, retiring from it, would be carried off *in infinitum.*

And as those bodies are equipollent in the congress and reflexion, whose velocities are reciprocally as their innate forces, so in the use of mechanic instruments those agents are equipollent, and mutually sustain each the contrary pressure of the other, whose velocities, estimated according to the determination of the forces, are reciprocally as the forces.

So those weights are of equal force to move the arms of a balance; which during the play of the balance are reciprocally as their velocities upwards and downwards; that is, if the ascent or descent is direct, those weights are of equal force, which are reciprocally as the distances of the points at which they are suspended from the axis of the balance; but if they are turned aside by the interposition of oblique planes, or other obstacles, and made to ascend or descend obliquely, those bodies will be equipollent, which are reciprocally as the heights of their ascent and descent taken according to the perpendicular; and that on account of the determination of gravity downwards.

And in like manner in the pully, or in a combination of pullies, the force of a hand drawing the rope directly, which is to the weight, whether ascending directly or obliquely, as the velocity of the perpendicular ascent of the weight to the velocity of the hand that draws the rope, will sustain the weight.

In clocks and such like instruments, made up from a combination of wheels, the contrary forces that promote and impede the motion of the wheels, if they are reciprocally as the velocities of the parts of the wheel on which they are impressed, will mutually sustain the one the other.

The force of the screw to press a body is to the force of the hand that turns the handles by which it is moved as the circular velocity of the handle in that part where it is impelled by the hand is to the progressive velocity of the screw towards the pressed body.

The forces by which the wedge presses or drives the two parts of the wood it cleaves are to the force of the mallet upon the wedge as the progress of the wedge in the direction of the force impressed upon it by the mallet is to the velocity with which the parts of the wood yield to the wedge, in the direction of lines perpendicular to the sides of the wedge. And the like account is to be given of all machines.

The power and use of machines consist only in this, that by diminishing the velocity we may augment the force, and the contrary: from whence in all sorts of proper machines, we have the solution of this problem; *To move a given weight with a given power,* or with a given force to overcome any other given resistance. For if machines are so contrived that the velocities of the agent and resistant are reciprocally as their forces, the agent will just sustain the resistant, but with a greater disparity of velocity will overcome it. So that if the disparity of velocities is so great as to overcome all that resistance which commonly arises either from the attrition of contiguous bodies as they slide by one another, or from the cohesion of continuous bodies that are to be separated, or from the weights of bodies to be raised, the excess of the force remaining, after all those resistances are overcome, will produce an acceleration of motion proportional thereto, as well in the parts of the machine as in the resisting body. But to treat of mechanics is not my present business. I was only willing to show by those examples the great extent and certainty of the third Law of motion. For if we estimate the action of the agent from its force and velocity conjunctly, and likewise the reaction of the impediment conjunctly from the velocities of its several parts, and from the forces of resistance arising from the attrition, cohesion, weight, and acceleration of those parts, the action and reaction in the use of all sorts of machines will be found always equal to one another. And so far as the action is propagated by the intervening instruments, and at last impressed upon the resisting body, the ultimate action will be always contrary to the reaction.

"Therefore, Astronomers have a large field
wherein to exercise themselves for many ages, before
they will be able to know the number of these many and great
Bodies, revolving about the common center of the Sun,
and to reduce their motions to certain rules."

Edmund Halley

1656 — 1742

THE ELLIPTICAL ORBITS OF COMETS ARE DESCRIBED, AND THE RETURN OF A COMET IS PREDICTED

Newton's *Principia* was published in 1687, as the result of a revival of his interest in work done in his youth. The man directly responsible for this was Edmund Halley, a member of a group within the Royal Society, who desired Newton's views on the elliptical orbits of the planets. Halley had begun his study of the planets while he was a student at Queen's College, Oxford, and his first paper on the planetary orbits was published in 1676. After his graduation, he spent some time on the lonely island of St. Helena, where, 170 years later, Napoleon Bonaparte died in exile. Here Halley studied the stars of the southern hemisphere, adding 341 to the catalogues.

Halley's whole life, first as professor of geometry at Oxford and later as Astronomer Royal at the Greenwich Observatory, was dedicated to the study of the heavens. Like Sarton, his interest in his field induced him even to learn Arabic, to give him access to early texts not otherwise available. He was always on hand to support Newton in his work, whether by financing the publication of the *Principia* or by helping to iron out the disputes which arose with Hooke.

Halley's principal project was an eighteen-year study (started when he was already 64 years old) of the moon, but his major, and perhaps best known, scientific contribution was his discovery of the comet of 1682, subsequently named for him. He connected the comet with earlier appearances of comets, in 1531 and 1607, which had followed the same course; and he ventured a prediction that this comet "would reappear after approximately 75½ years." This certainty about an otherwise mysterious phenomenon helped to dissipate the superstitious fear of comets, long regarded as forerunners of disaster; more important, it offered strong confirmation for the belief that the universe was a comprehensible mechanism.

Halley was a practical astronomer and established many procedures which assisted later generations to work out the implications of Newton's synthesis.

The selection that follows has been taken from Gregory's *The Elements of Astronomy*, Vol. 2, 1715. It appears in *A Source Book in Astronomy*.

A DISCUSSION OF ELLIPTICAL ORBITS OF COMETS

Hitherto I have consider'd the Orbits of Comets as exactly Parabolic; upon which supposition it wou'd follow, that Comets being impell'd towards the Sun by a Centripetal Force, would descend as from spaces infinitely distant, and by their so falling acquire such a Velocity, as that they may again fly off into the remotest parts of the Universe, moving upwards with a perpetual tendency, so as never to return again to the Sun. But since they appear frequently enough, and since some of them can be found to move with a Hyperbolic Motion, or a Motion swifter than what a Comet might acquire by its Gravity to the Sun, 'tis highly probable they rather move in very Excentric Elliptic Orbits, and make their returns after long periods of Time: For so their number will be determinate, and, perhaps, not so very great. Besides, the space between the Sun and the Fix'd Stars is so immense, that there is room enough for a Comet to revolve, tho' the Period of its revolution be vastly long. Now, the Latus Rectum of an Ellipsis, is to the Latus Rectum of a Parabola, which has the same Distance in its Perihelium; as the distance in the Aphelium in the Ellipses, is to the whole Axis of the Ellipsis. And the Velocities are in a Sub-duplicate ratio of the same: Wherefore in very Excentric Orbits the ratio comes very near to a ratio of Equality; and the very small difference which happens on account of the greater Velocity in the Parabola, is easily compensated in determining the situation of the Orbit. The principal use therefore, of this Table of the Elements of their Motions, and that which indeed induced me to construct it, is, that whenever a new Comet shall appear, we may be able to know, by comparing together the Elements, whether it be any of those which has appear'd before, and consequently to determine its Period, and the Axis of its Orbit, and to foretel its Return. And, indeed there are many things which make me believe that the Comet which Apian observ'd on the Year 1531, was the same with that which Kepler and Longomontanus more accurately describ'd in the Year 1607; and which I myself have seen return, and observ'd in the Year 1682. All the Elements agree, and nothing seems to contradict this my opinion, besides the Inequality of the Periodic revolutions. Which Inequality is not so great neither, as that it may not be owing to Physical Causes. For the Motion of Saturn is so disturbed by the rest of the Planets, especially Jupiter, that the Periodic time of that Planet is uncertain for some whole days together. How much more therefore will a Comet be subject to such like errors, which rises almost four times higher than Saturn, and whose Velocity, tho' increased but a very little, would be sufficient to change its Orbit, from an Elliptical to a Parabolical one. And I am the more confirmed in my opinion of its being the same; for that in the Year 1456, in the Summer time, a Comet was seen passing Retrograde between the Earth and the Sun, much after the same manner: Which tho' nobody made observations upon it, yet from its Period and the manner of its Transit, I cannot think different from those I have just now mention'd. And since looking over the Histories of Comets I find, at an equal interval of Time, a Comet to have been seen about Easter in the Year 1305, which is another double Period of 151 Years before the former. Hence I think I may venture to foretel, that it will return again in the Year 1758. And, if it should then so return, we shall have no reason to doubt but the rest may return also: Therefore, Astronomers have a large field wherein to exercise themselves for many ages, before they will be able to know the number of these many and great Bodies revolving about the common Center of the Sun, and to reduce their Motions to certain Rules.

*"All events, even those which on account
of their insignificance do not seem to follow the great laws of
nature, are a result of it just as necessarily as
the revolutions of the sun."*

Pierre Simon Laplace

1749 – 1827

THE NEBULAR HYPOTHESIS IS SUGGESTED
AS AN EXPLANATION OF THE ORIGIN
OF THE SOLAR SYSTEM

Pierre Simon Laplace, the man who examined Napoleon
Bonaparte in mathematics, is sometimes called the French Newton. The son of a Norman farmer, Laplace was sent to school by
wealthy neighbors and, in due course, became a professor of
mathematics at L'Ecole Militaire at Paris. By the age of 24 he
had published the first stage of his thesis to prove the essential
stability of the solar system. In this he was to oppose Newton's
view that the planets were affected in their movement not only
by the sun but also by other planets, so that eventually an irregularity would develop which only Divine intervention could ad-
just!

By 1825 Laplace had published his six-volume *Mécanique
Céleste (Celestial Mechanics),* in which he provided "a complete
solution of the great mechanical problem presented by the solar
system." He also advanced his "nebular hypothesis" (described
in the following selection), in which he traced the origin of the
planets to masses of hot, rotating gases thrown off by the sun
because of its increasing acceleration. This would account for the

similarity of the direction of the rotation of the planets and their satellites. It is not known if Laplace was aware that the philosopher Immanuel Kant (1724-1804) had, in 1755, when he was still a practicing scientist, put forth the same idea. Laplace's theory held ground for some time until it was ascertained that, among other technical objections, the sun, instead of increasing its rate of rotation, is, in fact, hardly rotating at all.

Laplace combined his scientific work with politics, becoming an active supporter of Napoleon, who appointed him Minister of the Interior. His geometry, however, was better than his administrative ability, and he was soon removed from office and promoted to the Senate. When the time came he transferred his loyalty from Napoleon to the Bourbons and became a marquis for his pains. Newton can be considered to have inspired Laplace's scientific career. Perhaps the knighthood given to the Englishman stimulated the Frenchman's hunt for a title!

With Laplace, the development of cosmology entered the nineteenth century. After three hundred years, a cosmic order had been discovered; the sun, stars, and earth had been observed in their true relations to one another; and a mathematical set of tools had been provided to serve those who wished to refine the theories of the great cosmic discoverers.

The following selection has been taken from *The System of the World,* translated by H. H. Harte in *A Source Book in Astronomy.*

THE NEBULAR HYPOTHESIS

However arbitrary the elements of the system of the planets may be, there exists between them some very remarkable relations, which may throw light on their origin. Considering it with attention, we are astonished to see all the planets move round the Sun from west to east, and nearly in the same plane, all the satellites moving round their respective planets in the same direction, and nearly in the same plane with the planets. Lastly, the Sun, the planets, and those satellites in which a motion of rotation have been observed, turn on their own axes, in the same direction, and nearly in the same plane as their motion of projection.

The satellites exhibit in this respect a remarkable peculiarity. Their motion of rotation is exactly equal to their motion of revolution; so that they always present the same hemisphere to their primary. At least, this has been observed for the Moon, for the four satellites of Jupiter, and for the last satellite of Saturn, the only satellites whose rotation has been hitherto recognized.

Phenomena so extraordinary, are not the effect of irregular causes. By subjecting their probability to computation, it is found that there is more than two thousand to one against the hypothesis that they are the effect of chance, which is a probability much greater than that on which most of the events of history, respecting which there does not exist a doubt, depends. We ought, therefore, to be assured with the same confidence, that a primitive cause has directed the planetary motions.

Another phenomenon of the solar system, equally remarkable, is the small eccentricity of the orbits of the planets and their satellites, while those of comets are very much extended. The orbits of this system present no intermediate shades between a great and small eccentricity. We are here again compelled to acknowledge the effect of a regular cause; chance alone could not have given a form nearly circular to the orbits of all the planets. It is, therefore, necessary that the cause which determined the motions of these bodies, rendered them also nearly circular. This cause then must also have influenced the great eccentricity of the orbits of comets, and their motion in every direction; for, considering the orbits of retrograde comets, as being inclined more than one hundred degrees to the ecliptic, we find that the mean inclination of the orbits of all the observed comets, approaches near to one hundred degrees, which would be the case if the bodies had been projected at random.

What is this primitive cause? In the concluding note of this work I will suggest an hypothesis which appears to me to result with a great degree of probability, from the preceding phenomena, which, however, I present with that diffidence, which ought always to attach to whatever is not the result of observation and computation.

Whatever be the true cause, it is certain that the elements of the planetary system are so arranged as to enjoy the greatest possible stability, unless it is deranged by the intervention of foreign causes. From the sole circumstance that the motions of the planets and satellites are performed in orbits nearly circular, in the same direction, and in planes which are inconsiderably inclined to each other, the system will always oscillate about a mean state, from which it will deviate but by very small quantities. The mean motions of rotation and of revolution of these different bodies are uniform, and their mean distances from the foci of the principal forces which actuate them are constant; all the secular inequalities are periodic. . . .

NOTE VII, AND LAST

From the preceding chapter it appears, that we have the five following phenomena to assist us in investigating the cause of the primitive motions of the planetary system. The motions of the planets in the same direction, and very nearly in the same plane; the motions of the satellites in the same direction as those of the planets; the motions of rotation of these different bodies and also of the Sun, in the same direction as their motions of projection, and in planes very little inclined to each other; the small eccentricity of the orbits of the planets and satellites; finally, the great eccentricity of the orbits of the comets, their inclinations being at the same time entirely indeterminate.

Buffon is the only individual that I know of, who, since the discovery of the true system of the world, endeavoured to investigate the origin of the planets and satellites. He supposed that a comet, by impinging on the Sun, carried away a torrent of matter, which was reunited far off, into globes of different magnitudes, and at different distances from this star. These globes, when they cool and become hardened, are the planets and their satellites. This hypothesis satisfied the first of the five preceding phenomena for it is evident that all bodies thus formed should move very nearly in the plane which passes through the centre of the Sun, and through the direction of the torrent of matter which has produced them: but the four remaining phenomena appear to me inexplicable on this supposition. Indeed the absolute motion of the molecules of a planet ought to be in the same direction as the motion of its centre of gravity; but it by no means follows from this, that the motion of rotation of a planet should be also in the same direction. Thus the Earth may revolve from east to west, and yet the absolute motion of each of its molecules may be directed from west to east. This observation applies also to the revolution of the satellites, of which the direction, in the same hypothesis, is not necessarily the same as that of the motion of projection of the planets.

The small eccentricity of the planetary orbits is a phenomenon, not only difficult to explain on this hypothesis, but altogether inconsistent with it. We know from the theory of central forces, that if a body which moves in a re-entrant orbit about the Sun, passes very near the body of the Sun, it will return constantly to it, at the end of each revolution. Hence it follows that if the planets were originally detached from the Sun, they would touch it, at each return to his star; and their orbits, instead of being nearly circular, would be very eccentric. Indeed it must be admitted that a torrent of matter detached from the Sun, cannot be compared to a globe which just skims by its surface: from the impulsions which the parts of this torrent receive from each other, combined with their mutual attraction, they may, by changing the direction of their motions, increase the distances of their perihelions from the Sun. But their orbits should be extremely eccentric, or at least all the orbits would not be circular, except by the most extraordinary chance. Finally, no reason can be assigned on the hypothesis of Buffon, why the orbits of more than one hundred comets, which have been already observed, should be all very eccentric. This hypothesis, therefore, is far from satisfying the preceding phenomena. Let us consider whether we can assign the true cause.

Whatever may be its nature, since it has produced or influenced the direction of the planetary motions, it must have embraced them all within the sphere of its action; and considering the immense distance which intervenes between them, nothing could have effected this but a fluid of almost indefinite extent. In order to have impressed on them all a motion circular and in the same direction about the Sun, this fluid must environ this star, like an atmosphere. From a consideration of the planetary motions, we are, therefore, brought to the conclusion, that in consequence of an excessive heat, the solar atmosphere originally extended beyond the orbits of all the planets, and that it has successively contracted itself within its present limits.

In the primitive state in which we have supposed the Sun to be, it resembles those substances which are termed nebulæ, which, when seen through telescopes, appear to be composed of a nucleus, more or less brilliant, surrounded by a nebulosity, which, by condensing on its surface, transforms it into a star. If all the stars are conceived to be similarly formed, we can suppose their anterior state of nebulosity to be preceded by other states, in which the nebulous matter was more or less diffuse, the nucleus being at the same time more or less brilliant. By going back in this manner, we shall arrive at a state of nebulosity so diffuse, that its existence can with difficulty be conceived.

For a considerable time back, the particular arrangement of some stars visible to the naked eye, has engaged the attention of philosophers. Mitchel remarked long since how extremely improbable it was that the stars composing the constellation called the Pleiades, for example, should be confined within the narrow space which contains them, by the sole chance of hazard; from which he inferred that this group of stars, and the similar groups which the heavens present to us, are the effects of a primitive cause, or of a primitive law of nature. These groups are a general result of the condensation of nebulæ of several nuclei; for it is evident that the nebulous matter being perpetually attracted by these different nuclei, ought at length to form a group of stars, like to that of the Pleiades. The condensation of nebulæ consisting of two nuclei, will in like manner form stars very near to each other, revolving the one about the other like to the double stars, whose respective motions have been already recognized.

But in what manner has the solar atmosphere determined the motions of rotation and revolution of the planets and satellites? If these bodies had penetrated deeply into this atmosphere, its resistance would cause them to fall on the Sun. We may, therefore, suppose that the planets were formed at its successive limits, by the condensation of zones of vapours, which it must, while it was cooling, have abandoned in the plane of its equator.

Let us resume the results which we have given in the tenth chapter of the preceding book. The Sun's atmosphere cannot extend indefinitely; its limit is the point where the centrifugal force arising from the motion of rotation balances the gravity; but according as the cooling contracts the atmosphere, and condenses the molecules which are near to it, on the surface of the star, the motion of rotation increases; for in virtue of the principle of areas, the sum of the areas described by the radius vector of each particle of the Sun and of its atmosphere, and projected on the plane of its equator, is always the same. Consequently, the rotation ought to be quicker, when these particles approach to the centre of the Sun. The centrifugal force arising from this motion becoming thus greater, the point where the

gravity is equal to it, is nearer to the centre of the Sun. Supposing, therefore, what is natural to admit, that the atmosphere extended at any epoch
as far as this limit, it ought, according as it cooled, to abandon the molecules, which are situated at this limit, and at the successive limits produced
by the increased rotation of the Sun. These particles, after being abandoned,
have continued to circulate about this star, because their centrifugal force
was balanced by their gravity. But as this equality does not obtain for those
molecules of the atmosphere which are situated on the parallels to the
Sun's equator, these have come nearer by their gravity to the atmosphere
according as it condensed, and they have not ceased to belong to it, inasmuch as by this motion, they have approached to the plane of this equator.

Let us now consider the zones of vapours, which have been successively abandoned. These zones ought, according to all probability, to form
by their condensation, and by the mutual attraction of their particles, several concentrical rings of vapours circulating about the Sun. The mutual
friction of the molecules of each ring ought to accelerate some and retard
others, until they all had acquired the same angular motion. Consequently,
the real velocities of the molecules which are farther from the Sun, ought
to be greatest. The following cause ought, likewise, to contribute to this
difference of velocities: The most distant particles of the Sun, which, by
the effects of cooling and of condensation, have collected so as to constitute
the superior part of the ring, have always described areas proportional to
the times, because the central force by which they are actuated has been
constantly directed to this star; but this constancy of areas requires an increase of velocity, according as they approach more to each other. It appears
that the same cause ought to diminish the velocity of the particles, which,
situated near the ring, constitute its inferior part.

If all the particles of a ring of vapours continued to condense without
separating, they would at length constitute a solid or a liquid ring. But the
regularity which this formation requires in all the parts of the ring, and
in their cooling, ought to make this phenomenon very rare. Thus the solar
system presents but one example of it; that of the rings of Saturn. Almost
always each ring of vapours ought to be divided into several masses, which,
being moved with velocities which differ little from each other, should
continue to revolve at the same distance about the Sun. These masses should
assume a spheroidical form, with a rotatory motion in the direction of
that of their revolution, because their inferior particles have a less real

velocity than the superior; they have, therefore, constituted so many planets in a state of vapour. But if one of them was sufficiently powerful, to unite successively by its attraction, all the others about its centre, the ring of vapours would be changed into one sole spheroidical mass, circulating about the Sun, with a motion of rotation in the same direction with that of revolution. This last case has been the most common; however, the solar system presents to us the first case, in the four small planets which revolve between Mars and Jupiter, at least unless we suppose with Olbers, that they originally formed one planet only, which was divided by an explosion into several parts, and actuated by different velocities. Now if we trace the changes which a farther cooling ought to produce in the planets formed of vapours, and of which we have suggested the formation, we shall see to arise in the centre of each of them, a nucleus increasing continually, by the condensation of the atmosphere which environs it. In this state, the planet resembles the Sun in the nebulous state, in which we have first supposed it to be; the cooling should, therefore, produce at the different limits of its atmosphere, phenomena similar to those which have been described, namely, rings and satellites circulating about its centre in the direction of its motion of rotation, and revolving in the same direction on their axes. The regular distribution of the mass of rings of Saturn about its centre and in the plane of its equator, results naturally from this hypothesis, and, without it, is inexplicable. Those rings appear to me to be existing proofs of the primitive extension of the atmosphere of Saturn, and of its successive condensations. Thus the singular phenomena of the small eccentricities of the orbits of the planets and satellites, of the small inclination of these orbits to the solar equator, and of the identity in the direction of the motions of rotation and revolution of all those bodies with that of the rotation of the Sun, follow from the hypothesis which has been suggested, and render it extremely probable. If the solar system was formed with perfect regularity, the orbits of the bodies which compose it would be circles, of which the planes, as well as those of the various equators and rings, would coincide with the plane of the solar equator. But we may suppose that the innumerable varieties which must necessarily exist in the temperature and density of different parts of these great masses, ought to produce the eccentricities of their orbits, and the deviations of their motions, from the plane of this equator.

In the preceding hypothesis, the comets do not belong to the solar system. If they be considered, as we have done, as small nebulæ, wandering from one solar system to another, and formed by the condensation of the nebulous matter, which is diffused so profusely throughout the universe, we may conceive that when they arrive in that part of space where the attraction of the Sun predominates, it should force them to describe elliptic or hyperbolic orbits. But as their velocities are equally possible in every direction, they must move indifferently in all directions, and at every possible inclination to the ecliptic; which is conformable to observation. Thus the condensation of the nebulous matter, which explains the motions of rotation and revolution of the planets and satellites in the same direction, and in orbits very little inclined to each other, likewise explains why the motions of the comets deviate from this general law.

The great eccentricity of the orbits of the comets, is also a result of our hypothesis. If those orbits are elliptic, they are very elongated, since their greater axes are at least equal to the radius of the sphere of activity of the Sun. But these orbits may be hyperbolic; and if the axes of these hyperbolæ are not very great with respect to the mean distance of the Sun from the Earth, the motion of the comets which describe them will appear to be sensibly hyperbolic. However, with respect to the hundred comets, of which the elements are known, not one appears to move in a hyperbola; hence the chances which assign a sensible hyperbola, are extremely rare relatively to the contrary chances. The comets are so small, that they only become sensible when their perihelion distance is inconsiderable. Hitherto this distance has not surpassed twice the diameter of the Earth's orbit, and most frequently, it has been less than the radius of this orbit. We may conceive, that in order to approach so near to the Sun, their velocity at the moment of their ingress within its sphere of activity, must have an intensity and direction confined within very narrow limits. If we determine by the analysis of probabilities, the ratio of the chances which, in these limits, assign a sensible hyperbola to the chances which assign an orbit, which may without sensible error be confounded with a parabola, it will be found that there is at least six thousand to unity that a nebula which penetrates within the sphere of the Sun's activity so as to be observed, will either describe a very elongated ellipse, or an hyperbola, which, in consequence of the magnitude of its axis will be as to sense confounded with a parabola in the part of its orbit which is observed. It is not, therefore, surprising that hitherto no hyperbolic motions have been recognised.

The attraction of the planets, and perhaps also the resistance of the ethereal media, ought to change several cometary orbits into ellipses, of which the greater axes are much less than the radius of the sphere of the solar activity. It is probable that such a change was produced in the orbit of the comet of 1759, the greater axis of which was not more than thirty-five times the distance of the Sun from the Earth. A still greater change was produced in the orbits of the comets of 1770 and of 1805.

If any comets have penetrated the atmospheres of the Sun and planets at the moment of their formation, they must have described spirals, and consequently fallen on these bodies, and in consequence of their fall, caused the planes of the orbits and of the equators of the planets to deviate from the plane of the solar equator.

If in the zones abandoned by the atmosphere of the Sun, there are any molecules too volatile to be united to each other, or to the planets, they ought, in their circulation about this star, to exhibit all the appearances of the zodiacal light, without opposing any sensible resistance to the different bodies of the planetary system, both on account of their great rarity, and also because their motion is very nearly the same as that of the planets which they meet.

An attentive examination of all the circumstances of this system renders our hypothesis still more probable. The primitive fluidity of the planets is clearly indicated by the compression of their figure, conformably to the laws of the mutual attraction of their molecules; it is, moreover, demonstrated by the regular diminution of gravity, as we proceed from the equator to the poles. This state of primitive fluidity to which we are conducted by astronomical phenomena, is also apparent from those which natural history points out. But in order fully to estimate them, we should take into account the immense variety of combinations formed by all the terrestrial substances which were mixed together in a state of vapour, when the depression of their temperature enabled their elements to unite; it is necessary, likewise, to consider the wonderful changes which this depression ought to cause in the interior and at the surface of the earth, in all its productions, in the constitution and pressure of the atmosphere, in the ocean, and in all substances which it held in a state of solution. Finally, we should take into account the sudden changes, such as great volcanic eruptions, which must at different epochs have deranged the regularity of these changes. Geology, thus studied under the point of view which connects it with astronomy, may, with respect to several objects, acquire both precision and certainty.

One of the most remarkable phenomena of the solar system is the rigorous equality which is observed to subsist between the angular motions of rotation and revolution of each satellite. It is infinity to unity that this is not the effect of hazard. The theory of universal gravitation makes infinity to disappear from this improbability, by shewing that it is sufficient for the existence of this phenomenon, that at the commencement these motions did not differ much. Then, the attraction of the planet would establish between them a perfect equality; but at the same time it has given rise to a periodic oscillation in the axis of the satellite directed to the planet, of which oscillation the extent depends on the primitive difference between these motions. As the observations of Mayer on the libration of the Moon, and those which Bouvard and Nicollet made for the same purpose, at my request, did not enable us to recognize this oscillation; the difference on which it depends must be extremely small, which indicates with every appearance of probability the existence of a particular cause, which has confined this difference within very narrow limits, in which the attraction of the planet might establish between the mean motions of rotation and revolution a rigid equality, which at length terminated by annihilating the oscillation which arose from this equality. Both these effects result from our hypothesis; for we may conceive that the Moon, in a state of vapour, assumed in consequence of the powerful attraction of the earth the form of an elongated spheroid, of which the greater axis would be constantly directed towards this planet, from the facility with which the vapours yield to the slightest force impressed upon them. The terrestrial attraction continuing to act in the same manner, while the Moon is in a state of fluidity, ought at length, by making the two motions of this satellite to approach each other, to cause their difference to fall within the limits, at which their rigorous equality commences to establish itself. Then this attraction should annihilate, by little and little, the oscillation which this equality produced on the greater axis of the spheroid directed towards the earth. It is in this manner that the fluids which cover this planet, have destroyed by their friction and resistance the primitive oscillations of its axis of rotation, which is only now subject to the nutation resulting from the actions of the Sun and Moon. It is easy to be assured that the equality of the motions of rotation and revolution of the satellites ought to oppose the formation of rings and secondary satellites, by the atmospheres of these bodies. Consequently observation has not hitherto indicated the existence of any such. The motions of the three first satellites of Jupiter present a phenomenon still more extraordinary than the preceding; which consists in this, that the mean longitude of the first, minus three times that of the second, plus twice that of the third, is constantly equal to two right angles. There is the ratio of infinity to one, that this equality is not the effect of chance. But we have seen, that in order to produce it, it is sufficient, if at the commencement, the mean motions of these three bodies approached very near to the relation which renders the mean motion of the first, minus three times that of the second, plus twice that of the third, equal to nothing. Then their mutual attraction rendered this ratio rigorously exact, and it has moreover made the mean longitude of the first minus three times that of the second, plus twice that of the third, equal to a semicircumference. At the same time, it gave rise to a periodic inequality, which depends on the small quantity, by which the mean motions originally deviated from the relation which we have just announced. Notwithstanding all the care Delambre took in his observations, he could not recognise this inequality, which; while it evinces its extreme smallness, also indicates, with a high degree of probability, the existence of a cause which makes it to disappear. In our hypothesis, the satellites of Jupiter, immediately after their formation, did not move in a perfect vacuo; the less condensible molecules of the primitive atmospheres of the Sun and planet would then constitute a rare medium, the resistance of which being different for each of the [bodies], might make the mean motions to approach by degrees to the ratio in question; and when these movements had thus attained the conditions requisite, in order that the mutual attraction of the three satellites might render this relation accurately true, it perpetually diminished the inequality which this relation originated, and eventually rendered it insensible. We cannot better illustrate these effects than by comparing them to the motion of a pendulum, which, actuated by a great velocity, moves in a medium, the resistance of which is inconsiderable. It will first describe a great number of circumferences; but at length its motion of circulation perpetually decreasing, it will be converted into an oscillatory motion, which itself diminishing more and more, by the resistance of the medium, will eventually be totally destroyed, and then the pendulum, having attained a state of repose, will remain at rest for ever.

" . . . how little mystery there really is in the
business of experimental philosophy, and with how little
sagacity, *or even* design, *discoveries (which some persons are*
pleased to consider as great and wonderful things)
have been made. . . ."
—Joseph Priestley

DISCOVERY OF THE
INFINITELY SMALL

The progress of science depends upon a great deal more than the exploration of the heavens. Many of us would be quite content to leave to a few specialists the explanation of a distant mystery; and it is likely that during the great cosmological debates of the sixteenth and seventeenth centuries the layman was completely unmoved. There were many things happening in his everyday experience which demanded explanation—matters in which any educated person might take an interest because the results of investigation could be reduced to terms which he could understand. The period we are about to examine was still far from the climax of the scientific revolution, when science was, in effect, to become a paramount influence in the life of society. This is a period of transition, and the group of readings here must be read in that context.

In a sense, this group of readings pays tribute to the emergence of a new element in the scientific life of Europe. We have already seen that the influence which caused Newton to publish his *Principia* came not from his university but from a group of members of the Royal Society of London for Promoting Natural Knowledge. Of the eight writers represented here, three were members of the Royal Society; another was a member of the nucleus out of which came the French *Académie des Sciences,* a fifth was a member of both the *Académie* and the Royal Society. Both of these societies came into being as a result of the voluntary association of like-minded men. Some were scholars; some were amateurs. They met informally, long before their associations were given the charters which ensured their continued existence as corporate bodies; the societies set an example which was followed throughout the civilized world, and they have survived to this day as vital elements in the scientific life not only of the countries of their origin but of the world.

The story of the Royal Society indicates clearly the social forces in the sixteenth century which were favorable to the growth of science. It begins in 1597 with the founding of Gresham College, in the City of London, one of the earliest attempts to bring the universities to the people who, especially in those days, could not attend them. Seven unmarried professors were appointed to give lectures, open (as they are today in a slightly different form) to any citizen. The lectures attracted men from all walks of life, and they put men of learning in contact with representatives of the active life of the community—businessmen and craftsmen, sea captains and shipbuilders. In this climate of education-in-touch-with-life (so different from that of the cloistered universities), a group of young men started a club to meet once a week to discuss science. It was called "the invisible college" because it had no buildings or professors. When it could not meet at Gresham College, the group repaired to a neighboring inn, and discussed everything from the Copernican hypothesis to the valves in the veins. By 1662, the club had become important enough to justify incorporation; a Royal charter was granted, thus giving formal recognition to the fact that the work of the club had real significance to society. Among the original fellows were Robert Boyle, Robert Hooke—and, surprisingly, but significantly in view of the close association between British and American scientists,

John Winthrop, Governor of Connecticut, probably the first chemist and metallurgist in the American colonies.

The selections that follow begin with William Gilbert, a contemporary of Francis Bacon and a brilliant exponent of Bacon's faith in the value of experimentation. Galileo represents the new scientific movement as it was developing in Italy. His work, like that of Torricelli, was among the earliest to receive the attention of the Royal Society. Blaise Pascal, often the host of a French group similar to the invisible college, frequently entertained visitors from the Royal Society. Christian Huygens had close contacts with London and Paris which gave him a place where his theories could be discussed and his inventions tested.

The readings cover a wide range of topics basic to the future development of science in those areas in which, unlike astronomy and mathematics, little development had yet taken place. Ptolemy had established a workable system to describe the universe, but little had been done to observe the nature of gases, to explain the behavior of light, or to put the science of mechanics upon a sound basis. The investigators here represented were not aware that they were working in areas in which the phenomena were manifestations of the infinitely small in nature—quanta, electrons, atoms, and molecules—although some of them unquestionably were influenced by a revival of atomistic thinking. Here we see the pioneering efforts in these important directions.

*". . . in the discovery of secret things and in the
investigation of hidden causes, stronger reasons are obtained
from sure experiments and demonstrated arguments than
from probable conjectures and the opinions
of philosophical speculators."*

William Gilbert

1544 – 1603

THE SCIENCE OF MAGNETISM AND
ELECTRICITY IS INITIATED

While Francis Bacon (see page 36) was developing his
ideas about the virtues of the experimental method, William
Gilbert was actually laying its foundations by intensive experimentation. Gilbert's researches began in medicine, in which he
was distinguished enough to be a member of the committee appointed to prepare a pharmacopoeia (published in 1618, after
his death) and to be Court Physician to Queen Elizabeth I.

Gilbert's major work, *De Magnete* (from which this selection has been taken, translated by E. F. Mottelay), published
in 1600, did more than show the usefulness of experiment; it
established magnetism and electricity as sciences, influencing
thought on these subjects down to the time of Michael Faraday
(1791-1867). The magnetic needle, which was invented by the
Chinese in the eleventh century and introduced to Western navigation by Mediterranean sailors in the twelfth century, may have
stimulated Gilbert's inquiries and experiments. He had first to
overcome the superstitions which were associated with the lode-
stone and provide a reasonable explanation for magnetic phe-

nomena. He detected the poles of a magnet and discovered the magnetic field of force. From these ideas and his experiments with a spherical magnet (a *terella*), Gilbert arrived at the hypothesis that the earth itself is a gigantic magnet, a hypothesis which would explain the tendency of the compass needle to turn toward the north. In some of this work, Gilbert was, in fact, reviving some thirteenth-century studies of Peter Peregrinus, who described the "poles" of strongest attraction which attracted needles. Moreover, in his application of these ideas to explain the planetary motions, Gilbert followed the general theories of Giordano Bruno (*c.* 1548-1600).

Gilbert distinguished between electricity and magnetism, but his explanation was inaccurate and took him into metaphysics; for him electricity was a force binding the particles of matter together. He made many experiments based on a fact which had been observed even in antiquity: that when a piece of amber was rubbed in the proper way it developed the power to attract objects to it. Thus Gilbert introduced the word *electricity* into our language (from the Greek word meaning amber). He observed the differences between what we now call conductors and insulators, though he got no farther than describing the two types of material as *electrics* and *non-electrics*.

Gilbert accepted the Copernican theory and tried to explain the rotation of the earth as the result of its magnetic character. However, it is as an experimenter that we read Gilbert today, impressed by his great skill and imagination.

MAGNETISM AND ELECTRICITY

The Loadstone Possesses Parts Differing In Their Natural Powers, And Has Poles Conspicuous For Their Properties

THE MANY QUALITIES exhibited by the loadstone itself, qualities hitherto recognized yet not well investigated, are to be pointed out in the first place, to the end the student may understand the powers of the loadstone and of iron, and not be confused through want of knowledge at the threshold of the arguments and demonstrations. In the heavens, astronomers give to each moving sphere two poles; thus do we find two natural poles of excelling importance even in our terrestrial globe, constant points related to the movement of its daily revolution, to wit, one pole pointing to Arctos (Ursa) and the north; the other looking toward the opposite part of the heavens. In like manner the loadstone has from nature its two poles, a northern and a southern; fixed, definite points in the stone, which are the primary termini of the movements and effects, and the limits and regulators of the several actions and properties. It is to be understood, however, that not from a mathematical point does the force of the stone emanate, but from the parts themselves; and all these parts in the whole—while they belong to the whole—the nearer they are to the poles of the stone, the stronger virtues do they acquire and pour out on other bodies. These poles look toward the poles of the earth, and move toward them, and are subject to them. The magnetic poles may be found in every loadstone, whether strong and powerful (male, as the term was in antiquity) or faint, weak, and female; whether its shape is due to design or to chance, and whether it be long, or flat, or four-square, or three-cornered, or polished; whether it be rough, broken-off, or unpolished: the loadstone ever has and ever shows its pole. . . .

One Loadstone Appears To Attract Another In The Natural Position; But In The Opposite Position Repels It And Brings It To Rights

First we have to describe in popular language the potent and familiar properties of the stone; afterward, very many subtle properties, as yet recondite and unknown, being involved in obscurities, are to be unfolded; and the causes of all these (nature's secrets being unlocked) are in their place to be demonstrated in fitting words and with the aid of apparatus. The fact is trite and familiar, that the loadstone attracts iron; in the same way, too, one loadstone attracts another. Take the stone on which you have designated the poles, *N.* and *S.*, and put it in its vessel so that it may float; let the poles lie just in the plane of the horizon, or at least in a plane not very oblique to it; take in your hand another stone the poles of which are also known, and hold it so that its south pole shall lie toward the north pole of the floating stone, and near it alongside; the floating loadstone will straightway follow the other (provided it be within the range and dominion of its powers), nor does it cease to move nor does it quit the other till it clings to it, unless by moving your hand away, you manage skilfully to prevent the conjunction.

In like manner, if you oppose the north pole of the stone in your hand to the south pole of the floating one, they come together and follow each other. For opposite poles attract opposite poles. But, now, if in the same way you present N. to N. or S. to S., one stone repels the other; and as though a helmsman were bearing on the rudder it is off like a vessel making all sail, nor stands nor stays as long as the other stone pursues. One stone also will range the other, turn the other around, bring it to right about and make it come to agreement with itself. But when the two come together and are conjoined in nature's order, they cohere firmly. For example, if you present the north pole of the stone in your hand to . . . any point between the equator and the south pole: immediately the floating stone turns round and so places itself that its south pole touches the north pole of the other and is most closely joined to it.

In the same way you will get like effect at the other side of the equator by presenting pole to pole; and thus by art and contrivance we exhibit attraction and repulsion, and motion in a circle toward the concordant position, and the same movements to avoid hostile meetings. Furthermore, in one same stone we are thus able to demonstrate all this: but also we are able to show how the self-same part of one stone may by division become either north or south. Take the oblong stone ad in which a is the north pole and d the south. Cut the stone in two equal parts, and put part a in a vessel and let it float in water.

You will find that a, the north point, will turn to the south [1] as before; and in like manner the point d will move to the north, in the divided stone, as before division. But b and c, before connected, now separated from each other, are not what they were before. b is now south while c is north. b attracts c, longing for union and for restoration of the original continuity. They are two stones made out of one, and on that account the c of one turning toward the b of the other, they are mutually attracted, and being freed from all impediments and from their own weight, borne as they are on the surface of the water, they come together and into conjunction. But if you

[1] Today we name the poles the other way. The "north pole" of a magnet is the "north-seeking" pole.

bring the part or point *a* up to *c* of the other, they repel one another and turn away; for by such a position of the parts nature is crossed and the form of the stone is perverted: but nature observes strictly the laws it has imposed upon bodies: hence the flight of one part from the undue position of the other, and hence the discord unless everything is arranged exactly according to nature. And nature will not suffer an unjust and inequitable peace, or agreement, but makes war and employs force to make bodies acquiesce fairly and justly. Hence, when rightly arranged the parts attract each other, i.e., both stones, the weaker and the stronger, come together and with all their might tend to union: a fact manifest in all loadstones, and not, as Pliny supposed, only in those from Ethiopia.

The Ethiopic stones if strong, and those brought from China, which are all powerful stones, show the effect most quickly and most plainly, attract with most force in the parts nighest the pole, and keep turning till pole looks straight on pole. The pole of a stone has strongest attraction for that part of another stone which answers to it (the *adverse* as it is called); e.g., the north pole of one has strongest attraction for, has the most vigorous pull on, the south part of another; so too it attracts iron more powerfully, and iron clings to it more firmly, whether previously magnetized or not. Thus it has been settled by nature, not without reason, that the parts nigher the pole shall have the greatest attractive force; and that in the pole itself shall be the seat, the throne as it were, of a high and splendid power; and that magnetic bodies brought near thereto shall be attracted most powerfully and relinquished with most reluctance. So, too, the poles are readiest to spurn and drive away what is presented to them amiss, and what is inconformable and foreign. . . .

Of Magnetic Coition; And, First, Of The Attraction Exerted By Amber, or More Properly The Attachment of Bodies to Amber

Great has ever been the fame of the loadstone and of amber in the writings of the learned: many philosophers cite the loadstone and also amber whenever, in explaining mysteries, their minds become obfuscated and reason can no farther go. Over-inquisitive theologians, too, seek to light up God's mysteries and things beyond man's understanding by means of the loadstone as a sort of Delphic sword and as an illustration of all sorts of things. Medical men also (at the bidding of Galen), in proving that purgative medicines exercise attraction through likeness of substance and kinships of juices (a silly error and gratuitous!), bring in as a witness the loadstone, a substance of great authority and of noteworthy efficiency, and a body of no common order.

Thus in very many affairs persons who plead for a cause the merits of which they cannot set forth, bring in as masked advocates the loadstone and amber. But all these, besides sharing the general misapprehension, are ignorant that the causes of the loadstone's movements are very different from those which give to amber its properties; hence they easily fall into errors, and by their own imaginings are led farther and farther astray. For in other bodies is seen a considerable power of attraction, differing from that of the loadstone,—in amber, for example. Of this substance a few words must be said, to show the nature of the attachment of bodies to it, and to point out the vast difference between this and the magnetic actions; for men still continue in ignorance, and deem that inclination of bodies to amber to be an attraction, and comparable to the magnetic coition. . . .

The ancients as well as moderns tell (and their report is confirmed by experience) that amber attracts straws and chaff. The same is done by jet, a stone taken out of the earth in Britain, Germany, and many other regions: it is a hard concretion of black bitumen—a sort of transformation of bitumen to stone. Many modern authors have written about amber and jet as attracting chaff and about other facts unknown to the generality, or have copied from other writers; with the results of their labors booksellers' shops are crammed full. Our generation has produced many volumes about recondite, abstruse, and occult causes and wonders, and in all of them amber and jet are represented as attracting chaff; but never a proof from experiments, never a demonstration do you find in them. The writers deal only in words that involve in thicker darkness subject-matter; they treat the subject esoterically, miracle-mongeringly, abstrusely, reconditely, mystically.

Hence such philosophy bears no fruit; for it rests simply on a few Greek or unusual terms—just as our barbers toss off a few Latin words in the hearing of the ignorant rabble in token of their learning, and thus win reputation—bears no fruit, because few of the philosophers themselves are investigators, or have any first-hand acquaintance with things; most of them are indolent and untrained, add nothing to knowledge by their writings, and are blind to the things that might throw a light upon their reasonings. For not only do amber and jet, as they suppose attract light

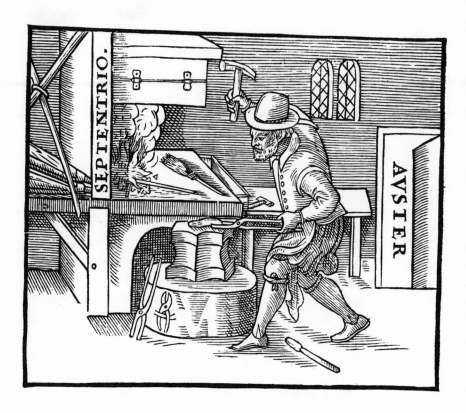

A blacksmith pounds a glowing iron bar which is held so that its ends point north *(septentrio)* and south *(auster)*. In this way the bar is magnetized. From William Gilbert's *De Magnete,* London, 1600. (Courtesy of the Burndy Library.)

substances: the same is done by diamond, sapphire, carbuncle, iris stone, opal, amethyst, vincentina, Bristol stone, beryl, rock crystal. Like powers of attracting are possessed by glass, especially clear, brilliant glass; by artificial gems made of (paste) glass or rock crystal, antimony glass, many fluor-spars, and belemnites. Sulphur also attracts, and likewise mastich, and sealing-wax (of lac), hard resin, orpiment (weakly). Feeble power of attraction is also possessed in favoring dry atmosphere by sal gemma [native chloride of sodium], mica, rock alum. This we may observe when in mid-winter the atmosphere is very cold, clear, and thin; when the electrical effluvia of the earth offers less impediment, and electric bodies are harder: of all this later. These several bodies (electric) not only draw to themselves straws and chaff, but all metals, wood, leaves, stones, earths, even water and oil; in short, whatever things appeal to our senses or are solid: yet we are told that it attracts nothing but chaff and twigs. Hence Alexander Aphrodiseus incorrectly declares the question of amber to be unsolvable, because that amber does attract chaff, yet not the leaves of basil; but such stories are false, disgracefully inaccurate.

Now in order clearly to understand by experience how such attraction takes place, and what those substances may be that so attract other bodies (and in the case of many of these electrical substances, though the bodies influenced by them lean toward them, yet because of the feebleness of the attraction they are not drawn clean up to them, but are easily made to rise), make yourself a rotating-needle (electroscope—*versorium*) (See fig.), of any sort of metal, three or four fingers long, pretty light, and poised on a sharp point after the manner of a magnetic pointer. Bring near to one end of it a piece of amber or a gem, lightly rubbed, polished and shining: at once the instrument revolves. Several objects are seen to attract not only natural objects, but things artificially prepared, or manufactured, or formed by mixture. Nor is this a rare property possessed by one object or two (as is commonly supposed), but evidently belongs to a multitude of objects, both simple and compound, e.g., sealing-wax and other unctuous mixtures. But why this inclination and what these forces,—on which points a few writers have given a very small amount of information, while the common run of philosophers give us nothing—these questions must be considered fully. . . .

*"The works I have to finish are chiefly: . . .
three books on local motion, a science entirely new,
no one, ancient or modern, having discovered any of the many
admirable consequences which I demonstrate in natural
and violent motions, so that I may with reason
call it a new science invented by me from
its very first principles. . . ."*

Galileo Galilei

1564 – 1642

THE LAWS OF ACCELERATION AND OF
FALLING BODIES ARE ESTABLISHED

We have already dealt with the facts of Galileo's life (see
page 240). The present selection from the *Dialogues Concerning
Two New Sciences* (translated by Henry Crew and A. DeSalvio
in 1914) describes one of Galileo's most important contributions to modern science—his work in mechanics. To understand
the significance of his discovery, we must first consider the system
which he replaced.

Until the time of Galileo, the Western world accepted the
Aristotelian mechanical theory. All matter consisted of a combination of two or more of the four elements: earth, air, water,
and fire. Every element possessed a tendency to move toward its
natural place: air and fire upward and water and earth downward.
The element which was most abundant in any object would determine the direction of its natural movement. Fire added to water
produces steam; fire dominates; therefore steam rises. On the
other hand, if fire is withdrawn from steam, water regains its

dominance and the movement becomes downward. Similarly, the speed of motion is proportionate to the amount of the dominant element; and, clearly, a heavy object will fall faster than a lighter one.

This neat explanation could easily have been shown to be contrary to observation; but it must be remembered that, absurd as it may appear to us, this mechanical theory formed part of an integrated scheme and, so long as it was left alone, it served the purpose of the times. Experiments spelled danger, because even if only a small part of that structure were damaged, the whole might topple over. Galileo's attacks on the structure were at two levels: the explanation of the universe and the analysis of the minor phenomena of life about which men were, in general, not yet very curious.

In recalling Galileo's experiments demonstrating that bodies fall with velocities which increase regularly with the time of the fall, we must remember that Galileo lacked any means of recording the minute fractions of time involved. His experiments with vertically falling bodies (such as the legendary tests made from the Leaning Tower at Pisa) could not properly be verified. Resorting to inclined planes, Galileo found that he could obtain the same data by observing the time taken by a brass sphere to roll down a groove designed to minimize friction. To measure the short intervals of time fairly accurately, or rather to discover the relationship between the time intervals, Galileo weighed the quantities of water which escaped from a hole in a container during the various movements of the ball; a masterpiece of laboratory improvisation.

Galileo was also able to show that a body would, in the absence of friction, continue in motion after the force which provided it was withdrawn. This principle was afterwards developed by Newton in his first law of motion.

It will be noted in the selection that Simplicius, the anti-Copernican, appears to be out of his depth for he intervenes in the discussion hardly at all. Here was less meat for controversy than in the discussions about the mechanics of the universe.

NATURALLY ACCELERATED MOTION

SAGR. Although I can offer no rational objection to this or indeed to any other definition, devised by any author whomsoever, since all definitions are arbitrary, I may nevertheless without offense be allowed to doubt whether such a definition as the above, established in an abstract manner, corresponds to and describes that kind of accelerated motion which we meet in nature in the case of freely falling bodies. And since the Author apparently maintains that the motion described in his definition is that of freely falling bodies, I would like to clear my mind of certain difficulties in order that I may later apply myself more earnestly to the propositions and their demonstrations.

SALV. It is well that you and Simplicio raise these difficulties. They are, I imagine, the same which occurred to me when I first saw this treatise, and which were removed either by discussion with the Author himself, or by turning the matter over in my own mind.

SAGR. When I think of a heavy body falling from rest, that is, starting with zero speed and gaining speed in proportion to the time from the beginning of the motion; such a motion as would, for instance, in eight beats of the pulse acquire eight degrees of speed; having at the end of the fourth beat acquired four degrees; at the end of the second, two; at the end of the first, one: and since time is divisible without limit, it follows from all these considerations that if the earlier speed of a body is less than its present speed in a constant ratio, then there is no degree of speed however small (or, one may say, no degree of slowness however great) with which we may not find this body travelling after starting from infinite slowness, i. e., from rest. So that if that speed which it had at the end of the fourth beat was such that, if kept uniform, the body would traverse two miles in an hour, and if keeping the speed which it had at the end of the second beat, it would traverse one mile an hour, we must infer that, as the instant of starting is more and more nearly approached, the body moves so slowly that, if it kept on moving at this rate, it would not traverse a mile in an hour, or in a day, or in a year or in a thousand years; indeed, it would not traverse a span in an even greater time; a phenomenon which baffles the imagination, while our senses show us that a heavy falling body suddenly acquires great speed.

SALV. This is one of the difficulties which I also at the beginning, experienced, but which I shortly afterwards removed; and the removal was effected by the very experiment which creates the difficulty for you. You say the experiment appears to show that immediately after a heavy body starts from rest it acquires a very considerable speed: and I say that the same experiment makes clear the fact that the initial motions of a falling body, no matter how heavy, are very slow and gentle. Place a heavy body upon a yielding material, and leave it there without any pressure except that owing to its own weight; it is clear that if one lifts this body a cubit or two and allows it to fall upon the same material, it will, with this impulse, exert a new and greater pressure than that caused by its mere weight; and this effect is brought about by the [weight of the] falling body together with the velocity acquired during the fall, an effect which will be greater and greater according to the height of the fall, that is according as the velocity of the falling body becomes greater. From the quality and intensity of the blow we are thus enabled to accurately estimate the speed of a falling body. But tell me, gentlemen, is it not true that if a block be allowed to fall upon a stake from a height of four cubits and drives it into the earth, say, four finger-breadths, that coming from a height of two cubits it will drive the stake a much less distance, and from the height of one cubit a still less distance; and finally if the block be lifted only one finger-breadth how much more will it accomplish than if merely laid on top of the stake without percussion? Certainly very little. If it be lifted only the thickness of a leaf, the effect will be altogether imperceptible. And since the effect of the blow depends upon the velocity of this striking body, can any one doubt the motion is very slow and the speed more than small whenever the effect [of the blow] is imperceptible? See now the power of truth; the same experiment which at first glance seemed to show one thing, when more carefully examined, assures us of the contrary.

But without depending upon the above experiment, which is doubt-less very conclusive, it seems to me that it ought not to be difficult to estab-lish such a fact by reasoning alone. Imagine a heavy stone held in the air at rest; the support is removed and the stone set free; then since it is heavier than the air it begins to fall, and not with uniform motion but slowly at the beginning and with a continuously accelerated motion. Now since velocity can be increased and diminished without limit, what reason is there to believe that such a moving body starting with infinite slowness, that is, from rest, immediately acquires a speed of ten degrees rather than one of four, or of two, or of one, or of a half, or of a hundredth; or, indeed, of any of the infinite number of small values [of speed]? Pray listen. I hardly think you will refuse to grant that the gain of speed of the stone falling from rest follows the same sequence as the diminution and loss of this same speed when, by some impelling force, the stone is thrown to its former elevation: but even if you do not grant this, I do not see how you can doubt that the ascending stone, diminishing in speed, must before coming to rest pass through every possible degree of slowness.

SIMP. But if the number of degrees of greater and greater slowness is limitless, they will never be all exhausted, therefore such an ascending heavy body will never reach rest, but will continue to move without limit always at a slower rate; but this is not the observed fact.

SALV. This would happen, Simplicio, if the moving body were to maintain its speed for any length of time at each degree of velocity; but it merely passes each point without delaying more than an instant: and since each time-interval however small may be divided into an infinite number of instants, these will always be sufficient [in number] to correspond to the infinite degrees of diminished velocity.

That such a heavy rising body does not remain for any length of time at any given degree of velocity is evident from the following: because if, some time-interval having been assigned, the body moves with the same speed in the last as in the first instant of that time-interval, it could from this second degree of elevation be in like manner raised through an equal height, just as it was transferred from the first elevation to the second, and by the same reasoning would pass from the second to the third and would finally continue in uniform motion forever.

SAGR. From these considerations it appears to me that we may obtain a proper solution of the problem discussed by philosophers, namely, what causes the acceleration in the natural motion of heavy bodies? Since, as it seems to me, the force [virtù] impressed by the agent projecting the body upwards diminishes continuously, this force, so long as it was greater than the contrary force of gravitation, impelled the body upwards; when the two are in equilibrium the body ceases to rise and passes through the state of rest in which the impressed impetus [impeto] is not destroyed, but only its excess over the weight of the body has been consumed—the excess which caused the body to rise. Then as the diminution of the outside impetus [impeto] continues, and gravitation gains the upper hand, the fall begins, but slowly at first on account of the opposing impetus [*virtù impressa*], a large portion of which still remains in the body; but as this continues to diminish it also continues to be more and more overcome by gravity, hence the continuous acceleration of motion.

SIMP. The idea is clever, yet more subtle than sound; for even if the argument were conclusive, it would explain only the case in which a natural motion is preceded by a violent motion, in which there still remains active a portion of the external force [*virtù esterna*]; but where there is no such remaining portion and the body starts from an antecedent state of rest, the cogency of the whole argument fails.

SAGR. I believe that you are mistaken and that this distinction between cases which you make is superfluous or rather non-existent. But, tell me, cannot a projectile receive from the projector either a large or a small force [*virtù*] such as will throw it to a height of a hundred cubits, and even twenty or four or one?

SIMP. Undoubtedly, yes.

SAGR. So therefore this impressed force [*virtù impressa*] may exceed the resistance of gravity so slightly as to raise it only a finger-breadth; and finally the force [*virtù*] of the projector may be just large enough to exactly balance the resistance of gravity so that the body is not lifted at all but merely sustained. When one holds a stone in his hand does he do anything but give it a force impelling [*virtù impellente*] it upwards equal to the power [*facoltà*] of gravity drawing it downwards? And do you not continuously impress this force [*virtù*] upon the stone as long as you hold it in the hand? Does it perhaps diminish with the time during which one holds the stone?

And what does it matter whether this support which prevents the stone from falling is furnished by one's hand or by a table or by a rope from which it hangs? Certainly nothing at all. You must conclude, therefore, Simplicio, that it makes no difference whatever whether the fall of the stone is preceded by a period of rest which is long, short, or instantaneous provided only the fall does not take place so long as the stone is acted upon by a force [*virtù*] opposed to its weight and sufficient to hold it at rest.

SALV. The present does not seem to be the proper time to investigate the cause of the acceleration of natural motion concerning which various opinions have been expressed by various philosophers, some explaining it by attraction to the center, others to repulsion between the very small parts of the body, while still others attribute it to a certain stress in the surrounding medium which closes in behind the falling body and drives it from one of its positions to another. Now, all these fantasies, and others too, ought to be examined; but it is not really worth while. At present it is the purpose of our Author merely to investigate and to demonstrate some of the properties of accelerated motion (whatever the cause of this acceleration may be)—meaning thereby a motion, such that the momentum of its velocity [*i momenti della sua velocità*] goes on increasing after departure from rest, in simple proportionality to the time, which is the same as saying that in equal time-intervals the body receives equal increments of velocity; and if we find the properties [of accelerated motion] which will be demonstrated later are realized in freely falling and accelerated bodies, we may conclude that the assumed definition includes such a motion of falling bodies and that their speed [*accelerazione*] goes on increasing as the time and the duration of the motion.

SAGR. So far as I see at present, the definition might have been put a little more clearly perhaps without changing the fundamental idea, namely, uniformly accelerated motion is such that its speed increases in proportion to the space traversed; so that, for example, the speed acquired by a body in falling four cubits would be double that acquired in falling two cubits and this latter speed would be double that acquired in the first cubit. Because there is no doubt but that a heavy body falling from the height of six cubits has, and strikes with, a momentum [*impeto*] double that it had at the end of three cubits, triple that which it had at the end of one.

SALV. It is very comforting to me to have had such a companion in error; and moreover let me tell you that your proposition seems so highly probable that our Author himself admitted, when I advanced this opinion to him, that he had for some time shared the same fallacy. But what most surprised me was to see two propositions so inherently probable that they commanded the assent of everyone to whom they were presented, proven in a few simple words to be not only false, but impossible.

SIMP. I am one of those who accept the propositon, and believe that a falling body acquires force [*vires*] in its descent, its velocity increasing in proportion to the space, and that the momentum [*momento*] of the falling body is doubled when it falls from a doubled height; these propositions, it appears to me, ought to be conceded without hesitation or controversy.

SALV. And yet they are as false and impossible as that motion should be completed instantaneously; and here is a very clear demonstration of it. If the velocities are in proportion to the spaces traversed, or to be traversed, then these spaces are traversed in equal intervals of time; if, therefore, the velocity with which the falling body traverses a space of eight feet were double that with which it covered the first four feet (just as the one distance is double the other) then the time-intervals required for these passages would be equal. But for one and the same body to fall eight feet and four feet in the same time is possible only in the case of instantaneous [discontinuous] motion; but observation shows us that the motion of a falling body occupies time, and less of it in covering a distance of four feet than of eight feet; therefore it is not true that its velocity increases in proportion to the space.

The falsity of the other proposition may be shown with equal clearness. For if we consider a single striking body the difference of momentum in its blows can depend only upon difference of velocity; for if the striking body falling from a double height were to deliver a blow of double momentum, it would be necessary for this body to strike with a doubled velocity; but with this doubled speed it would traverse a doubled space in the same time-interval; observation however shows that the time required for fall from the greater height is longer.

SAGR. You present these recondite matters with too much evidence and ease; this great facility makes them less appreciated than they would be had they been presented in a more abstruse manner. For, in my opinion, people esteem more lightly that knowledge which they acquire with so little labor than that acquired through long and obscure discussion.

SALV. If those who demonstrate with brevity and clearness the fallacy of many popular beliefs were treated with contempt instead of gratitude the injury would be quite bearable; but on the other hand it is very unpleasant and annoying to see men, who claim to be peers of anyone in a certain field of study, take for granted certain conclusions which later are quickly and easily shown by another to be false. I do not describe such a feeling as one of envy, which usually degenerates into hatred and anger against those who discover such fallacies; I would call it a strong desire to maintain old errors, rather than accept newly discovered truths. This desire at times induces them to unite against these truths, although at heart believing in them, merely for the purpose of lowering the esteem in which certain others are held by the unthinking crowd. Indeed, I have heard from our Academician many such fallacies held as true but easily refutable; some of these I have in mind.

SAGR. You must not withhold them from us, but, at the proper time, tell us about them even though an extra session be necessary. But now, continuing the thread of our talk, it would seem that up to the present we have established the definition of uniformly accelerated motion which is expressed as follows:

> A motion is said to be equally or uniformly accelerated when, starting from rest, its momentum (*celeritatis momenta*) receives equal increments in equal times.

SALV. This definition established, the Author makes a single assumption, namely,

> The speeds acquired by one and the same body moving down planes of different inclinations are equal when the heights of these planes are equal.

By the height of an inclined plane we mean the perpendicular let fall from the upper end of the plane upon the horizontal line drawn through the lower end of the same plane. Thus, to illustrate, let the line AB be horizontal, and let the planes CA and CD be inclined to it; then the Author calls the perpendicular CB the "height" of the planes CA and CD; he supposes that the speeds acquired by one and the same body, descending along the planes CA and CD to the terminal points A and D are equal since the heights of these planes are the same, CB; and also it must be understood that this speed is that which would be acquired by the same body falling from C to B.

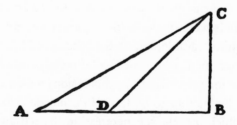

SAGR. Your assumption appears to me so reasonable that it ought to be conceded without question, provided of course there are no chance or outside resistances, and that the planes are hard and smooth, and that the figure of the moving body is perfectly round, so that neither plane nor moving body is rough. All resistance and opposition having been removed, my reason tells me at once that a heavy and perfectly round ball descending along the lines CA, CD, CB would reach the terminal points A, D, B, with equal momenta [*impeti eguali*].

SALV. Your words are very plausible; but I hope by experiment to increase the probability to an extent which shall be little short of a rigid demonstration.

Imagine this page to represent a vertical wall, with a nail driven into it; and from the nail let there be suspended a lead bullet of one or two ounces by means of a fine vertical thread, AB, say from four to six feet long, on this wall draw a horizontal line DC, at right angles to the vertical thread AB, which hangs about two finger-breadths in front of the wall. Now bring the thread AB with the attached ball into the position AC and set it free; first it will be observed to descend along the arc CBD, to pass the point B, and to travel along the arc BD, till it almost reaches the horizontal CD, a slight shortage being caused by the resistance of the air and the string; from this we may rightly infer that the ball in its descent through the arc CB acquired a momentum [*impeto*] on reaching B, which was just sufficient to carry it through a similar arc BD to the same height. Having repeated this experiment many times, let us now drive a nail into the wall close to the perpendicular AB, say at E or F, so that it projects out some five or six finger-breadths in order that the thread, again carrying the bullet through the arc CB, may strike upon the nail E when the bullet reaches B, and thus compel it to traverse the arc BG, described about E as center. From this we can see what can be done by the same momentum [*impeto*] which previously starting at the same point B carried the same body through the arc BD to the horizontal CD. Now, gentlemen, you will observe with pleasure that the ball swings to the point G in the horizontal, and you would see the same thing happen if the obstacle were placed at some lower point, say at F, about which the ball would describe the arc BI, the rise of the ball always terminating exactly on the line CD. But when the nail is placed so low that the remainder of the thread below it will not reach to the height CD (which would happen if the nail were placed nearer B than to the intersection of AB with the horizontal CD) then the thread leaps over the nail and twists itself about it.

This experiment leaves no room for doubt as to the truth of our supposition; for since the two arcs CB and DB are equal and similarly placed, the momentum [*momento*] acquired by the fall through the arc CB is the same as that gained by fall through the arc DB; but the momentum [*momento*] acquired at B, owing to fall through CB, is able to lift the same body [*mobile*] through the arc BD; therefore, the momentum acquired in the fall BD is equal to that which lifts the same body through the same arc from B to D; so, in general, every momentum acquired by fall through an arc is equal to that which can lift the same body through the same arc. But all these momenta [*momenti*] which cause a rise through the arcs BD, BG, and BI are equal, since they are produced by the same momentum, gained by fall through CB, as experiment shows. Therefore all the momenta gained by fall through the arcs DB, GB, IB are equal.

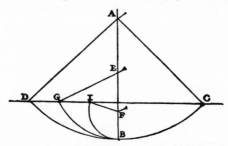

SAGR. The argument seems to me so conclusive and the experiment so well adapted to establish the hypothesis that we may, indeed, consider it as demonstrated.

SALV. I do not wish, Sagredo, that we trouble ourselves too much about this matter, since we are going to apply this principle mainly in motions which occur on plane surfaces, and not upon curved, along which acceleration varies in a manner greatly different from that which we have assumed for planes.

So that, although the above experiment shows us that the descent of the moving body through the arc CB confers upon it momentum [*momento*] just sufficient to carry it to the same height through any of the arcs BD, BG, BI, we are not able, by similar means, to show that the event would be identical in the case of a perfectly round ball descending along planes whose inclinations are respectively the same as the chords of these arcs. It seems likely, on the other hand, that, since these planes form angles at the point B, they will present an obstacle to the ball which has descended along the chord CB, and starts to rise along the chord BD, BG, BI.

In striking these planes some of its momentum [*impeto*] will be lost and it will not be able to rise to the height of the line CD; but this obstacle, which interferes with the experiment, once removed, it is clear that the momentum [*impeto*] (which gains in strength with descent) will be able to carry the body to the same height. Let us then, for the present, take this as a postulate, the absolute truth of which will be established when we find that the inferences from it correspond to and agree perfectly with experiment. The author having assumed this single principle passes next to the propositions which he clearly demonstrates; the first of these is as follows:

THEOREM I, PROPOSITION I

The time in which any space is traversed by a body starting from rest and uniformly accelerated is equal to the time in which that same space would be traversed by the same body moving at a uniform speed whose value is the mean of the highest speed and the speed just before acceleration began.

Let us represent by the line AB the time in which the space CD is traversed by a body which starts from rest at C and is uniformly accelerated; let the final and highest value of the speed gained during the interval AB be represented by the line EB drawn at right angles to AB; draw the line AE, then all lines drawn from equidistant points on AB and parallel to BE will represent the increasing values of the speed, beginning with the instant A. Let the point F bisect the line EB; draw FG parallel to BA, and GA parallel to FB, thus forming a parallelogram AGFB which will be equal in area to the triangle AEB, since the side GF bisects the side AE at the point I; for if the parallel lines in the triangle AEB are extended to GI, then the sum of all the parallels contained in the quadrilateral is equal to the sum of those contained in the triangle AEB; for those in the triangle IEF are equal to those contained in the triangle GIA, while those included in the trapezium AIFB are common. Since each and every instant of time in the time-interval AB has its corresponding point on the line AB, from which points parallels drawn in and limited by the triangle AEB represent the increasing values of the growing velocity, and since parallels contained within the rectangle represent the values of a speed which is not increasing, but constant, it appears, in like manner, that the momenta [*momenta*] assumed by the moving body may also be represented, in the case of the accelerated motion, by the increasing parallels of the triangle AEB, and, in the case of the uniform motion, by the parallels of the rectangle GB. For, what the momenta may lack in the first part of the accelerated motion (the deficiency of the momenta being represented by the parallels of the triangle AGI) is made up by the momenta represented by the parallels of the triangle IEF.

Hence it is clear that equal spaces will be traversed in equal times by two bodies, one of which, starting from rest, moves with a uniform acceleration, while the momentum of the other, moving with uniform speed, is one-half its maximum momentum under accelerated motion.   Q. E. D.

THEOREM II, PROPOSITION II

The spaces described by a body falling from rest with a uniformly accelerated motion are to each other as the squares of the time-intervals employed in traversing these distances.

Let the time beginning with any instant A be represented by the straight line AB in which are taken any two time-intervals AD and AE. Let HI represent the distance through which the body, starting from rest at H, falls with uniform acceleration. If HL represents the space traversed during the time-interval AD, and HM that covered during the interval AE, then the space MH stands to the space LH in a ratio which is the square of the ratio of the time AE to the time AD; or we may say simply that the distances HM and HL are related as the squares of AE and AD.

Draw the line AC making any angle whatever with the line AB; and from the points D and E, draw the parallel lines DO and EP; of these two lines, DO represents the greatest velocity attained during the interval AD, while EP represents the maximum velocity acquired during the interval AE. But it has just been proved that so far as distances traversed are concerned it is precisely the same whether a body falls from rest with a uniform acceleration or whether it falls during an equal time-interval with a constant speed which is one-half the maximum speed attained during the accelerated motion. It follows therefore that the distances HM and HL are the same as would be traversed, during the time-intervals AE and AD, by uniform velocities equal to one-half those represented by DO and EP respectively. If, therefore, one can show that the distances HM and HL are in the same ratio as the squares of the time-intervals AE and AD, our proposition will be proven.

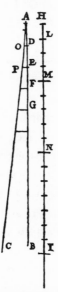

But in the fourth proposition of the first book . . . it has been shown that the spaces traversed by two particles in uniform motion bear to one another a ratio which is equal to the product of the ratio of the velocities by the ratio of the times. But in this case the ratio of the velocities is the same as the ratio of the time-intervals (for the ratio of AE to AD is the same as that of ½ EP to ½ DO or of EP to DO). Hence the ratio of the spaces traversed is the same as the squared ratio of the time-intervals. Q. E. D.

Evidently then the ratio of the distances is the square of the ratio of the final velocities, that is, of the lines EP and DO, since these are to each other as AE to AD.

*"We live submerged in the bottom of an ocean
of air which, by experiment, undoubtedly has weight, with
greatest density near the surface of the earth."*

Evangelista Torricelli

1608 – 1647

THE INVENTION OF THE BAROMETER IS
DESCRIBED AND ITS OPERATION
EXPLAINED

When Galileo found that his water pump would not raise
water above the height of 32 feet, he did not ask why; he explained the fact by saying that the column of water broke under
its own weight. His disciple, Torricelli, who is known also for
his improvements to the microscope and telescope, began experiments which led to a new understanding of atmospheric pressure.
As will be seen from the selection, he made his discovery in connection with his search for "a plainly apparent cause for the resistance which is felt when one needs to produce a vacuum."

The 46-inch glass tubes that were made by Torricelli and
his colleague, Viviani, in 1643, reflect the advance of the craft
of glass-making in Italy at the period. It is unlikely that such
tubes could have been produced anywhere else in Europe. Filling such a tube with mercury and inserting its open end into a
bowl of mercury, Torricelli found that a column of some 30
inches of mercury was supported in the tube not, as he pointed
out, by the vacuum inside, as was previously thought, but by an
external force. This remark, incidentally, suggests that other
people had performed the experiment but had not realized, as

Torricelli did, that there was a relation between the height of the column of mercury and that of a column of water in a similar but longer tube.

It was Blaise Pascal who discovered the significance of Torricelli's experiment to the measurement of variations in the pressure of the atmosphere. Torricelli himself was interested in the vacuum he created at the head of his tube, using it for experiments in the transmission of light, sound, and magnetic forces.

This selection has been taken from *The Physical Treatises of Pascal,* translated by I. H. B. and A. G. H. Spiers (Columbia, 1937).

ON THE PRESSURE OF THE ATMOSPHERE

LETTER FROM TORRICELLI TO MICHELANGELO RICCI

Florence, June 11, 1644

My most illustrious Sir and most cherished Master:

Several weeks ago I sent some demonstrations of mine on the area of the cycloid to Signor Antonio Nardi, entreating him to send them directly to you or to Signor Magiotti after he had seen them. I have already intimated to you that a certain physical experiment was being performed on the vacuum; not simply to produce a vacuum, but to make an instrument which would show the changes in the air, which is at times heavier and thicker and at times lighter and more rarefied. Many have said that a vacuum cannot be produced, others that it can be produced, but with repugnance on the part of Nature and with difficulty; so far, I know of no one who has said that it can be produced without effort and without resistance on the part of Nature. I reasoned in this way: if I were to find a plainly apparent cause for the resistance which is felt when one needs to produce a vacuum, it seems to me that it would be vain to try to attribute that action, which patently derives from some other cause, to the vacuum; indeed, I find that by making certain very easy calculations, the cause I have proposed (which is the weight of air) should in itself have a greater effect than it does in the attempt to produce a vacuum. I say this because some Philosopher, seeing that he could not avoid the admission that the weight of the air causes the resistance which is felt in producing a vacuum, did not say that he admitted the effect of the weight of the air, but persisted in asserting that Nature also contributes at least to the abhorrence of a vacuum.

We live submerged at the bottom of an ocean of the element of air, which by unquestioned experiments is known to have weight, and so much, indeed, that near the surface of the earth where it is most dense it weighs [volume for volume] about the four-hundredth part of the weight of water.[1] Those who have written about twilight, moreover, have observed that the vaporous and visible air rises above us about fifty or fifty-four miles; I do not, however, believe its height is a great as this, since if it were, I could show that the vacuum would have to offer much greater resistance than it does—even though there is in their favor the argument that the weight referred to by Galileo applies to the air in very low places where men and animals live, whereas that on the tops of high mountains begins to be distinctly rare and of much less weight than the four-hundredth part of the weight of water.

We have made glass vessels like the following marked A and B with necks two cubits.[2] We filled these with quicksilver, and then, the mouths being stopped with a finger and being inverted in a basin where there was quicksilver C, they seemed to become empty and nothing happened in the vessel that was emptied; the neck AD, therefore, remained always filled to the height of a cubit and a quarter and an inch besides [29¾ inches]. To show that the vessel was perfectly empty, the underlying basin was filled with water up to D, and as the vessel was slowly raised, when its mouth reached the water, one could see the quicksilver fall from the neck, whereupon with a violent impetus the vessel was filled with water completely to the top. This experiment was performed when the vessel was empty and the quicksilver, although very heavy, was held up in the neck AD.

The force which holds up that quicksilver, against its nature to fall

---

[1] Modern computations show that the density of water is 775 times that of air, at sea level.

[2] About 46 inches.

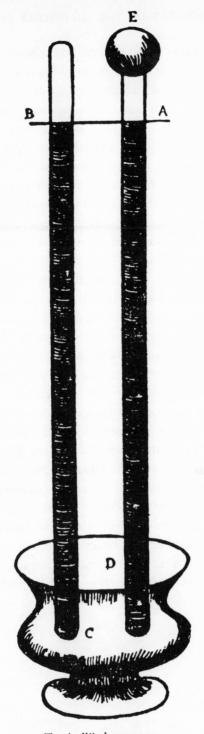

Torricelli's barometer.

down again, has been believed hitherto to be inside of the vessel, and to be due either to vacuum or to that material [mercury] highly rarefied; but I maintain that it is external and that the force comes from without. On the surface of the liquid which is in the basin, there gravitates a mass of air fifty miles high; is it therefore to be wondered at if in the glass CE, where the mercury is not attracted nor indeed repelled, since there is nothing there, it enters and rises to such an extent as to come to equilibrium with the weight of this outside air which presses upon it? Water also, in a similar but much longer vessel, will rise up to almost eighteen cubits, that is, as much further than the quicksilver rises as quicksilver is heavier than water, in order to come to equilibrium with the same force, which presses alike the one and the other.

The above conclusion was confirmed by an experiment made at the same time with a vessel A and a tube B, in which the quicksilver always came to rest at the same level, AB. This is an almost certain indication that the force was not within; because if that were so, the vessel AE would have had greater force, since within it there was more rarefied material to attract the quicksilver, and a material much more powerful than that in the very small space B, on account of its greater rarefaction.

I have since tried to consider from this point of view all the kinds of repulsions which are felt in the various effects attributed to vacuum, and thus far I have not encountered anything which does not go [to confirm my opinion]. I know that you will think up many objections, but I also hope that, as you think about them, you will overcome them. I must add that my principal intention—which was to determine with the instrument EC when the air was thicker and heavier and when it was more rarefied and light—has not been fulfilled; for the level AB changes from another cause (which I never would have believed), namely, on account of heat and cold; and changes very appreciably, exactly as if the vase AE were full of air.

"Thus it appears that a vessel full of water (or oil)
is a new principle in mechanics and a new machine which can
multiply force to any degree we choose."

Blaise Pascal

1623 — 1662

THE FACTS OF AIR PRESSURE ARE
DEMONSTRATED BY EXPERIMENT

Blaise Pascal is best remembered, perhaps, for his *Pensées,*
which were the philosophical fruit of a short but intense life. A
precocious child, Pascal was trained by the Jesuits, but afterwards
he came under the influence of the Jansenites, a sect which denied
the possibility of free will. All of his scientific work was done
before the age of 31, and the degree of his brilliance is indicated
by its variety. His development of the theory of probability, a
type of applied mathematics which was to prove of great importance in such fields as biological statistics, was, in its time,
what we should now call "a major break-through." At the age of
19, Pascal had devised and constructed an automatic machine
which helped to avoid errors in reading the recently introduced
logarithmic scales.

Pascal's studies in the equilibrium of fluids, which extended
the work of Galileo, produced the discovery that pressures exerted
by such fluids as the atmosphere were exerted equally in all directions. The laws of fluid pressures which Pascal developed
became one of the foundation stones of the science of hydro-
dynamics. He carried Torricelli's work on the barometer on to
its next logical stage. Reasoning, as we see from the following

351

selection from *The Physical Treatises,* that if air has weight, the pressure exerted by it will vary according to the amount of it, he sent his brother to the high mountains of the Puy-de-Dôme in Central France with a Torricelli barometer. The results showed that the column of mercury supported by atmospheric pressure varied with the height of the land above sea level.

The full implications of this and his other experiments with fluid pressures are clearly expressed in the quotation above. We should, perhaps, recall Pascal every time we use the hydraulic brakes in a modern automobile.

TREATISE ON THE WEIGHT OF THE MASS OF THE AIR

CHAPTER I

The Mass of the Air Has Weight, and with This Weight Presses Upon All the Bodies It Surrounds

IT IS NO LONGER open to discussion that the air has weight. It is common knowledge that a balloon is heavier when inflated than when empty, which is proof enough. For if the air were light, the more the balloon was inflated, the lighter the whole would be, since there would be more air in it. But since, on the contrary, when more air is put in, the whole becomes heavier, it follows that each part has a weight of its own, and consequently that the air has weight.

Whoever wishes for more elaborate proofs can find them in the writings of those who have devoted special treatises to the subject.

If it be objected that air is light when pure, but that the air that surrounds us is not pure, being mixed with vapor and impurities which alone give it weight, my answer is brief: I am not acquainted with "pure" air, and believe that it might be very difficult to find it. But throughout this treatise I am referring solely to the air such as we breathe, regardless of its component elements. Whether it be compound or simple, that is the body which I call the air, and which I declare to have weight. This cannot be denied, and I require nothing more for my further proof.

This principle being laid down, I will now proceed to draw from it certain consequences.

1. Since every part of the air has weight, it follows that the whole mass of the air, that is to say, the whole sphere of the air, has weight, and as the sphere of the air is not infinite in extent, but limited, neither is the weight of the whole mass of the air infinite.

2. The mass of the water of the sea presses with its weight that part of the earth which is beneath it; if it surrounded the whole earth instead of only a part, its weight would press upon the whole surface of the earth. In the same way, since the mass of the air covers the whole face of the earth, its weight presses upon the earth at every point.

3. Just as the bottom of a bucket containing water is pressed more heavily by the weight of the water when it is full than when it is half empty, and the more heavily the deeper the water is, similarly the high places of the earth, such as the summits of mountains, are less heavily pressed than the lowlands are by the weight of the mass of the air. This is because there is more air above the lowlands than above the mountain tops; for all the air along a mountain side presses upon the lowlands but not upon the summit, being above the one but below the other.

4. Bodies immersed in water are pressed on all sides by the weight of the water above them, as we have shown in the Treatise on The Equilibrium of Liquids. In the same way bodies in the air are pressed on all sides by the weight of the air above them.

5. Animals in water do not feel its weight; neither do we the weight of the air and for the same reason. Just as it would be a mistake to infer that, because we do not feel the weight of the water when immersed in it, water has no weight; so it would be a mistake to infer that air has no weight because we do not feel its pressure. We have shown the reason of this in the Treatise on The Equilibrium of Liquids.

6. If there were collected a great bulk of wool, say twenty or thirty fathoms high, this mass would be compressed by its own weight; the bottom layers would be far more compressed than the middle or top layers, because they are pressed by a greater quantity of wool. Similarly the mass of the air, which is a compressible and heavy body like wool, is compressed by its own weight, and the air at the bottom, in the lowlands, is far more compressed than the higher layers on the mountain tops, because it bears a greater load of air.

7. In the case of that bulk of wool, if a handful of it were taken from the bottom layer, compressed as it it, and lifted, in the same state of compression, to the middle of the mass, it would expand of its own accord; for it would then be nearer the top and subjected there to the pressure of a smaller quantity of wool. Similarly if a body of air, as found here below in its natural state of compression, were by some device transferred to a mountain top, it would necessarily expand and come to the condition of the air around it on the mountain; for then it would bear a lesser weight of air than it did below. Hence if a balloon, only half inflated—not fully so, as they generally are—were carried up a mountain, it would necessarily be more inflated at the mountain top, and would expand in the degree to which it was less burdened. The difference will be visible, provided the quantity of air along the mountain slope, from the pressure of which it is now relieved, has a weight great enough to cause a sensible effect.

There is so necessary a bond between these consequences and their principle that if the principle is true the consequences will be true also. Since, therefore, it is acknowledged that the air, reaching from the earth to the periphery of its sphere, has weight, all the conclusions we have inferred from this fact are equally correct.

But, however certain these conclusions may be deemed, it appears to me that all who accept them would nevertheless be eager to see this last consequence confirmed by experiment, because it involves all the others and indeed directly verifies the principle itself. There is no doubt that if a balloon such as we have described were seen to expand as it was lifted up, the conclusion could not be avoided that the expansion was due to a pressure, which was greater below than above. Nothing else could cause that expansion, the more so as the mountains are colder than the lowlands. The compression of the air in the balloon could have no other cause than the weight of the mass of the air, since this air was taken in its actual condition at low altitudes and was uncompressed, the balloon being even limp and only half inflated. This would be proof positive that air has weight; that the mass of the air is heavy; that its weight presses all the bodies it contains; that its pressure is greater on the lowlands than on the highlands that it compresses itself by its own weight, and is more highly compressed below than above. And, since in physical science experience is far more convincing than argument, I do not doubt that everyone will wish to see this reasoning confirmed by experiment. Moreover, should the experiment be performed, I should enjoy this advantage: that if no expansion of the balloon were observed even on the highest mountains, my conclusions, nevertheless, would not be invalidated; for I might then claim that the mountains were still not high enough to cause a perceptible difference. Whereas if a considerable and very marked change occurred, say of one-eighth or one-ninth in volume, the proof, to me, would be absolutely convincing, and there could remain no doubt as to the truth of all that I had asserted.

But I delay too long. It is time to say, in a word, that the trial has been made and with the following successful result.

An Experiment Made at Two High Places, the One about 500 Fathoms Higher than the Other

If one takes a balloon half-filled with air, shrunken and flabby, and carries it by a thread to the top of a mountain 500 fathoms high, it will expand of its own accord as it rises, until at the top it will be fully inflated as if more air had been blown into it. As it is brought down it will gradually shrink by the same degrees, until at the foot of the mountain it has resumed its former condition.

This experiment proves all that I have said of the mass of the air, with wholly convincing force; but it must be fully confirmed, since the whole of my discourse rests on this foundation. Meanwhile it remains to be pointed out only that the mass of the air weighs more or less at different times, according as it is more charged with vapor or more contracted by cold.

Let it then be set down, (1) that the mass of air has weight; (2) that its weight is limited; (3) that it is heavier at some times than at others; (4) that its weight is greater in some places than in others, as in [highlands and] lowlands; (5) that by its weight it presses all the bodies it surrounds, the more strongly when its weight is greater.

CHAPTER II

The Weight of the Mass of the Air Produces all the Effects That Are Commonly Ascribed to the Abhorrence of a Vacuum

THIS CHAPTER IS DIVIDED into two parts: the first describes the principal effects which have been commonly ascribed to the abhorrence of a vacuum; the second shows that they are due to the weight of the air.

PART I

An account of the effects ascribed to the abhorrence of a vacuum

There are several effects which nature is said to produce by an abhorrence of a vacuum, of which the most striking are the following:

I. When all the apertures of a bellows are closed, it is hard to open. Any attempt to do this meets with a resistance as if its two sides were stuck together. And similarly the piston of a sealed syringe resists the effort to withdraw it, as though it adhered to the base of its case.

This resistance is commonly explained as an instance of nature's abhorrence of the vacuum which would be produced if the bellows could be opened: and this theory is supported by the fact that the resistance ceases as soon as an aperture is made by which air can enter to fill the bellows when it is opened.

II. Two polished surfaces laid one upon the other are difficult to separate and seem glued together. Thus a hat laid on a table is hard to jerk up. A piece of leather pressed against a paving stone and jerked up, will wrench out and lift the stone.

It is claimed that this adhesion is due to nature's abhorrence of the vacuum that would exist while the air was passing from the periphery to the center.

III. When a syringe is dipped in water and the piston is drawn back, the water follows it, and rises as if it adhered to the plunger. In the same way, in a suction pump, which is really but a long syringe, the water rises and follows its piston when this is drawn back, as if it adhered to it.

It is claimed that this rising of the water is due to nature's abhorrence of the vacuum which would be left when the piston is withdrawn, if water did not take its place, since air cannot enter. This explanation is supported by the fact that if slits are cut through which air can penetrate, the water no longer rises.

Similarly, if the nozzle of a bellows is thrust into water and the bellows is opened suddenly, water enters to fill it because no air can get in, especially if the vents in the sides are sealed.

Again, if a man sucks up water, the same cause produces the result; for the lungs act like a bellows of which the nozzle is the mouth.

Again, in breathing, the air is drawn in as a bellows draws in air, to fill its emptiness.

Again, if lighted tow is put in a saucer full of water and covered with an inverted glass, then, as the fire dies out the water rises in the glass, because the air within it, rarefied by the fire, is condensed as it cools and draws the water up with it to fill the place which its condensation has left empty; just as the piston of a syringe draws the water up behind it.[1]

Again, in cupping, the flesh is drawn up into a swelling; because the air inside the cup, rarefied by the flame of the candle, is condensed as it cools when the flame dies, and draws up the flesh to fill the vacated space, as the water was drawn up in the foregoing instance.

IV. If a bottle, filled with water, is set upside down in a water-filled vessel, the water hangs in the bottle and does not fall out.

It is claimed that this retention of the water is due to nature's abhorrence of the vacuum which would be produced were the water to drop away while no air could enter to fill the vacancy left behind. This explanation is supported by the fact that if a vent is made through which the air can flow in, the water drops immediately.

The same test may be made with a tube, say ten feet in length, sealed at the top and open at the bottom. If the tube is filled with water and the open end [temporarily closed] is dipped into a vessel full of water, the water will be wholly retained in the tube, whereas it would run out at once if the top were opened.

The same thing may be done with a similar tube, sealed at the top but bent backward at the lower [open] end, without dipping it in a water-filled vessel as in the preceding case. For if the tube is filled with water, the water will be retained, whereas if the top were opened a jet of water would instantly and violently escape from the bent extremity.[2]

Lastly, the same thing may be done with a simple straight tube, provided it be very narrow at its lower end. If it is sealed at the top the water will be retained, whereas the water would rush out below if the upper end were opened. This is why a wine-filled cask does not release a single drop, though the spigot be open, until a vent is opened at the top.

---

[1] In this case, as is implied, the tow is only partially submerged, and is not at once extinguished. At first, some of the warmed air would probably bubble out through the water and thus suggest this interpretation. The chemistry of combustion was not, at this time, understood.

[2] The instrument now called the siphon barometer.

V. If a tube bent in the shape of an inverted horseshoe (which is commonly called a siphon) is filled with water, and its legs are placed so as to dip in separate water-filled vessels, then, however small the difference of level between the two vessels may be, all the water from the higher vessel will rise up the leg immersed in it to the top of the siphon and will pass down by the other leg into the lower vessel in which that leg is immersed; so that, if a sufficiency of water be supplied to the higher vessel, the flow will be continuous.

It is claimed that this retention of the water is due to nature's abhorrence of the vacuum that would be left in the siphon if the water from these two legs were to fall from each into its own. So it does, if any vent is made at the top of the siphon, whereby the air can enter.

There are several other similar effects which I do not describe because they are all like those I have mentioned. In all of them the one outstanding cause is that all bodies in contact resist any effort to part them when the air cannot insinuate itself between them, whether that effort be due to their own weight, as in the cases where the water rises and is retained in spite of its weight, or to the force exerted to part them as in the earlier examples.

Such are the effects commonly ascribed to nature's abhorrence of a vacuum. We will now show that they are due to the weight of the air.

PART II

The Weight of the Mass of the Air Produces all the Effects Hitherto Ascribed to the Abhorrence of a Vacuum

If it has been well understood, from the Treatise on the Equilibrium of Liquids, how their weight presses all the bodies immersed in them, there will be no difficulty in understanding how the weight of the mass of the air bearing on all bodies produces on them the effects that might be ascribed to abhorrence of a vacuum: for they are quite alike, as we shall prove in each case.

I. *The weight of the mass of the air causes the difficulty in opening a sealed bellows.*

To make it clear how the weight of the mass of air causes the resistance encountered in opening a bellows from which the air is excluded, I will point to a similar resistance due to the weight of water. It needs only to be remembered, as I said in the Equilibrium of Liquids, that if a bellows with a tube twenty or more feet long is set in a tank full of water with the tip of the nozzle extending above the surface, it is hard to open; and that the greater the depth of water above it the harder it is to open. This is obviously due to the weight of the water above: for if there is no water there, it is easy to open. The more water you pour in, the greater is the resistance, which is always equal to the weight of the water sustained. The reason is that as the nozzle projects above the water, and therefore excludes it, the bellows cannot be opened without raising and holding up the whole mass of water. The water that is pushed aside in the act of opening cannot enter the bellows, is forced to find room elsewhere, and thus raises the water level—a process attended with some difficulty; whereas if the bellows were so perforated that water could get in, it could be freely opened and closed because the water could enter through the perforations as fast as room was made for it, and would not, therefore, be lifted. I do not think that anyone can be tempted to ascribe this resistance to the abhorrence of a vacuum. It is absolutely certain that it is due solely to the weight of water.

Now what we say about water must be taken to apply to any other liquid: for if the bellows is set in a vessel full of wine, the same resistance to its opening will be experienced; likewise with milk, oil, quicksilver, and indeed with any liquid whatsoever. Thus it is a general rule and a necessary effect of the weight of liquids, that if a bellows is so immersed in any one of them that the liquid is excluded from its interior, the weight of the liquid above makes it impossible to open the bellows without overcoming a resistance due to the fact that it has to be lifted. Applying this general rule to air in particular, it follows as a certain consequence that when a bellows is so sealed as to exclude all air, the weight of the air above prevents its opening without overcoming some resistance: since it cannot be opened without lifting the whole mass of air. But as soon as a perforation is made in the bellows, it can be freely opened and closed, because now the act of opening no longer lifts the mass of the air. All this is completely analogous to the action of the bellows immersed in water.

Whence it is evident that the difficulty in opening a sealed bellows is but a particular case of the general rule that it is hard to open a bellows in any fluid whatsoever which is prevented from entering it.

What we have said about this effect we will say of all the rest, but more briefly.

II. The weight of the mass of the air is the cause of the difficulty that one feels in separating two polished bodies in close contact.

To explain how the weight of the mass of the air causes the resistance felt when the attempt is made to separate two polished surfaces in close contact, I will give an example of a wholly similar resistance due to the weight of water, which will put it beyond doubt that the air causes this effect. Here again what was stated in the Equilibrium of Liquids must be recalled.

Let a copper cylinder carefully ground on a lathe be placed in the mouth of a funnel made with equal care, until they fit so perfectly that the cylinder enters smoothly into the funnel without any leakage of water between them; and let this device be plunged into a tank full of water so that the stem of the funnel—which may be made twenty feet long if necessary—just emerges. If, now, while the funnel is held in one hand, the cylinder, at a depth of fifteen feet in the water, is released and left to move as it will, not only will it remain in position, although it seems to be quite unsupported; but furthermore, there will be difficulty in withdrawing it from the funnel, although it is in no way attached to it. On the other hand it would drop violently of its own weight if it were only four feet below the surface of the water in the tank, and more violently still if it were entirely out of the water. The reason for this I have already made clear. It is that water is in contact with the cylinder below but not above (since the funnel prevents its contact with the upper surface); it presses the face it touches toward the face it does not touch, and thus drives the cylinder up against the funnel.

The same reasoning applies to any other liquid. Consequently, when two polished surfaces are laid together, if the upper is held in the hand while the lower is left free, the latter must remain suspended, because it is in contact with the air below, but not with the air above, since there is no opening between the two plates, and the air, consequently, cannot reach the surfaces in contact. Whence it follows, as a necessary effect of the weight of all fluids, that the weight of the air must drive the lower body up and press it against the upper so strongly that a great resistance will be felt to the effort of separating them: an effect completely analogous to the effect of the weight of water.

Thus it is evident that the difficulty of separating two smooth bodies is but a particular case of the general rule that applies to the pressure of all fluids whatever when they are in contact with one of the surfaces of a body, but not with the surface opposite.

III. *The weight of the mass of the air is the cause of the rise of water in syringes and pumps.*

To explain how the weight of the mass of the air makes water rise in pumps as the plunger is drawn back, I will explain an entirely similar effect of the weight of water, which will account for it perfectly.

If a syringe is provided with a long piston, say ten feet in length and hollow throughout, with a valve at its base opening downwards and not upwards, it cannot suck water nor any other liquid above the level of the liquid, because air can freely enter through the hollow of the piston. When the mouth of this syringe is plunged into a vessel full of quicksilver, and the whole apparatus is placed in a tank full of water so that the top of the piston shall just emerge, then if the piston is drawn up, the quicksilver will also rise behind it, as though adhering; though it would not rise at all if there were no water in the tank, because the air would then have free access to the body of the syringe through the hollow neck of the piston.

There is here no abhorrence of a vacuum, for even if the quicksilver did not rise to fill the space vacated by the piston, there would be no vacuum; since the air could enter freely. The sole cause is the mass of water which presses on the quicksilver in the vessel from every side except at the mouth of the syringe (which it is prevented from reaching by the body of the syringe and by the piston). This quicksilver, then, pressed on all sides but one, is forced by the weight of the water towards that one side as soon as the rising piston leaves it entrance room, and balances, within the syringe, the weight of the water outside. But if slits are made to admit water into the syringe, the quicksilver will cease to rise, because the water enters by them and is now in the same contact with the mouth of the syringe as with the other parts. Since its pressure then affects all parts equally, no liquid rises. All this has been clearly demonstrated in the Equilibrium of Liquids.

This illustration makes it clear how the weight of the water causes the quicksilver to rise. The same effect might be produced by the weight of sand. If all the water is removed from this vessel, and sand is poured in, in its place, the weight of the sand will cause the quicksilver to rise in the syringe because, just as the water did before, the sand now presses it on every side save that which is at the mouth of the syringe; and pressing it, compels it to rise. And if you bear on the sand with your hands, you will drive the quicksilver further up the syringe until it reaches such a height that it can balance the extra pressure.

The explanation of these effects makes it very easy to see why the weight of the air causes water to rise in common syringes to the height that the piston is drawn back. The air, in contact with the water of the vessel on every side except at the mouth of the syringe (from which it is excluded by the syringe itself and by its piston), pressing by its weight upon that water on every side except that single one, cannot fail to drive it up as far as the withdrawing piston makes room for it to enter, and to counterbalance, within the syringe, the weight of the air outside. It does so for the same reason that the quicksilver rose under the pressure of the water, and under that of the sand in the case that we have just given, and by the same necessity.

Thus it is obvious that the rising of water in syringes is but a particular case of the general rule that any liquid pressed in every one of its parts save one by the weight of another fluid is thereby driven towards that part against which no pressure is exerted.

*   *   *

V. The weight of the mass of the air causes water to rise in siphons.

To make it apparent how the weight of the air causes water to rise in a siphon, we will show that the weight of water makes quicksilver rise in a siphon which is fully open at the top and to which, therefore, air has free access. From this it will be clearly seen how the weight of the air produces this effect. And we will do so thus:

Let a siphon with one leg some twelve inches long and the other thirteen be opened at the top and let a tube twenty feet in length be soldered hermetically to this opening. Then let it be filled with quicksilver and placed with its legs dipping into separate vessels also filled with quicksilver; and let the whole apparatus be set up in a water-filled tank to a depth of some fifteen or sixteen feet, the upper end of the open tube remaining out of water. Now if one of the vessels be never so little, say one inch, higher than the other, all the quicksilver in the higher vessel will rise to the top of the siphon and make its way by the other leg to the lower vessel in a continuous stream; and if more quicksilver is fed to the higher vessel the flow will be continuous. But if the siphon is punctured so that water may enter it, instantly the quicksilver will drop out of each leg into its vessel, and water will take its place.

This rising of the quicksilver is not due to the abhorrence of a vacuum, for the air has perfectly free access to the siphon. Again, if the water were removed from the tank, the quicksilver from each leg would drop into its separate vessel, and air would take its place through the now freely open tube. Thus manifestly it is the weight of the water that causes this rising, because it presses upon the quicksilver in the vessels and not upon that in the siphon. This weight forces the quicksilver to rise and to flow as it does. But no sooner is water admitted by a perforation than, pressing now inside as well as outside the siphon, it ceases to force the quicksilver upwards.

For the same reason that water must necessarily cause the quicksilver to rise in a siphon when it presses upon the vessels without any access to the inside of the siphon, similarly the weight of the air must cause the water to rise in common siphons: it exerts its weight upon the water held by the vessels into which their legs dip, without any access to the inside of the siphon; but if a perforation is made so as to provide that access, the water ceases to rise, and on the contrary drops into each vessel and is replaced by air which now exerts its weight both inside and outside the siphon.

It is apparent that this last effect is but a particular case of the general rule, and that if it is clearly understood why the weight of the water makes the quicksilver rise in the example we have given, it will be apparent likewise why the weight of the air raises the water in common siphons. Hence we must make very clear the reason why the weight of the water produces this effect, and explain why it is the higher vessel that empties itself into the lower and not the lower into the other.

To do so, it must be observed that the water weighs upon the quicksilver in each vessel, but not on the quicksilver inside the legs that dip into it. Thus the quicksilver in the vessels is pressed, by the weight of the water, up each leg of the siphon to its top, and would rise farther if this were possible, for the water in the tank is sixteen feet deep while the siphon is but one foot in height; and one foot of quicksilver is equal to only fourteen of water. So, obviously, the weight of the water drives the quicksilver to the top of each leg, with some power left over. Thus the quicksilver in each leg being driven up by the weight of the water, the pressures in the two legs oppose each other at the top, and the stronger must prevail. It will be easy to calculate which this will be. Since the water has a greater height by one inch above the lower vessel, it drives up the quicksilver in the longer leg with more power than in the other leg, by the margin of the power derived from one inch of height. From this it would seem at first glance that the result would be to drive the quicksilver from the longer leg into the shorter. But it must be taken into consideration that the weight of quicksilver in each leg opposes the effort of water to press it up. These two resistances are not equal. Since the quicksilver in the longer leg is the deeper, by one inch, it offers a resistance which is greater by the force derived from one inch of height. Hence the quicksilver in the longer leg is driven up by a force of water the greater by the height of one inch. But it is borne down by its own weight, that is by the excess weight of one inch of quicksilver. Now one inch of quicksilver weighs more than one inch of water; therefore the quicksilver in the shorter leg is driven up with the greater force and consequently must continue to rise so long as there is quicksilver in the vessel into which it dips.

From this it is apparent that the reason why the higher vessel empties itself into the lower is that quicksilver is heavier than water. The contrary would be the effect if the siphon, and also the vessels in which the siphon is plunged, were filled with oil, which is lighter than water, while the whole apparatus was immersed in the same tank of water. For then the oil from the lower vessel would rise and flow through the top of the siphon into the higher for the reasons aforesaid. The water would press the oil continuously from the lower vessel more strongly by the weight of one inch of height, and the oil of the longer leg would oppose this with the weight of one inch of greater height. As one inch of oil is lighter than one inch of water, the oil of the longer leg would be driven up more forcibly than that in the other and consequently would make its way from the lower vessel to the higher. And lastly, if the siphon were filled with a liquid of the same weight as the water in the tank, then there would be no exchange. Equilibrium would prevail. Calculating all the forces, you will find that they cancel one another.

Such are the effects that had to be clearly understood in order to grasp the reason for the rise of these liquids in siphons. After this it is perfectly easy to see why the weight of the air lifts the water in simple siphons from the higher to the lower vessel. We need not dilate upon the subject, as the case is only another one of the general rule that we have stated above.

* * *

IX. *The weight of the mass of the air causes the in-drawing of air which occurs in breathing.*

For the same reason, in breathing, the air enters the lungs. When the lungs open while the nose and all passages are also free and open, the air in these passages, driven by the weight of its whole mass, enters and drops down by the natural and necessary action of its weight. These facts are so intelligible, easy, and simple, that it is strange that recourse should have been had to the abhorrence of a vacuum, occult qualities and other such far-fetched and chimerical causes for the purpose of accounting for them. It is just as natural for air to enter and drop down into the lungs when they open, as for wine to drop into a bottle when it is poured in.

Thus it is that the weight of the air produces all the effects hitherto ascribed to the abhorrence of a vacuum. I have now explained the more important of them. If any remain unexplained, they are so easy to account for by the same processes as the rest, that to look for them and explain them in detail would seem to me idle and tedious. Indeed they have all been seen, we may say, in their common origin, in the preceding treatise, since all these effects are but particular cases of the general rule concerning the Equilibrium of Fluids.

"I esteem that it becomes a naturalist not only to devise hypotheses and experiments, but to examine and improve those that are already found out."

Robert Boyle

1627 – 1691

THE RELATIONSHIP BETWEEN THE PRESSURE AND THE VOLUME OF A GAS IS DEVELOPED EXPERIMENTALLY

Robert Boyle is another example of precocity though, unlike Pascal, Boyle managed to continue his work through a long life uncomplicated by religious crises. At the age of 11, Boyle was taken from school and sent abroad with a tutor, and at 14 he was studying the work of Galileo in Italy. When he returned to England, he soon came under the influence of a coterie of men known, as we have seen above, as the Invisible College, who had adopted the Baconian principles of experimentation. The group included Robert Hooke and Isaac Newton; indeed, the latter found in Boyle a sponsor for his magnum opus—the *Principia*—the publication of which Boyle inspired and financed. The story goes that his epitaph described Boyle as "Father of Chemistry and Uncle of the Earl of Cork." It is as the former that he is included in these readings.

Boyle attacked one aspect of scholasticism which had survived the general attacks made by Galileo—the concept that matter was composed of four "elements" or "principles" or "essences." In his *Sceptical Chymist,* Boyle anticipated many of the ideas of modern chemistry and came close to a definition of an element which would satisfy today's scientists. Matter, he found, was composed of corpuscles—minute particles—which were capable of combining in various arrangements to form substances as we know them, the compound having qualities different from those of the components.

He made many experiments on the relation between pressure and the volume of gases; in this connection he is best remembered for the law named for him, which states that at a given temperature, pressure is inversely proportional to the volume. With the help of Hooke (see page 387), Boyle constructed a pump which was an improvement on the first air pump made by von Guericke in 1654.

It seems, too, that Boyle almost discovered oxygen when he noticed, in air, what he called a "little vital quintessence which restores our vital spirits." His studies of combustion, in which he described heat as a "brisk agitation of the particles," suggest that some continuation of his work might have been fruitful in accelerating the course of chemical investigation had not the phlogiston doctrine of Stahl been so influential.

Boyle, a true Baconian experimenter, collected data on electricity and magnetism. He improved Galileo's thermometer by sealing it hermetically and, as we can read in the following selection, he developed Torricelli's barometer into the U-shaped form in which we know it today.

The following selection is from the second edition of *A Defense of the Doctrine Touching the Spring and Weight of the Air,* in W. F. Magie's *A Source Book in Physics* (Harvard, 1935).

A spectacular demonstration by von Guericke of the pressure exerted
by the atmosphere on a globe of fitted bronze hemispheres from which
the air has been exhausted. Two teams of eight horses each could not
pull the globe apart, although it fell apart when air was permitted to
enter. From Otto von Guericke's *Experimenta Nova* (*ut Vocantur*)
Magdeburgica de Vacuo Spatio, Amstelodami, 1672. (Courtesy of the
Burndy Library.)

RELATIONS OF PRESSURE AND VOLUME OF AIR

Two New Experiments Touching the Measure of the Force of the Spring of Air Compressed and Dilated.

We took then a long glass-tube, which, by a dexterous hand and the help of a lamp, was in such a manner crooked at the bottom, that the part turned up was almost parallel to the rest of the tube, and the orifice of this shorter leg of the siphon (if I may so call the whole instrument) being hermetically sealed, the length of it was divided into inches (each of which was subdivided into eight parts) by a streight list of paper, which containing those divisions, was carefully pasted all along it. Then putting in as much quicksilver as served to fill the arch or bended part of the siphon, that the mercury standing in a level might reach in the one leg to the bottom of the divided paper, and just to the same height or horizontal line in the other; we took care, by frequently inclining the tube, so that the air might freely pass from one leg into the other by the sides of the mercury (we took, I say, care) that the air at last included in the shorter cylinder should be of the same laxity with the rest of the air about it. This done, we began to pour quicksilver into the longer leg of the siphon, which by its weight pressing up that in the shorter leg, did by degrees streighten the included air: and continuing this pouring in of quicksilver till the air in the shorter leg was by condensation reduced to take up by half the space it possessed (I say, possessed, not filled) before; we cast our eyes upon the longer leg of the glass, on which was likewise pasted a list of paper carefully divided into inches and parts, and we observed, not without delight and satisfaction, that the quicksilver in that longer part of the tube was 29 inches higher than the other. Now that this observation does both very well agree with and confirm our hypothesis, will be easily discerned by him that takes notice what we teach; and Monsieur Paschal and our English friend's experiments prove, that the greater the weight is that leans upon the air, the more forcible is its endeavour of dilatation, and consequently its power of resistance (as other springs are stronger when bent by greater weights). For this being considered, it will appear to agree rarely-well with the hypothesis, that as according to it the air in that degree of density and correspondent measure of resistance, to which the weight of the incumbent atmosphere had brought it, was able to counter-balance and resist the pressure of a mercurial cylinder of about 29 inches, as we are taught by the Torricellian experiment; so here the same air being brought to a degree of density about twice as great as that it had before, obtains a spring twice as strong as formerly. As may appear by its being able to sustain or resist a cylinder of 29 inches in the longer tube, together with the weight of the atmospherical cylinder, that leaned upon those 29 inches of mercury; and, as we just now inferred from the Torricellian experiment, was equivalent to them.

We were hindered from prosecuting the trial at that time by the casual breaking of the tube. But because an accurate experiment of this nature would be of great importance to the doctrine of the spring of the air, and has not yet been made (that I know) by any man; and because also it is more uneasy to be made than one would think, in regard of the difficulty as well of procuring crooked tubes fit for the purpose, as of making a just estimate of the true place-of the protuberant mercury's surface; I suppose it will not be unwelcome to the reader to be informed, that after some other trials, one of which we made in a tube whose longer leg was perpendicular, and the other, that contained the air, parallel to the horizon, we at last procured a tube of the figure expressed in the scheme; which tube, though of a pretty bigness, was so long, that the cylinder, whereof the shorter leg of it consisted, admitted a list of paper, which had before been divided into 12 inches and their quarters, and the longer leg admitted another list of paper of divers feet in length, and divided after the same manner. Then quicksilver being poured in to fill up the bended part of the glass, that the surface of it in either leg might rest in the same horizontal line, as we lately taught, there was more and more quicksilver poured into the longer tube; and notice being watchfully taken how far the mercury was risen in that longer tube, when it appeared to have ascended to any of the divisions in the shorter tube, the several observations that were thus successively made, and as they were made set down, afforded us the ensuing table.

And to let you see, that we did not (as a little above) inconsiderately mention the weight of the incumbent atmospherical cylinder as a part of the weight resisted by the imprisoned air, we will here annex, that we took care, when the mercurial cylinder in the longer leg of the pipe was about

A TABLE OF THE CONDENSATION OF THE AIR

A	A	B	C	D	E	
48	12	00		29 2/16	29 2/16	AA. The number of equal spaces in the shorter leg, that contained the same parcel of air diversely extended.
46	11½	01 7/16		30 9/16	30 6/16	
44	11	02 13/16		31 15/16	31 12/16	
42	10½	04 6/16		33 8/16	33 1/7	
40	10	06 3/16		35 5/16	35	
38	9½	07 14/16		37	36 15/19	B. The height of the mercurial cylinder in the longer leg, that compressed the air into those dimensions.
36	9	10 2/16		39 5/16	38 7/8	
34	8½	12 8/16		41 10/16	41 2/17	
32	8	15 1/16		44 3/16	43 11/16	
30	7½	17 15/16	Added to 29⅛ makes	47 1/16	46 3/5	
28	7	21 3/16		50 5/16	50	C. The height of the mercurial cylinder, that counterbalanced the pressure of the atmosphere.
26	6½	25 3/16		54 5/16	53 10/13	
24	6	29 11/16		58 13/16	58 2/8	
23	5¾	32 3/16		61 5/16	60 18/23	
22	5½	34 15/16		64 1/16	63 6/11	
21	5¼	37 15/16		67 1/16	66 4/7	D. The aggregate of the two last columns, B and C, exhibiting the pressure sustained by the included air.
20	5	41 9/16		70 11/16	70	
19	4¾	45		74 2/16	73 11/19	
18	4½	48 12/16		77 14/16	77 2/3	
17	4¼	53 11/16		82 12/16	82 4/17	
16	4	58 2/16		87 14/16	87 3/8	E. What that pressure should be according to the hypothesis, that supposes the pressures and expansions to be in reciprocal proportion.
15	3¾	63 15/16		93 1/16	93 1/5	
14	3½	71 5/16		100 7/16	99 6/7	
13	3¼	78 11/16		107 13/16	107 7/13	
12	3	88 7/16		117 9/16	116 4/8	

an hundred inches high, to cause one to suck at the open orifice; whereupon (as we expected) the mercury in the tube did notably ascend. . . . And therefore we shall render this reason of it that the pressure of the incumbent air being in part taken off by its expanding itself into the sucker's dilated chest, the imprisoned air was thereby enabled to dilate itself manifestly, and repel the mercury, that comprest it, till there was an equality of force betwixt the strong spring of the comprest air on the one part, and the tall mercurial cylinder, together with the contiguous dilated air, on the other part.

Now, if to what we have thus delivered concerning the compression of the air, we add some observations concerning its spontaneous expansion, it will the better appear, how much the phænomena of these mercurial experiments depend upon the differing measures of strength to be met with in the air's spring, according to its various degrees of compression and laxity.

A TABLE OF THE RAREFACTION OF THE AIR

	A	B	C	D	E
A. The number of equal spaces at the top of the tube, that contained the same parcel of air.	1	00		$29\frac{3}{4}$	$29\ \frac{3}{4}$
	$1\frac{1}{2}$	$10\frac{5}{8}$		$19\frac{1}{8}$	$19\ \frac{5}{6}$
	2	$15\frac{3}{8}$		$14\frac{3}{8}$	$14\ \frac{7}{8}$
	3	$20\frac{2}{8}$		$9\frac{1}{8}$	$9\frac{15}{12}$
B. The height of the mercurial cylinder, that together with the spring of the included air counterbalanced the pressure of the atmosphere.	4	$22\frac{5}{8}$		$7\frac{1}{8}$	$7\ \frac{7}{16}$
	5	$24\frac{1}{8}$		$5\frac{5}{8}$	$5^{19}/_{25}$
	6	$24\frac{7}{8}$		$4\frac{7}{8}$	$4^{23}/_{24}$
	7	$25\frac{4}{8}$		$4\frac{2}{8}$	$4\ \frac{1}{4}$
	8	26		$3\frac{6}{8}$	$3^{23}/_{32}$
	9	$26\frac{3}{8}$		$3\frac{3}{8}$	$3^{11}/_{36}$
C. The pressure of the atmosphere.	10	$26\frac{6}{8}$		3	$2^{39}/_{40}$
	12	$27\frac{1}{8}$		$2\frac{5}{8}$	$2^{23}/_{48}$
D. The complement of B to C, exhibiting the pressure sustained by the included air.	14	$27\frac{4}{8}$		$2\frac{2}{8}$	$2\ \frac{1}{8}$
	16	$27\frac{6}{8}$		2	$1^{55}/_{64}$
	18	$27\frac{7}{8}$		$1\frac{7}{8}$	$1^{47}/_{72}$
	20	28		$1\frac{6}{8}$	$1\ ^9/_{80}$
	24	$28\frac{2}{8}$		$1\frac{4}{8}$	$1^{23}/_{96}$
E. What that pressure should be according to the hypothesis.	28	$28\frac{3}{8}$		$1\frac{3}{8}$	$1\ \frac{1}{16}$
	32	$28\frac{4}{8}$		$1\frac{2}{8}$	$0^{119}/_{128}$

Column C: Subtracted from $29\frac{3}{4}$ leaves

"In true philosophy . . . we conceive the cause
of all natural effects in terms of mechanics. That is what we
must do, according to my opinion, or renounce all hope
of ever understanding anything in physics."

Christian Huygens
1629 – 1695

THE WAVE THEORY OF LIGHT IS SET FORTH

Although he was born in the Netherlands, Huygens was a close associate of a number of men with whom we are already familiar. A correspondent of Newton's, he was elected to membership of the Royal Society at the age of 34 and was thus given official recognition of his association with Newton, Halley, Boyle, and the rest of this most interesting group.

Huygens began his scientific work with the study of lenses, for the grinding and polishing of which he discovered better methods. As a result of this improvement, he was able to detect a satellite of Saturn and to observe more accurately the constellation of Orion. His studies in optics were paralleled by his work on the pendulum. Huygens determined the relation between the length of the pendulum and its period of vibration and developed the theory of evolutes. He applied his discovery about the pendulum to the regulation of clocks, making possible, for the first time, the construction of accurate time pieces. His theory of centrifugal forces in circular motion was of great help to Newton in the formulation of the latter's concepts of gravity. Huygens rejected Newton's theory of gravitation as a universal quality of matter, though he accepted his contemporary's explanation of planetary motions.

After some years of work in France, under the patronage of Louis XIV, Huygens returned to Holland and published the results of his studies on light. He made lenses of very great focal length and, like Newton, studied the refraction of light through prisms. As a result of his investigations, he evolved the wave theory of light. This theory presented Huygens with the problem of explaining shadows and the propagation of light in straight lines, which Newton achieved by resorting to a corpuscular theory. For this reason, and perhaps because of the greater prestige of Newton, Huygens's theory was ignored for a hundred years or so, until the study of his work by Thomas Young and Augustin Jean Fresnel revived interest in it. As work on the quantum theory was to show later, both Newton's and Huygens's theories were necessary to a full explanation of light.

In the following selection will be found a reference to Roemer (1644-1710). There was, at this time, uncertainty as to whether light had a finite velocity, and Roemer had made experiments in 1676, the results of which were not immediately accepted, which showed that light was not instantaneous but required time in which to travel. Roemer had observed the eclipses of the moons of Jupiter in two cases: when the earth was between the sun and Jupiter and when the earth was on the other side of the sun. The difference in the times observed was as much as fifteen minutes, which, if the moon's motions were uniform, would clearly indicate the time taken by light to travel the greater distance. These observations were used by Huygens in support of his wave theory, which stated that light was propagated in a pulse movement which could be subjected to mathematical analysis.

As a mathematical physicist, Huygens is considered as second only to Newton. Evidently, each owed much to the other, if only for the values derived from that skepticism of another's results which is the essence of scientific controversy.

The selection is from Huygens's *Traité de la Lumière*, composed in France in 1678 but published in Holland in 1690 and translated by S. P. Thompson as *Treatise on Light* in 1912.

TREATISE ON LIGHT

PREFACE

I WROTE THIS TREATISE during my sojourn in France twelve years ago, and I communicated it in the year 1678 to the learned persons who then composed the Royal Academy of Science, to the membership of which the King had done me the honour of calling me. Several of that body who are still alive will remember having been present when I read it, and above the rest those amongst them who applied themselves particularly to the study of Mathematics; of whom I cannot cite more than the celebrated gentlemen Cassini, Römer, and De la Hire. And although I have since corrected and changed some parts, the copies which I had made of it at that time may serve for proof that I have yet added nothing to it save some conjectures touching the formation of Iceland Crystal, and a novel observation on the refraction of Rock Crystal. I have desired to relate these particulars to make known how long I have meditated the things which now I publish, and not for the purpose of detracting from the merit of those who, without having seen anything that I have written, may be found to have treated of like matters: as has in fact occurred to two eminent Geometricians, Messieurs Newton and Leibniz, with respect to the Problem of the figure of glasses for collecting rays when one of the surfaces is given.

One may ask why I have so long delayed to bring this work to the light. The reason is that I wrote it rather carelessly in the Language in which it appears, with the intention of translating it into Latin, so doing in order to obtain greater attention to the thing. After which I proposed to myself to give it out along with another Treatise on Dioptrics, in which I explain the effects of Telescopes and those things which belong more to that Science. But the pleasure of novelty being past, I have put off from time to time the execution of this design, and I know not when I shall ever come to an end of it, being often turned aside either by business or by some new study. Considering which I have finally judged that it was better worth while to publish this writing, such as it is, than to let it run the risk, by waiting longer, of remaining lost.

There will be seen in it demonstrations of those kinds which do not produce as great a certitude as those of Geometry, and which even differ much therefrom, since whereas the Geometers prove their Propositions by fixed and incontestable Principles, here the Principles are verified by the conclusions to be drawn from them; the nature of these things not allowing of this being done otherwise. It is always possible to attain thereby to a degree of probability which very often is scarcely less than complete proof. To wit, when things which have been demonstrated by the Principles that have been assumed correspond perfectly to the phenomena which experiment has brought under observation; especially when there are a great number of them, and further, principally, when one can imagine and foresee new phenomena which ought to follow from the hypothesis which one employs, and when one finds that therein the fact corresponds to our prevision. But if all these proofs of probability are met with in that which I propose to discuss, as it seems to me they are, this ought to be a very strong confirmation of the success of my inquiry; and it must be ill if the facts are not pretty much as I represent them. I would believe then that those who love to know the Causes of things and who are able to admire the marvels of Light, will find some satisfaction in these various speculations regarding it, and in the new explanation of its famous property which is the main foundation of the construction of our eyes and of those great inventions which extend so vastly the use of them. I hope also that there will be some who by following these beginnings will penetrate much further into this question than I have been able to do, since the subject must be far from being exhausted. This appears from the passages which I have indicated where I leave certain difficulties without having resolved them, and still more from matters which I have not touched at all, such as Luminous Bodies of several sorts, and all that concerns Colours; in which no one until now can boast of having succeeded. Finally, there remains much more to be investigated touching the nature of Light which I do not pretend to have disclosed, and I shall owe much in return to him who shall be able to supplement that which is here lacking to me in knowledge. The Hague. The 8 January 1690.

*   *   *

CHAPTER I

On Rays Propagated in Straight Lines

AS HAPPENS IN ALL THE SCIENCES in which Geometry is applied to matter, the demonstrations concerning Optics are founded on truths drawn from experience. Such are that the rays of light are propagated in straight lines; that the angles of reflexion and of incidence are equal; and that in refraction the ray is bent according to the law of sines, now so well known, and which is no less certain than the preceding laws.

The majority of those who have written touching the various parts of Optics have contented themselves with presuming these truths. But some, more inquiring, have desired to investigate the origin and the causes, considering these to be in themselves wonderful effects of Nature. In which they advanced some ingenious things, but not however such that the most intelligent folk do not wish for better and more satisfactory explanations. Wherefore I here desire to propound what I have meditated on the subject, so as to contribute as much as I can to the explanation of this department of Natural Science, which, not without reason, is reputed to be one of its most difficult parts. I recognize myself to be much indebted to those who were the first to begin to dissipate the strange obscurity in which these things were enveloped, and to give us hope that they might be explained by intelligible reasoning. But, on the other hand I am astonished also that even here these have often been willing to offer, as assured and demonstrative, reasonings which were far from conclusive. For I do not find that any one has yet given a probable explanation of the first and most notable phenomena of light, namely why it is not propagated except in straight lines, and how visible rays, coming from an infinitude of diverse places, cross one another without hindering one another in any way.

I shall therefore essay in this book, to give, in accordance with the principles accepted in the Philosophy of the present day, some clearer and more probable reasons, firstly of these properties of light propagated rectilinearly; secondly of light which is reflected on meeting other bodies. Then I shall explain the phenomena of those rays which are said to suffer refraction on passing through transparent bodies of different sorts; and in this part I shall also explain the effects of the refraction of the air by the different densities of the Atmosphere.

Thereafter I shall examine the causes of the strange refraction of a certain kind of Crystal which is brought from Iceland. And finally I shall treat of the various shapes of transparent and reflecting bodies by which rays are collected at a point or are turned aside in various ways. From this it will be seen with what facility, following our new Theory, we find not only the Ellipses, Hyperbolas, and other curves which Mr. Des Cartes has ingeniously invented for this purpose; but also those which the surface of a glass lens ought to possess when its other surface is given as spherical or plane, or of any other figure that may be.

It is inconceivable to doubt that light consists in the motion of some sort of matter. For whether one considers its production, one sees that here upon the Earth it is chiefly engendered by fire and flame which contain without doubt bodies that are in rapid motion, since they dissolve and melt many other bodies, even the most solid; or whether one considers its effects, one sees that when light is collected, as by concave mirrors, it has the property of burning as a fire does, that is to say it disunites the particles of bodies. This is assuredly the mark of motion, at least in the true Philosophy, in which one conceives the causes of all natural effects in terms of mechanical motions. This, in my opinion, we must necessarily do, or else renounce all hopes of ever comprehending anything in Physics.

And as, according to this Philosophy, one holds as certain that the sensation of sight is excited only by the impression of some movement of a kind of matter which acts on the nerves at the back of our eyes, there is here yet one reason more for believing that light consists in a movement of the matter which exists between us and the luminous body.

Further, when one considers the extreme speed with which light spreads on every side, and how, when it comes from different regions, even from those directly opposite, the rays traverse one another without hindrance, one may well understand that when we see a luminous object, it cannot be by any transport of matter coming to us from this object, in the way in which a shot or an arrow traverses the air; for assuredly that would too greatly impugn these two properties of light, especially the second of them. It is then in some other way that light spreads; and that which can lead us to comprehend it is the knowledge which we have of the spreading of Sound in the air.

We know that by means of the air, which is an invisible and impalpable body, Sound spreads around the spot where it has been produced, by a movement which is passed on successively from one part of the air to another; and that the spreading of this movement, taking place equally rapidly on all sides, ought to form spherical surfaces ever enlarging and which strike our ears. Now there is no doubt at all that light also comes from the luminous body to our eyes by some movement impressed on the matter which is between the two; since, as we have already seen, it cannot be by the transport of a body which passes from one to the other. If, in addition, light takes time for its passage—which we are now going to examine—it will follow that this movement, impressed on the intervening matter, is successive; and consequently it spreads, as Sound does, by spherical surfaces and waves: for I call them waves from their resemblance to those which are seen to be formed in water when a stone is thrown into it, and which present a successive spreading as circles, though these arise from another cause, and are only in a flat surface.

To see then whether the spreading of light takes time, let us consider first whether there are any facts of experience which can convince us to the contrary. As to those which can be made here on the Earth, by striking lights at great distances, although they prove that light takes no sensible time to pass over these distances, one may say with good reason that they are too small, and that the only conclusion to be drawn from them is that the passage of light is extremely rapid. Mr. Des Cartes, who was of opinion that it is instantaneous, founded his views, not without reason, upon a better basis of experience, drawn from the Eclipses of the Moon; which, nevertheless, as I shall show, is not at all convincing. I will set it forth, in a way a little different from his, in order to make the conclusion more comprehensible.

Let A be the place of the sun, BD a part of the orbit or annual path of the Earth: ABC a straight line which I suppose to meet the orbit of the Moon, which is represented by the circle CD, at C.

Now if light requires time, for example one hour, to traverse the space which is between the Earth and the Moon, it will follow that the Earth having arrived at B, the shadow which it casts, or the interruption of the light, will not yet have arrived at the point C, but will only arrive there an hour after. It will then be one hour after, reckoning from the moment when the Earth was at B, that the Moon, arriving at C, will be obscured: but this obscuration or interruption of the light will not reach the Earth till after another hour. Let us suppose that the Earth in these two hours will have arrived at E. The Earth then, being at E, will see the Eclipsed Moon at C, which it left an hour before, and at the same time will see the sun at A. For it being immovable, as I suppose with Copernicus, and the light moving always in straight lines, it must always appear where it is. But one has always observed, we are told, that the eclipsed Moon appears at the point of the Ecliptic opposite to the Sun; and yet here it would appear in arrear of that point by an amount equal to the angle GEC, the supplement of AEC. This, however, is contrary to experience, since the angle GEC would be very sensible, and about 33 degrees. Now according to our computation, which is given in the Treatise on the causes of the phenomena of Saturn, the distance BA between the Earth and the Sun is about twelve thousand diameters of the Earth, and hence four hundred times greater than BC the distance of the Moon, which is 30 diameters. Then the angle ECB will be nearly four hundred times greater than BAE, which is five minutes; namely, the path which the earth travels in two hours along its orbit; and thus the angle BCE will be nearly 33 degrees; and likewise the angle CEG, which is greater by five minutes.

But it must be noted that the speed of light in this argument has been assumed such that it takes a time of one hour to make the passage from here to the Moon. If one supposes that for this it requires only one minute of time, then it is manifest that the angle CEG will only be 33 minutes; and if it requires only ten seconds of time, the angle will be less than six minutes. And then it will not be easy to perceive anything of it in observations of the Eclipse; nor, consequently, will it be permissible to deduce from it that the movement of light is instantaneous.

It is true that we are here supposing a strange velocity that would be a hundred thousand times greater than that of Sound. For Sound, according to what I have observed, travels about 180 Toises[1] in the time of one Second, or in about one beat of the pulse. But this supposition ought not to seem to be an impossibility; since it is not a question of the transport of a body with so great a speed, but of a successive movement which is passed on from some bodies to others. I have then made no difficulty, in meditating on these things, in supposing that the emanation of light is accomplished with time, seeing that in this way all its phenomena can be explained, and that in following the contrary opinion everything is incomprehensible. For it has always seemed to me that even Mr. Des Cartes, whose aim has been to treat all the subjects of Physics intelligibly, and who assuredly has succeeded in this better than any one before him, has said nothing that is not full of difficulties, or even inconceivable, in dealing with Light and its properties.

[1] About 1,115 feet. [Ed. note.]

But that which I employed only as a hypothesis, has recently received great seemingness as an established truth by the ingenious proof of Mr. Römer which I am going here to relate, expecting him himself to give all that is needed for its confirmation. It is founded as is the preceding argument upon celestial observations, and proves not only that Light takes time for its passage, but also demonstrates how much time it takes, and that its velocity is even at least six times greater than that which I have just stated.

For this he makes use of the Eclipses suffered by the little planets which revolve around Jupiter, and which often enter his shadow: and see what is his reasoning. Let A be the Sun, BCDE the annual orbit of the Earth, F Jupiter, GN the orbit of the nearest of his Satellites, for it is this one which is more apt for this investigation than any of the other three, because of the quickness of its revolution. Let G be this Satellite entering into the shadow of Jupiter, H the same Satellite emerging from the shadow.

Let it be then supposed, the Earth being at B some time before the last quadrature, that one has seen the said Satellite emerge from the shadow; it must needs be, if the Earth remains at the same place, that, after 42½ hours, one would again see a similar emergence, because that is the time in which it makes the round of its orbit, and when it would come again into opposition to the Sun. And if the Earth, for instance, were to remain always at B during 30 revolutions of this Satellite, one would see it again emerge from the shadow after 30 times 42½ hours. But the Earth having been carried along during this time to C, increasing thus its distance from Jupiter, it follows that if Light requires time for its passage the illumination of the little planet will be perceived later at C than it would have been at B, and that there must be added to this time of 30 times 42½ hours that which the Light has required to traverse the space MC, the difference of the spaces CH, BH. Similarly at the other quadrature when the earth has come to E from D while approaching toward Jupiter, the immersions of the Satellite ought to be observed at E earlier than they would have been seen if the Earth had remained at D.

Now in quantities of observations of these Eclipses, made during ten consecutive years, these differences have been found to be very considerable, such as ten minutes and more; and from them it has been concluded that in order to traverse the whole diameter of the annual orbit KL, which is double the distance from here to the sun, Light requires about 22 minutes of time.

The movement of Jupiter in his orbit while the Earth passed from B to C, or from D to E, is included in this calculation; and this makes it evident that one cannot attribute the retardation of these illuminations or the anticipation of the eclipses, either to any irregularity occurring in the movement of the little planet or to its eccentricity.

If one considers the vast size of the diameter KL, which according to me is some 24 thousand diameters of the Earth, one will acknowledge the extreme velocity of Light. For, supposing that KL is no more than 22 thousand of these diameters, it appears that being traversed in 22 minutes this makes the speed a thousand diameters in one minute, that is 16⅔ diameters in one second or in one beat of the pulse, which makes more than 11 hundred times a hundred thousand toises; since the diameter of the Earth contains 2,865 leagues, reckoned at 25 to the degree, and each league is 2,282 Toises, according to the exact measurement which Mr. Picard made by order of the King in 1669. But Sound, as I have said above, only travels 180 toises in the same time of one second: hence the velocity of Light is more than six hundred thousand times greater than that of Sound. This, however, is quite another thing from being instantaneous, since there is all the difference between a finite thing and an infinite. Now the successive movement of Light being confirmed in this way, it follows, as I have said, that it spreads by spherical waves, like the movement of Sound.

But if the one resembles the other in this respect, they differ in many other things; to wit, in the first production of the movement which causes them; in the matter in which the movement spreads; and in the manner in which it is propagated. As to that which occurs in the production of Sound, one knows that it is occasioned by the agitation undergone by an entire body, or by a considerable part of one, which shakes all the contiguous air. But the movement of the Light must originate as from each point of the luminous object, else we should not be able to perceive all the different parts of that object, as will be more evident in that which follows. And I do not believe that this movement can be better explained than by supposing that all those of the luminous bodies which are liquid, such as flames, and apparently the sun and the stars, are composed of particles which float in a much more subtle medium which agitates them with great rapidity, and makes them strike against the particles of the ether which surrounds them, and which are much smaller than they. But I hold also that in luminous solids such as charcoal or metal made red hot in the fire, this same movement is caused by the violent agitation of the particles of the metal or of the wood; those of them which are on the surface striking similarly against the ethereal matter. The agitation, moreover, of the particles which engender the light ought to be much more prompt and more rapid than is that of the bodies which cause sound, since we do not see that the tremors of a body which is giving out a sound are capable of giving rise to Light, even as the movement of the hand in the air is not capable of producing Sound.

Now if one examines what this matter may be in which the movement coming from the luminous body is propagated, which I call Ethereal matter, one will see that it is not the same that serves for the propagation of Sound. For one finds that the latter is really that which we feel and which we breathe, and which being removed from any place still leaves there the other kind of matter that serves to convey Light. This may be proved by shutting up a sounding body in a glass vessel from which the air is withdrawn by the machine which Mr. Boyle has given us, and with which he has performed so many beautiful experiments. But in doing this of which I speak, care must be taken to place the sounding body on cotton or on feathers, in such a way that it cannot communicate its tremors either to the glass vessel which encloses it, or to the machine; a precaution which has hitherto been neglected. For then after having exhausted all the air one hears no Sound from the metal, though it is struck.

One sees here not only that our air, which does not penetrate through glass, is the matter by which Sound spreads; but also that it is not the same air but another kind of matter in which Light spreads; since if the air is removed from the vessel the Light does not cease to traverse it as before.

And this last point is demonstrated even more clearly by the celebrated experiment of Torricelli, in which the tube of glass from which the quicksilver has withdrawn itself, remaining void of air, transmits Light just the same as when air is in it. For this proves that a matter different from air exists in this tube, and that this matter must have penetrated the glass or the quicksilver, either one or the other, though they are both impenetrable to the air. And when, in the same experiment, one makes the vacuum after putting a little water above the quicksilver, one concludes equally that the said matter passes through glass or water, or through both.

As regards the different modes in which I have said the movements of Sound and of Light are communicated, one may sufficiently comprehend how this occurs in the case of Sound if one considers that the air is of such a nature that it can be compressed and reduced to a much smaller space than that which it ordinarily occupies. And in proportion as it is compressed the more does it exert an effort to regain its volume; for this property along with its penetrability, which remains notwithstanding its compression, seems to prove that it is made up of small bodies which float about and which are agitated very rapidly in the ethereal matter composed of much smaller parts. So that the cause of the spreading of Sound is the effort which these little bodies make in collisions with one another, to regain freedom when they are a little more squeezed together in the circuit of these waves than elsewhere.

But the extreme velocity of Light, and other properties which it has, cannot admit of such a propagation of motion, and I am about to show here the way in which I conceive it must occur. For this, it is needful to explain the property which hard bodies must possess to transmit movement from one to another.

When one takes a number of spheres of equal size, made of some very hard substance, and arranges them in a straight line, so that they touch one another, one finds, on striking with a similar sphere against the first of these spheres, that the motion passes as in an instant to the last of them, which separates itself from the row, without one's being able to perceive that the others have been stirred. And even that one which was used to strike remains motionless with them. Whence one sees that the movement passes with an extreme velocity which is the greater, the greater the hardness of the substance of the spheres.

But it is still certain that this progression of motion is not instantaneous, but successive, and therefore must take time. For if the movement, or the disposition to movement, if you will have it so, did not pass successively through all these spheres, they would all acquire the movement at the same time, and hence would all advance together; which does not happen. For the last one leaves the whole row and acquires the speed of the one which was pushed. Moreover there are experiments which demonstrate that all the bodies which we reckon of the hardest kind, such as quenched steel, glass, and agate, act as springs and bend somehow, not only when extended as rods but also when they are in the form of spheres or of other shapes. That is to say they yield a little in themselves at the place where they are struck, and immediately regain their former figure. For I have found that on striking with a ball of glass or of agate against a large and quite thick piece of the same substance which had a flat surface, slightly soiled with breath or in some other way, there remained round marks, of smaller or larger size according as the blow had been weak or strong. This makes it evident that these substances yield where they meet, and spring back: and for this time must be required.

* * *

I have then shown in what manner one may conceive Light to spread successively, by spherical waves, and how it is possible that this spreading is accomplished with as great a velocity as that which experiments and celestial observations demand. Whence it may be further remarked that although the particles are supposed to be in continual movement (for there are many reasons for this) the successive propagation of the waves cannot be hindered by this; because the propagation consists nowise in the transport of those particles but merely in a small agitation which they cannot help communicating to those surrounding, notwithstanding any movement which may act on them causing them to be changing positions amongst themselves.

But we must consider still more particularly the origin of these waves, and the manner in which they spread. And, first, it follows from what has been said on the production of Light, that each little region of a luminous body, such as the Sun, a candle, or a burning coal, generates its own waves of which that region is the centre. Thus in the flame of a candle, having distinguished the points A, B, C, concentric circles described about each of these points represent the waves which come from them. And one must imagine the same about every point of the surface and of the part within the flame.

But as the percussions at the centres of these waves possess no regular succession, it must not be supposed that the waves themselves follow one another at equal distances: and if the distances marked in the figure appear to be such, it is rather to mark the progression of one and the same wave at equal intervals of time than to represent several of them issuing from one and the same centre.

After all, this prodigious quantity of waves which traverse one another without confusion and without effacing one another must not be deemed inconceivable; it being certain that one and the same particle of matter can serve for many waves coming from different sides or even from contrary directions, not only if it is struck by blows which follow one another closely but even for those which act on it at the same instant. It can do so because the spreading of the movement is successive. This may be proved by the row of equal spheres of hard matter, spoken of above. If against this row there are pushed from two opposite sides at the same time two similar spheres A and D, one will see each of them rebound with the same velocity which it had in striking, yet the whole row will remain in its place, although the movement has passed along its whole length twice over. And if these contrary movements happen to meet one another at the middle sphere, B, or at some other such as C, that sphere will yield and act as a spring at both sides, and so will serve at the same instant to transmit these two movements.

But what may at first appear full strange and even incredible is that the undulations produced by such small movements and corpuscles, should spread to such immense distances; as for example from the Sun or from the Stars to us. For the force of these waves must grow feeble in proportion as they move away from their origin, so that the action of each one in particular will without doubt become incapable of making itself felt to our sight. But one will cease to be astonished by considering how at a great distance from the luminous body an infinitude of waves, though they have issued from different points of this body, unite together in such a way that they sensibly compose one single wave only, which, consequently, ought to have enough force to make itself felt. Thus this infinite number of waves which originate at the same instant from all points of a fixed star, big it may be as the Sun, make practically only one single wave which may well have force enough to produce an impression on our eyes. Moreover from each luminous point there may come many thousands of waves in the smallest imaginable time, by the frequent percussion of the corpuscles which strike the Ether at these points: which further contributes to rendering their action more sensible.

*"Wherever [the Reader] finds that I have ventured
at any small conjectures, at the causes of the things that I have
observed, I beseech him to look upon them only as uncertain
guesses and not as unquestionable conclusions,
or matters of unconfutable science."*

Robert Hooke

1635 – 1703

THE LAW OF ELASTICITY IS ESTABLISHED

Robert Hooke was a strange character who must have been a useful but somewhat disconcerting member of the Royal Society group. He is described as having originated much but perfected little. As a young man of twenty, he had constructed Boyle's new air pump. Boyle was, evidently, his patron and when the Royal Society was founded, Hooke became its Curator of Experiments. Elected a Fellow in 1663, he was later made the Secretary, which post he occupied from 1677 to 1683. He had many original ideas. It was he who introduced the wave theory of light which Huygens developed. He observed the colors in bubbles and other films, yet Newton systematized the study of light refraction. He was the first to describe the motions of the heavenly bodies as essentially a mechanical problem; others pursued the idea and elaborated theories. He used the pendulum as a measure of gravity; Huygens is credited with the effective development of the pendulum for scientific and horological purposes.

Hooke made several claims to priority—for example, that his theory of planetary motion anticipated Newton's; but if he had observed the motions of the planets, he was unable to apply the mathematics of curvilinear motion to his data. Perhaps Hooke's failure to achieve a more nearly equal stature with Boyle, Newton, and Huygens is to be attributed to his personality; he was an irascible person; he was penurious and, worst of all, in view of his intimacy with Boyle and others of the coterie, who were intellectually the most generous of men, he was prone to unreasonable jealousy. The others throve on scientific controversy. Hooke appears to have spent time nursing his grievances. He lacked that power of communication which, as is obvious from our readings, was becoming essential to the advancement of science.

The selection that follows is from *Early Science in Oxford,* by R. T. Gunther (Oxford, 1931).

THE THEORY OF SPRINGS

THE THEORY OF SPRINGS, though attempted by divers eminent Mathematicians of this Age, has hitherto not been Published by any. It is now about eighteen years since I first found it out, but designing to apply it to some particular use, I omitted the publishing thereof.

About three years since, His Majesty was pleased to see the Experiment that made out this Theory tried at *White-Hall,* as also my Spring Watch.

About two years since, I printed this Theory in an Anagram at the end of my Book of the Descriptions of Helioscopes, viz, ceiiino sssttuv,[1] *id est, Ut tensio sic vis;* That is, The Power of any Spring is in the same proportion with the Tension thereof; That is, if one power stretch or bend it one space, two will bend it two, and three will bend it three, and so forward. Now as the Theory is very short, so the way of trying it is very easie.

Take then a quantity of even-drawn wire, either Steel, Iron, or Brass, and coyl it on an even Cylinder into a Helix of what length or number of

---

[1] This "anagram" consists simply of the letters of the following Latin formula, "Ut tensio sic vis," which in English is literally, "As the tension, so the force."

turns you please, then turn the ends of the Wire into Loops, by one of which suspend this coyl upon a nail, and by the other sustain the weight that you would have to extend it, and hanging on several Weights observe exactly to what length each of the weights do extend it beyond the length that its own weight doth stretch it to, and shall find that if one ounce, or one pound, or one certain weight doth lengthen it one line, or one inch, or one certain length, then two ounces, two pounds, or two weights will extend it two lines, two inches, or two lengths; and three ounces, pounds, or weights, three lines, inches, or lengths; and so forward. And this is the Rule or Law of Nature, upon which all manner of Restituent of Springing motion doth proceed, whether it be of Rarefaction, or Extension, or Condensation and Compression.

Or take a Watch Spring, and coyl it into a Spiral, so as no part thereof may touch another, then provide a very light wheel of Brass, or the like, and fix it on an arbor that hath two small Pivots of Steel, upon which Pivot turn the edge of the said Wheel very even and smooth, so that a small silk may be coyled upon it; then put this Wheel into a Frame, so that the Wheel may move very freely on its Pivots; fasten the central end of the aforesaid Spring close to the Pivot hole or center of the frame in which the Arbor of the Wheel doth move, and the other end thereof to the rim of the Wheel, then coyling a fine limber thread of Silk upon the edge of the Wheel hang a small light scale at the end thereof fit to receive the weight that shall be put thereinto; then suffering the Wheel to stand in its own position by a little index fastened to the frame, and pointing to the Rim of the Wheel, make a mark with Ink, or the like, on that part of the Rim that the Index pointeth at; then put in a drachm weight into the scale, and suffer the Wheel to settle, and make another mark on the Rim where the Index doth point; then add a drachm more, and let the Wheel settle again, and note with Ink, as before, the place of the rim pointed at by the Index; then add a third drachm, and do as before, and so a fourth, fifth, sixth, seventh, eighth, etc. suffering the Wheel to settle, and marking the several places pointed at by the Index, then examine the Distances of all those marks, and comparing them together you shall find that they will all be equal the one to the other, so that if a drachm doth move the Wheel ten degrees, two drachms will move it twenty, and three thirty, and four forty, and five fifty, and so forwards.

Or take a Wire string of twenty, or thirty, or forty foot long, and fasten the upper part thereof to a nail, and to the other end fasten a Scale to receive the weights: Then with a pair of Compasses take the distance of the bottom of the scale from the ground or floor underneath, and set down the said distance, then put in weights into the said scale in the same manner as in the former trials, and measure the several stretchings of the said string, and set them down. Then compare the several stretchings of the said string, and you will find that they will always bear the same proportions one to the other that the weights do that made them.

The same will be found, if trial be made, with a piece of dry wood that will bend and return, if one end thereof be fixt in a horizontal posture, and to the other end be hanged weights to make it bend downwards.

The manner of trying the same thing upon a body of Air, whether it be for the rarefaction or for the compression thereof I did about fourteen years since publish in my *Micrographia,* and therefore I shall not need to add any further description thereof.

From all which it is very evident that the Rule or Law of Nature in every springing body is, that the force or power thereof to restore itself to its natural position is always proportionate to the Distance or space it is removed therefrom, whether it be by rarefaction, or separation of its parts the one from the other, or by a Condensation, or crowding of those parts nearer together. Nor is it observable in these bodies only, but in all other springy bodies whatsoever, whether Metal, Wood, Stones, baked Earths, Hair, Horns, Silk, Bones, Sinews, Glass and the like. Respect being had to the particular figures of the bodies bended and the advantagious or disadvantagious ways of bending them.

From this principle it will be easie to calculate the several strength of Bows, as of Long Bows or Cross-Bows, whether they be made of Wood, Steel, Horns, Sinews, or the like. As also of the *Balistæ* or *Catapultæ* used by the Ancients, which being once found, and Tables thereof calculated, I shall anon shew a way how to calculate the power they have in shooting or casting Arrows, Bullets, Stones, Granadoes, or the like.

From these principles also it will be easie to calculate the proportionate strength of the spring of a Watch upon the Fusey thereof, and consequently of adjusting the Fusey to the Spring so as to make it draw or move the Watch always with an equal force.

From the same also it will be easie to give the reason of the *Isochrone* motion of a Spring or extended string, and of the uniform sound produced

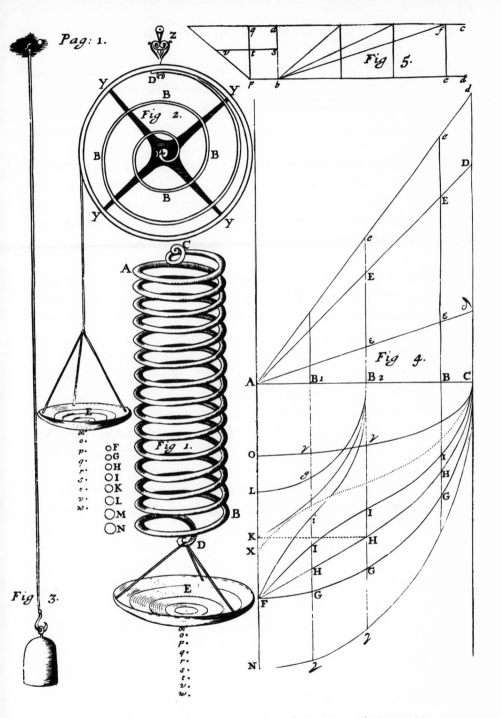

Hooke's apparatus for establishing the law of elasticity and his graphic
representation of the results. From Robert Hooke's *Lectiones Cutlerianae,*
London, 1674-1679. (Courtesy of the Burndy Library.)

by those whose Vibrations are quick enough to produce an audible sound, and likewise the reason of the sounds, and their variations in all manner of sonorous or springing Bodies, of which more on another occasion.

From this appears the reason, as I shall shew by and by, why a Spring applied to the balance of a Watch doth make the vibrations thereof equal, whether they be greater or smaller, one of which kind I shewed to the right Honourable Robert Boyle Esq.; and Sir Robert Morey in the year 1660, in order to have gotten Letters Patents for the use and benefit thereof.

From this it will be easy to make a Philosophical Scale to examine the weight of any body without putting in weights. . . .

This Scale I contrived in order to examine the gravitation of bodies towards the Center of the Earth, viz, to examine whether bodies at a further distance from the Center of the Earth did not lose somewhat of their power or tendency towards it. And propounded it as one of the Experiments to be tried at the top of the Pike of *Teneriff,* and attempted the same at the top of the Tower of St. *Paul's* before the burning of it in the late great Fire;[2] as also at the top and bottom of the Abbey of St. *Peter's* in *Westminster* though these being by but small distances removed from the Surface I was not able certainly to perceive any manifest difference. I propounded the same also to be tried at the bottom and several station of deep Mines; and D. *Power* did make some trials to that end, by his Instruments not being good, nothing could be certainly concluded from them.

These are the Phenomena of Springs and springy bodies, which as they have not hitherto been by any that I know reduced to Rules so have all the attempts for the explications of the reason of their power, and of springiness in general, been very insufficient. . . .

[2] The great London fire of 1660, in which the medieval cathedral of St. Paul's was destroyed.

*"My design in this Book is not to explain
the properties of Light by Hypotheses but to propose and
prove them by Reason and Experiment."*

Isaac Newton

1642 — 1727

THE COMPOSITE NATURE OF WHITE LIGHT
IS DEMONSTRATED BY THE USE
OF PRISMS

Newton, the main facts of whose life have been already discussed (page 55), published as his first scientific paper a study of the phenomenon of light; and his general work on the subject of optics would alone justify the fame accorded to him. Although Descartes had accurately described the rainbow, and successfully applied mathematics to the measurement of the angle of the bow, Newton's experiments with prisms greatly extended knowledge of the subject. These experiments showed that white light is a composite of many colors of light which are refracted unequally in passing through the prism. Newton's explanation of the propagation of light as due to the emission of "small Bodies" from "shining Substances" was, as we have seen, only part of the explanation. In practical applications, Newton, by his invention of the reflecting telescope, successfully overcame the problem caused by the chromatic aberration due to the unequal refraction of different colors of light through the lenses of the telescope.

Newton's great achievement was in obtaining his explanations by controlled experiment and in his ability to present the results in precise language. The selection which follows provides a good example of both aspects of his skill. The language may be archaic, by modern standards, but there is no doubt, at any point, as to what he means and as to how he conducted his experiments.

The following selection, taken from W. F. Magie's *A Source Book in Physics,* originally appeared in *Philosophical Transactions, Abridged,* Vol. I (1672).

DISPERSION OF LIGHT

In the year 1666, (at which time I applied myself to the grinding of optick glasses of other figures than spherical) I procured me a triangular glass prism, to try therewith the celebrated phænomena of colours. And in order thereto, having darkened my chamber, and made a small hole in my window-shuts, to let in a convenient quantity of the sun's light, I placed my prism at its entrance, that it might be thereby refracted to the opposite wall. It was at first a very pleasing divertisement, to view the vivid and intense colours produced thereby; but after a while applying my self to consider them more circumspectly, I became surprised, to see them in an oblong form; which, according to the received laws of refraction, I expected should have been circular. They were terminated at the sides with straight lines, but at the ends, the decay of light was so gradual that it was difficult to determine justly, what was their figure; yet they seemed semicircular.

Comparing the length of this colour'd Spectrum with its breadth, I found it about five times greater, a disproportion so extravagant, that it excited me to a more than ordinary curiosity to examining from whence it might proceed. I could scarce think, that the various thicknesses of the glass, or the termination with shadow or darkness, could have any influence on light to produce such an effect; yet I thought it not amiss, first to examine those circumstances, and so try'd what would happen by transmitting light through parts of the glass of divers thicknesses, or through holes in the window of diverse bignesses, or by setting the prism without, so that the light might pass through it, and be refracted, before it was terminated by the hole: But I found none of those circumstances material. The fashion of the colours was in all these cases the same.

Then I suspected, whether by any unevenness in the glass or other contingent irregularity, these colours might be thus dilated. And to try this, I took another prism like the former, and so placed it, that the light passing through them both might be refracted contrary ways, and so by the latter returned into that course from which the former had diverted it. For by this means I thought the regular effects of the first prism would be destroyed by the second prism, but the irregular ones more augmented, by the multiplicity of refractions. The event was, that the light, which by the first prism was diffused into an oblong form was by the second reduced into an orbicular one, with as much regularity as when it did not at all pass through them.

* * *

Then I began to suspect, whether the rays, after their trajection through the prism, did not move in curve lines, and according to their more or less curvity tend to divers parts of the wall. And it increased my suspicion, when I remembered that I had often seen a tennis ball struck with an oblique racket, describe such a curve line. For, a circular as well as a progressive motion being communicated to it by that stroke, its parts on that side where the motions conspire, must press and beat the contiguous air more violently than on the other, and there excite a reluctancy and reaction of the air proportionably greater. And for the same reason, if the rays of light should possibly be globular bodies, and by their oblique passage out of one medium into another, acquire a circulating motion, they ought to feel the greater resistance from the ambient ether, on that side, where the motions conspire, and thence be continually bowed to the other. But notwithstanding this plausible ground of suspicion, when I came to examine it, I could observe no such curvity in them. And besides (which was enough for my purpose) I observed, that the difference 'twixt the length of the image, and the diameter of the hole, through which the light was transmitted, was proportionable to their distance.

The gradual removal of these suspicions at length led me to the *Experimentum Crucis,* which was this: I took two boards, and placed one of them close behind the prism at the window, so that the light might pass through a small hole, made in it for the purpose, and fall on the other board, which I placed at about 12 feet distance, having first made a small

hole in it also, for some of the incident light to pass through. Then I placed
another prism behind this second board, so that the light trajected through
both the boards might pass through that also, and be again refracted before
it arrived at the wall. This done, I took the first prism in my hand, and
turned it to and fro slowly about its axis, so much as to make the several
parts of the image cast, on the second board, successively pass through the
hole in it, that I might observe to what places on the wall the second prism
would refract them. And I saw by the variation of those places, that the
light, tending to that end of the image, towards which the refraction of the
first prism was made, did in the second prism suffer a refraction considerably greater than the light tending to the other end. And so the true
cause of the length of that image was detected to be no other, than the light
is not similar or homogenial, but consists of *Difform Rays, some of which
are more Refrangible than others;* so that without any difference in their
incidence on the same medium, some shall be more Refracted than others;
and therefore that, according to their *particular Degrees of Refrangibility,*
they were transmitted through the prism to divers parts of the opposite
wall.

Now I shall proceed to acquaint you with another more notable *Dif-
formity* in its rays, wherein the origin of colours is unfolded: concerning
which I shall lay down the doctrine first, and then for its examination give
you an instance or two of the experiments, as a specimen of the rest.

The doctrine you will find comprehended and illustrated in the following propositions:

1. As the rays of light differ in degrees of refrangibility so they also
differ in their disposition to exhibit, this or that particular colour. Colours
are not qualifications of light, derived from refractions, or reflections of
natural bodies (as 'tis generally believed) but original and connate properties, which in divers rays are divers. Some rays are disposed to exhibit a red
colour and no other; some a yellow and no other, some a green and no
other, and so of the rest. Nor are there only rays proper and particular to
the more eminent colours, but even to all their intermediate gradations.

2. To the same degree of refrangibility ever belongs the same colour,
and to the same colour ever belongs the same degree of refrangibility. The
least refrangible rays are all disposed to exhibit a red colour, and contrarily
those rays which are disposed to exhibit a red colour, are all the least
refrangible: so the most refrangible rays are all disposed to exhibit a deep

violet colour, and contrarily those which are apt to exhibit such a violet colour are all the most refrangible. And so to all the intermediate colours in a continued series belong intermediate degrees of refrangibility. And this Analogy 'twixt colours and refrangibility is very precise and strict; the rays always either exactly agreeing in both, or proportionally disagreeing in both.

3. The species of colour, and degree of refrangibility proper to any particular sort of rays, is not mutable by refraction, nor by reflection from natural bodies, nor by any other cause that I could yet observe. When any one sort of rays hath been well parted from those of other kinds, it hath afterwards obstinately retained its colour, notwithstanding my utmost endeavors to change it. I have refracted it with prisms, and reflected it with bodies, which in daylight were of other colours; I have intercepted it with the coloured film of air, interceeded two compressed plates of glass; transmitted it through coloured mediums, and through mediums irradiated with other sorts of rays, and diversely terminated it; and yet could never produce any new colour out of it. It would by contracting or dilating become more brisk, or faint, and by the loss of many rays, in some cases very obscure and dark; but I could never see it changed in specie.

4. Yet seeming transmutations of colours may be made, where there is any mixture of divers sorts of rays. For in such mixtures, the component colours appear not, but, by their mutual allaying each other, constitute a midling colour. And therefore, if by refraction, or any other of the aforesaid causes, the difform rays, latent in such a mixture, be separated, there shall emerge colours different from the colour of the composition. Which colours are not new generated, but only made apparent by being parted; for if they be again entirely mixt and blended together, they will again compose that colour, which they did before separation. And for the same reason, transmutations made by the convening of divers colours are not real; for when the difform rays are again severed, they will exhibit the very same colours which they did before they entered the composition; as you see blue and yellow powders, when finely mixed, appear to the naked eye, green, and yet the colours of the component corpuscles are not thereby really transmuted, but only blended. For when viewed with a good microscope they still appear blue and yellow interspersedly.

5. There are therefore two sorts of colours. The one original and simple, and the other compounded of these. The original or primary colours

are red, yellow, green, blue, and a violet-purple, together with orange, indico, and an indefinite variety of intermediate gradations.

6. The same colours in specie with these primary ones, may be also produced by composition. For a mixture of yellow and blue makes green; of red and yellow makes orange; of orange and yellowish green makes yellow. And in general, if any two colours be mixed, which in the series of those generated by the prism are not too far distant one from another, they by their mutual alloy compound that colour, which in the said series appeareth in the midway between them. But those which are situated at too great a distance, do not so. Orange and indico produce not the intermediate green, nor scarlet and green the intermediate yellow.

7. But the most surprising, and wonderful composition was that of whiteness. There is no one sort of rays which alone can exhibit this. 'Tis ever compounded, and to its composition, are requisite all the aforesaid primary colours, mixed in a due proportion. I have often with admiration beheld that all the colours of the prism being made to converge, and thereby to be again mixed, as they were in the light before it was incident upon the prism, reproduced light, entirely and perfectly white, and not at all sensibly differing from a direct light of the sun, unless when the glasses, I used, were not sufficiently clear; for then they would a little incline it to their colour.

8. Hence therefore it comes to pass, that whiteness is the usual colour of light; for light is a confused aggregate of rays indued with all sorts of colours, as they were promiscuously darted from the various parts of luminous bodies. And of such a confused aggregate, as I said, is generated whiteness, if there be a due proportion of the ingredients; but if any one predominate, the light must incline to that colour; as it happens in the blue flame of brimstone; the yellow flame of a candle; and the various colours of the fixed stars.

9. These things considered, the manner how colours are produced by the prism is evident. For, of the rays, constituting the incident light, since those which differ in colour proportionally differ in refrangibility, they by their unequal refractions must be severed and dispersed into an oblong form in an orderly succession, from the least refracted scarlet, to the most refracted violet. And for the same reason it is, that objects when looked upon through a prism, appear coloured. For the difform rays, by their unequal refractions, are made to diverge towards several parts of the Retina,

and these express the images of things coloured, as in the former case they did the sun's image upon a wall. And by this inequality of refractions, they become not only coloured, but also very confused and indistinct.

10. Why the colours of the rainbow appear in falling drops of rain, is also from hence evident. For those drops which refract the rays, disposed to appear purple, in greatest quantity to the spectator's eye, refract the rays of other sorts so much less, as to make them pass beside it; and such are the drops on the inside of the primary bow, and on the outside of the secondary or exterior one. So those drops, which refract in greatest plenty the rays, apt to appear red, toward the spectator's eye, refract those of other sorts so much more, as to make them pass beside it; and such are the drops on the exterior part of the primary, and interior part of the secondary bow.

11. The odd phænomena of an infusion of *Lignum Nephriticum,* leaf-gold, fragments of coloured glass, and some other transparently coloured bodies, appearing in one position of one colour, and of another in another, are on these grounds no longer riddles. For those are substances apt to reflect one sort of light, and transmit another; as may be seen in a dark room, by illuminating them with familiar or uncompounded light. For then they appear of that colour only, with which they are illuminated, but yet in one position more vivid and luminous than in another, accordingly as they are disposed more or less to reflect or transmit the incident colour.

12. From hence also is manifest the reason of an unexpected experiment which Mr. *Hook,* somewhere in his *Micrography* relates to have made with two wedge-like transparent vessels, filled the one with a red, the other with a blue liquor: namely, that though they were severally transparent enough, yet both together became opake; for if one transmitted only red, and the other only blue, no rays could pass through both.

13. I might add more instances of this nature, but I shall conclude with this general one. That the colours of all natural bodies have no other origin than this, that they are variously qualified, to reflect one sort of light in greater plenty than another. And this I have experimented in a dark room, by illuminating those bodies with uncompounded light of divers colours. For by that means any body may be made to appear of any colour. They have there no appropriate colour, but ever appear of the colour of the light cast upon them, but yet with this difference, that they are most brisk and vivid in the light of their own daylight colour. Minium appeareth

there of any colour indifferently, with which it is illustrated, but yet most luminous in red, and so bise appeareth indifferently of any colour, but yet most luminous in blue. And therefore minium reflecteth rays of any colour, but most copiously those endowed with red, and consequently when illustrated with daylight; that is, with all sorts of rays promiscuously blended, those qualified with red shall abound most in the reflected light, and by their prevalence cause it to appear of that colour. And for the same reason bise, reflecting blue most copiously, shall appear blue by the excess of those rays in its reflected light; and the like of other bodies. And that this is the entire and adequate cause of their colours, is manifest, because they have no power to change or alter the colours of any sort of rays incident apart, but put on all colours indifferently, with which they are enlightened.

These things being so, it can be no longer disputed, whether there be colours in the dark, or whether they be the qualities of the objects we see, no nor perhaps, whether light be a body. For, since colours are the qualities of light, having its rays for their entire and immediate subject, how can we think those rays qualities also, unless one quality may be the subject of, and sustain another; which in effect is to call it substance. We should not know bodies for substances; were it not for their sensible qualities, and the principal of those being now found due to something else, we have as good reason to believe that to be a substance also.

Besides, who ever thought any quality to be a heterogeneous aggregate, such as light is discovered to be? But to determine more absolutely what light is, after what manner refracted, and by what modes or actions it produceth in our minds the phantasms of colours, is not so easie; and I shall not mingle conjectures with certainties.

*"I have been informed that a book is published
at Rome, by a learned Jesuit named Philippo Bonanni,
wherein he maintains that animalcules, or small living
creatures, can be produced out of inanimate substances, such as
mud or sand, by spontaneous generation, according to the
doctrine of Aristotle; and it seems that this learned
gentleman is very desirous to see my observations on
the subject. I shall therefore proceed to consider
Signor Bonanni's position, and I doubt not,
that upon investigation they will be found
of no weight or substance, but will
vanish like smoke or vapour."*
—Antony van Leeuwenhoek

THE ORIGIN OF LIFE

Scientists have tried, during the past twenty-five centuries, to solve numerous scientific riddles. Many of these have responded to the routine of experiment, analysis, and synthesis; or, if they have not been completely solved, enough has been learned about them for the scientist to know that his approach is sound. He has been able to cross-check his results by more experiments, to correct previous errors of observation, and to tidy up loose ends. He is, often, well aware that even where a neat package of solutions has been laid on the table, he must be prepared to remove the wrappings and start his work again on some aspect of the problem. But at least he knows where to start.

Other problems remain tantalizingly unsolved. A long history of experiment, an ever increasing fund of observed data,

401

and innumerable "solutions" have left the scientist with his original question. Investigation has frequently increased the number of unanswered questions. Certainly no atomic physicist of today would say that the spectacular discoveries of the past twenty years have finally explained the nature of matter.

Perhaps the most challenging question of all is: "How did life begin?" The science of geology, through examination of rocks and the fossils found in them, now indicates that although the earth is between three and five billion years old, life itself has existed for less than one billion years. But if, for two or four billion years, the state of the earth was such that life could not exist on it, by what means did life appear when, at last, conditions became favorable? How, indeed, did life *begin?* The readings which follow describe some of the discoveries which have upset ancient ideas and set us on the road toward the final answer.

The first task of the biologists, after Galileo and others presented them with a practical microscope, was to show the error of the first answer given to this question. Because they had frequently discovered live animals in decaying timber, in rotting vegetation and dung, in mud, and even in the dew, the idea developed that under the influence of heat, water, air, and putrefaction, life was generated spontaneously. Much of this belief was crystallized by Aristotle in his *Historia Animalium,* in which he gathered much so-called first-hand observation in apparent support of it. Like so many of Aristotle's ideas, this one dominated the thinking of Western man for more than 2000 years. As we have already seen, to doubt the Aristotelian doctrine was to defy the evidence of the senses and the processes of reason and, what was much worse, to challenge the constituted religious authorities of the time.

In his *Georgics,* Virgil (70-19 B.C.) gives a graphic account of the generation of living bees from the carcass of a dead calf. And as late as the sixteenth century van Helmont provided a recipe for producing mice from rags and wheat grains. Even Harvey and Newton accepted some features of spontaneous generation as not incompatible with their other views. The work of Pasteur and Tyndall in the nineteenth century apparently settled two hundred years of controversy on the subject, but even to the present day the erroneous belief persists among laymen that some smaller living things are spontaneously generated.

The first attempt to examine the question in a modern manner was made late in the seventeenth century by Francesco Redi. Redi was pre-eminently an experimenter who showed an intuitive grasp of the significance of the scientific method. The selection from his writings reflects an amazingly modern way of putting questions to nature and of eliciting answers. Redi was perceptive enough to limit both his experiments and the conclusions he drew from them. He thought he had proved that the maggots found in decaying meat did not originate spontaneously but developed from eggs deposited in the meat by flies. He also showed that the maggots ultimately developed into flies—flies of the same type that had originally laid eggs in the meat. Redi erected no broad theories on the origin of living things, although his experiments unquestionably were responsible for overthrowing the notion of the spontaneous generation of the larger forms of life. Yet his acuteness in this direction did not prevent him from concluding that the wormlike larvae found in plant galls arose spontaneously in the gall—a view that was corrected by Vallisnieri (1661-1730), a favorite pupil of Redi's. Vallisnieri and others finally established the belief that all the larger forms of life originated from other living things by some reproductive process.

The development and use of microscopes by Leeuwenhoek reopened the question of spontaneous generation, for it revealed the existence of a world of microscopic life. It was inevitable that the question be asked again—where do the myriad microscopic plants and animals come from? And just as inevitably the answer seemed to be that they arose spontaneously from the water or other substances in which they were found. Early in the eighteenth century Joblot performed experiments on heated infusions to see whether they could produce microscopic life. He concluded that the teeming animalcules he found entered the infusion from the air and reproduced more animalcules like themselves.

Despite this experimental demonstration that microbic

originated from pre-existing life just as do the larger plants and animals, the idea of spontaneous generation of microscopic plants and animals persisted and even flourished. It was particularly supported by the experiments of Needham (1713-1781) and Buffon (1707-1788) among others. It was these experiments that stimulated the efforts of Spallanzani, who repeated many of Needham's experiments and showed that heating an infusion effectively prevents the appearance of microscopic life.

Spallanzani's experiments were brilliantly conceived and performed and should have dispelled the notion of spontaneous generation. The doctrine persisted, however, for almost another century, and scores of investigators applied themselves to the question, often with techniques which were primitive against the standard set by Spallanzani. By the middle of the nineteenth century, the question had aroused such keen interest that some new experimental refutation or confirmation was imperative. Pasteur, in a series of researches remarkable for their clarity, simplicity, and experimental skill, provided definitive refutation of the idea of spontaneous generation of microorganisms. Pasteur's was, in fact, the major work which led to the establishment of the germ theory of disease.

It seemed that the goal had been attained; but only the idea of spontaneous generation had been disposed of. The study of viruses has revealed the existence of entities which show some of the attributes of living matter at the molecular level. We are still tantalized by the question: "How did life begin?"

*"I have given myself all possible trouble
and have taken the greatest care to convince myself of
facts with my own eyes by means of accurate and continued
experiments before submitting them to my mind
as matter for reflection."*

Francesco Redi

1626 — 1697

THE DEVELOPMENT OF MAGGOTS IS
SHOWN BY EXPERIMENT TO RESULT
FROM THE EGGS OF FLIES

Distinguished scholar, philologist, physician, and poet, but pre-eminently a naturalist of wide interests, Redi is best remembered today for his experimental investigation of the concept of spontaneous generation. He was a physician to the Dukes of Tuscany, but his main interest was in investigation and his *Esperienze Intorno alla Generazione degli Insetti* is the record of an experimental examination of a biological problem which reaches almost modern standards.

Redi attempted no universal explanation. He tried to demonstrate the simple hypothesis that maggots found in decaying flesh were not the product of the putrefaction of the flesh but were produced by natural means by living animals (flies) which laid their eggs in the meat. His conclusion was: "Thus the flesh of dead animals cannot engender worms unless the eggs of the living be deposited therein." Redi fully recognized the limits of his experiments but they soon became accepted as proof that, for large animals at least, "if living causes be excluded, no living things arise."

Redi was evidently not a wholehearted opponent of the idea of spontaneous generation, for he used it to explain the origin of insect larvae found in many plant galls. Some galls have an obvious opening by which the egg of the insect could be deposited within the plant tissues before the gall developed. Many galls do not reveal this point of entrance and it was these which puzzled Redi. It remained for one of Redi's students, Vallisnieri (1661-1730), utilizing the techniques of his teacher, to explain the natural origin of these insect larvae and thus to generalize Redi's statement.

Redi's method of investigation was an early form of "control experiment" now almost standard practice in biological experimentation. The technique takes account of the number of variables in a problem and examines the results of testing one variable while keeping the others unchanged. A "control" case is established as a standard of comparison so that the investigator can ensure that only the variable being tested affects the results. The number of controls used will depend on the number of possible conditions to be accounted for. If, for example, two rats are kept under identical conditions except that one (the control) is fed normal food and the other a vitamin-reinforced diet, the effects of the diet can be observed and precise conclusions reached without fear of intrusion of unknown factors. Redi's sealed and open flasks, described in the following selection, were an insurance that his experiment with the closed flask was not affected by some internal condition which would have brought on a similar result in an open flask at that particular time.

Redi's application of the method of "control experiment" was not to be generally adopted in the biological sciences for two hundred years, but his general influence on contemporary science is shown by the fact that his *Esperienze,* first published in 1668, went through five editions before 1688. Nine men, of whom he was one, formed the Accademia del Cimento in 1657, actually providing a model for the Royal Society of London and similar groups of science-minded men. The Accademia went out of existence before Redi published his work, but the channels of communication had been well enough established for Redi's reports to become rapidly available in London, Paris, and Amsterdam.

The following selection is taken from the M. A. B. Bigelow translation of *Esperienze,* titled *Experiments on the Generation of Insects by Francesco Redi* (Open Court, 1909).

EXPERIMENTS ON THE GENERATION OF INSECTS

ALTHOUGH CONTENT to be corrected by any one wiser than myself, if I should make erroneous statements, I shall express my belief that the Earth, after having brought forth the first plants and animals at the beginning by order of the Supreme and Omnipotent Creator, has never since produced any kinds of plants or animals, either perfect or imperfect, and everything which we know in past or present times that she has produced, came solely from the true seeds of the plants and animals themselves, which thus, through means of their own, preserve their species. And, although it be a matter of daily observation that infinite numbers of worms are produced in dead bodies and decayed plants, I feel, I say, inclined to believe that these worms are all generated by insemination and that the putrefied matter in which they are found has no other office than that of serving as a place, or suitable nest where animals deposit their eggs at the breeding season, and in which they also find nourishment; otherwise, I assert that nothing is ever generated therein. And, in order, Signor Carlo, to demonstrate to you the truth of what I say, I will describe to you some of those insects, which being most common, are best known to us.

In being thus, as I have said, the dictum of ancients and moderns, and the popular belief, that the putrescence of a dead body, or the filth of any sort of decayed matter engenders worms; and being desirous of tracing the truth in the case, I made the following experiment:

At the beginning of June I ordered to be killed three snakes, the kind called eels of Aesculapius. As soon as they were dead, I placed them in an open box to decay. Not long afterwards I saw that they were covered with worms of a conical shape and apparently without legs. These worms were intent on devouring the meat, increasing meanwhile in size, and from day to day I observed that they likewise increased in number; but, although of the same shape, they differed in size, having been born on different days. But all, little and big, after having consumed the meat, leaving only the bones intact, escaped from a small aperture in the closed box, and I was unable to discover their hiding place. Being curious, therefore, to know their fate, I again prepared three of the same snakes, which in three days were covered with small worms. These increased daily in number and size remaining alike in form, though not in color. Of these, the largest were white outside, and the smallest ones, pink. When the meat was all consumed, the worms eagerly sought an exit, but I had closed every aperture. On the nineteenth day of the same month some of the worms ceased all movements, as if they were asleep, and appeared to shrink and gradually assume a shape like an egg. On the twentieth day all the worms had assumed the egg shape, and had taken on a golden white color, turning to red, which in some darkened, becoming almost black. At this point the red, as well as the black ones, changed from soft to hard, resembling somewhat those chrysalides formed by caterpillars, silkworms, and similar insects. My curiosity being thus aroused, I noticed that there was some difference in shape between the red and the black eggs (pupæ), though it was clear that all were formed alike of many rings joined together; nevertheless, these rings were more sharply outlined, and more apparent in the black than in the red, which last were almost smooth and without a slight depression at one end, like that in a lemon picked from its stalk, which further distinguished the black egg-like balls. I placed these balls separately in glass vessels, well covered with paper, and at the end of eight days, every shell of the red balls was broken, and from each came forth a fly of gray color, torpid and dull, misshapen as if half finished, with closed wings; but after a few minutes they commenced to unfold and to expand in exact proportion to the tiny body, which also in the meantime had acquired symmetry in all its parts. Then the whole creature, as if made anew, having lost its gray color, took on a most brilliant and vivid green; and the whole body had expanded and grown so that it seemed incredible that it could ever have been contained in the small shell. Though the red eggs (pupæ) brought forth green flies at the end of eight days, the black ones labored fourteen days to produce certain large black flies striped with white, having a hairy abdomen, of the kind that we see daily buzzing about the butchers' stalls.

Having considered these things, I began to believe that all worms found in meat were derived directly from the dropping of flies, and not from the putrefaction of the meat, and I was still more confirmed in this belief by having observed that, before the meat grew wormy, flies had hovered over it, of the same kind as those that later bred in it. Belief would be vain without the confirmation of experiment, hence in the middle of July I put a snake, some fish, some eels of the Arno, and a slice of milk-fed veal in four large, wide-mouthed flasks; having well closed and sealed them, I then filled the same number of flasks in the same way, only leaving these open. It was not long before the meat and the fish, in these second vessels, became wormy and flies were seen entering and leaving at will; but in the closed flasks I did not see a worm, though many days had passed since the dead flesh had been put in them. Outside on the paper cover there was now and then a deposit, or a maggot that eagerly sought some crevice by which to enter and obtain nourishment. Meanwhile the different things placed in the flasks had become putrid and stinking.

Not content with these experiments, I tried many others at different seasons, using different vessels. In order to leave nothing undone, I even had pieces of meat put under ground, but though remaining buried for weeks, they never bred worms, as was always the case when flies had been allowed to light on the meat. One day a large number of worms, which had bred in some buffalo-meat, were killed by my order; having placed part in a closed dish, and part in an open one, nothing appeared in the first dish, but in the second worms had hatched, which changing as usual into egg-shaped balls (pupae), finally became flies of the common kind. In the same experiment tried with dead flies, I never saw anything breed in the closed vessel.

Hence I might conjecture that Father Kircher, though a man worthy of esteem, was led into erroneous statements in the twelfth book of "The Subterranean World," where he describes the experiment of breeding flies in the dead bodies of the same. "The dead flies," says the good man, "should be besprinkled and soaked with honey-water, and then placed on a copper-plate exposed to the tepid heat of ashes; afterward very minute worms, only visible through the microscope, will appear, which little by little grow wings on the back and assume the shape of very small flies, that slowly attain perfect size." I believe, however, that the aforesaid honey-water only serves to attract the living flies to breed in the corpses of their comrades and to drop their eggs therein. . . .

Leaving this long digression and returning to my argument, it is necessary to tell you that although I thought I had proved that the flesh of dead animals could not engender worms unless the semina of live ones were deposited therein, still, to remove all doubt, as the trial had been made with closed vessels into which the air could not penetrate or circulate, I wished to attempt a new experiment by putting meat and fish in a large vase closed only with a fine Naples veil, that allowed the air to enter. For further protection against flies, I placed the vessel in a frame covered with the same net. I never saw any worms in the meat, though many were to be seen moving about on the net-covered frame. These, attracted by the odor of the meat, succeeded at last in penetrating the fine meshes and would have entered the vase had I not speedily removed them. It was interesting, in the meanwhile, to notice the number of flies buzzing about which, every now and then, would light on the outside net and deposit worms there. I noted that some left six or seven at a time there and others dropped them in the air before reaching the net. Perhaps these were of the same breed mentioned by Scaliger, in whose hand, by a lucky accident, a large fly deposited some small worms, whence he drew the conclusion that all flies bring forth live worms directly and not eggs. But what I have already said on the subject proves how much this learned man was in error. It is true that some kinds of flies bring forth live worms and some others eggs, as I have proved by experiment.

" . . . wherever I found out anything remarkable,
I have thought it my duty to put down my discovery on paper,
so that all ingenuous people might be
informed thereof."

Antony van Leeuwenhoek

1632 – 1723

BACTERIA AND PROTOZOA ARE SEEN AND ACCURATELY DESCRIBED FOR THE FIRST TIME

Van Leeuwenhoek represents a type of man that has now been virtually excluded from the pursuit of discovery in science. The modern laboratory is a highly specialized institution, and those who hope to join in its work must undergo a rigorous formal training, itself sometimes regrettably specialized. There was a time when the gifted amateur enjoying a modest income could indulge his curiosity about life's phenomena by making experiments or exploiting the possibilities of useful inventions. His interest might be indulged as a mere hobby or, as in the case of Leeuwenhoek, as the consuming passion of a lifetime. He might, like Boyle, propound laws or content himself for the most part with recording observations. His studies might be broad and, in a sense, undisciplined; or they might be confined to a single problem.

Born ten years before the death of Galileo into a period which saw the foundation of the great scientific societies, van

Leeuwenhoek started his life in Holland as a businessman. He soon abandoned Amsterdam for the peace of Delft. An income from a city appointment—that of sheriff's chamberlain—and ample leisure enabled him to indulge his fascination for microscopes. For the rest of his ninety-one years van Leeuwenhoek studied the world of microscopic life.

Leeuwenhoek's hobby, and later his specialization, was the magnifying glass. The compound microscope had already been developed by this time, but it was not to become a satisfactory instrument until the nineteenth century because of the difficulties in using two lenses. Leeuwenhoek contented himself with improving the single-lens or simple microscope. This was easier to make but much more difficult to use since the curvature required for high magnifications limited the coverage to an extremely small field. Leeuwenhoek made more than four hundred lenses, some of them magnifying up to 270×.

Having produced his lenses, van Leeuwenhoek went on to observe a wide range of materials. He was a most careful observer, even though untrained in science, and left a record of his observations in a series of hundreds of letters written in his native Dutch and sent to the secretary of the Royal Society of England, who published them in Latin and English translations.

The whole world of microscopic life was first seen and reported by Leeuwenhoek—protozoa, bacteria, and countless other smaller animals and plants. The descriptions were so accurate that it is possible for the reader today to identify the animal or plant being described. Some were represented by drawings which are even more strikingly accurate. Van Leeuwenhoek observed circulation in both eels and fish; he perceived the blood cells and confirmed Malpighi's discovery of the capillaries, thus completing the theory of circulation as developed by Harvey (1578-1657) some fifty-five years before. He recognized that the aphid was developed by parthenogenesis—that is, from unfertilized eggs; he made particularly accurate observations on the development of the ant and on the spinning and poison apparatus of spiders. Not least of his accomplishments was to make unusually accurate micrometric measurements.

Van Leeuwenhoek gave some of his microscopes away but never sold one and kept the best for himself. He did not even permit anyone to look through his best microscopes. On his death many of his microscopes were bequeathed to the Royal Society but most of these have disappeared. The letters used in these readings are his most famous ones and record his discovery of protozoa and of bacteria.

The life of van Leeuwenhoek amply demonstrates the thesis, recently presented to the American Chemical Society by Dr. W. S. Knoll, that "very great discoveries . . . are still so close to the surface that they can be unearthed with little expense by non-conformists with an inquisitive mind, with knowledge, the urge to create and who are prepared to accept sacrifice as a way of life" (*Nature,* London Vol. 181, p. 160).

The selection that follows has been taken from *Antony van Leeuwenhoek and his 'Little Animals'* (1932) by C. Dobell, who translated the letters from the original Dutch.

FIRST OBSERVATION ON RAIN-WATER

In the year 1675, about half-way through September (being busy with studying air, when I had much compressed it by means of water), I discovered living creatures in rain, which had stood but a few days in a new tub that was painted blue within. This observation provoked me to investigate this water more narrowly; and especially because these little animals were, to my eye, more than 10,000 times smaller than the animalcule which Swammerdam has portrayed, and called by the name of water-flea or water-louse, which you can see alive and moving in water with the bare eye. [Obviously Daphnia]

Of the first sort that I discovered in the said water [Obviously Vorticella sp.], I saw, after divers observations, that the bodies consisted of 5, 6, 7, or 8 very clear globules, but without being able to discern any membrane or skin that held these globules together, or in which they were inclosed. When these animalcules bestirred 'emselves, they sometimes stuck out two little horns, which were continually moved, after the fashion of horse's ears. The part between these little horns was flat, their body else being roundish, save only that it ran somewhat to a point at the hind end; at which pointed end it had a tail, near 4 times as long as the whole body, and looking as thick, when viewed through my microscope, as a spider's web. At the end of this tail there was a pellet, of the bigness of one of the globules of the body; and this tail I could not perceive to be used by them for their movements in very clear water. These little animals were the most wretched creatures that I have ever seen; for when, with the pellet, they did but hit on any particles or little filaments (of which there are many in water, especially if it hath but stood some days), they stuck entangled in them; and then pulled their body out into an oval, and did struggle by strongly stretching themselves, to get their tail loose; whereby their whole body then sprang back towards the pellet of the tail, and their tails then coiled up serpent-wise, after the fashion of a copper or wire that, having been wound close about a round stick, and then taken off, kept all its windings. This motion of stretching out and pulling together the tail continued; and I have seen several hundred animalcules, caught fast by one another in a few filaments, lying within the compass of a coarse grain of sand.

I also discovered a second sort of animalcule, whose figure was an oval; and I imagined that their head was placed at the pointed end. These were a little bit bigger than the animalcules first mentioned. Their belly is flat, provided with divers incredibly thin little feet, or little legs [cilia], which were moved very nimbly, and which I was able to discover only after sundry great efforts, and wherewith they brought off incredibly quick motions. The upper part of their body was round, and furnished inside with 8, 10 or 12 globules. Otherwise these animalcules were very clear. . . . Their body was also very yielding: for if they so much as brushed against a tiny filament, their body bent in, which bend presently sprang out again; just as if you stuck your finger into a bladder-full of water, and then, on removing the finger, the inpitting went away. Yet the greatest marvel was when I brought any of the animalcules on a dry place, for I then saw them change themselves at last into a round, and then the upper part of the body rose up pyramid-like, with a point jutting out in the middle; and after having thus lain moving with their feet for a little while, they burst asunder, and the globules and a watery humour flowed away on all sides, without my being able to discern even the least sign of any skin wherein these globules and the liquid had to all appearance been inclosed; and at such times I could discern more globules than when they were alive.

LETTER 39 DATED SEPTEMBER 17, 1683 TO F. ASTON

I have ere this sent you my observations concerning spittle, which I see have been made public in print in the 'Lecture and Collections' published by Mr. Robert Hooke, Secretary of the Royal Society, in the year 1678. Since that time I have made divers further observations on my spittle, with the idea that if there be any animalcules lying about in the body, they would get into the mouth, sooner or later, through the spit-ducts; but in what observations I made to this end, I could make out no animalcules there, nor could I say aught else but what I have hitherto writ.

'Tis my wont of a morning to rub my teeth with salt, and then swill my mouth out with water: and often, after eating, to clean my back teeth with a toothpick, as well as rubbing them hard with a cloth: wherefore my teeth back and front, remain as clean and white as falleth to the lot of few men of my years (51 at the time), and my gums (no matter how hard the salt be that I rub them with) never start bleeding. Yet notwithstanding, my teeth are not so cleaned thereby, but what there sticketh or groweth between some of my front ones and my grinders (whenever I inspected them with a magnifying mirror), a little white matter, which is as thick as if 'twere batter. On examining this, I judged (albeit I could discern nought a-moving in it) that there yet were living animalcules therein. I have therefore mixed it, at divers times, with clean rain water (in which there were no animalcules), and also with spittle, that I took out of my mouth, after ridding it of air bubbles (lest the bubbles should make any motion in the spittle): and I then most always saw, with great wonder, that in the said matter there were many very little living animalcules, very prettily a-moving. The biggest sort had the shape of Figure A: these had a very strong and swift motion and shot through the water (or spittle) like a pike does through the water. These were most always few in number.

The second sort had the shape of figure B. These oft-times spun

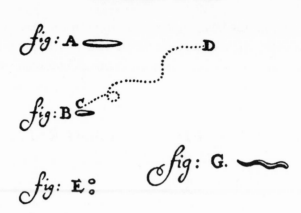

A drawing by Leeuwenhoek from his letter to The Royal Society of September 17, 1683. From *Arcana Naturae Detecta*, 1695. *A.* A bacillus. *B.* A bacillus from the mouth *(Selenomonas sputigena),* and *C., D.,* Its path of motion. *E.* Two small cocci. *G.* A spirillum.

around like a top, and every now and then took a course like that shown between C and D: and these were far more in number.

To the third sort I could assign no figure: for at times they seemed to be oblong, while anon they looked perfectly round. These were so small that I could see them no bigger than Fig. E: yet therewithal they went ahead so nimbly, and hovered so together, that you might imagine them to be a big swarm of gnats or flies, flying in and out among one another. These last seemed to me e'en as if there were, in my judgement, several thousand of 'em in an amount of water or spittle (mixed with the matter aforesaid) no bigger than a sand-grain; albeit there were quite nine parts of water, or spittle, to one part of the matter that I took from betwixt my front teeth, or my grinders.

Furthermore, the most part of this matter consisted of a huge number of little streaks, some greatly differing from others in their length, but of one and the same thickness withal; one being bent crooked, another straight, like Fig. F, and which lay disorderly ravelled together. And because I had formerly seen, in water, live animalcules that had the same figure, I did make every endeavour to see if there was any life in them; but I could make out not the least motion, that looked like anything alive in any of 'em.

*"We are therefore induced to believe that
those animalcula originate from germs there included, which
for a certain time withstand the effects of heat
but at length yield under it. . . ."*

Lazaro Spallanzani

1729 – 1799

IT IS DEMONSTRATED BY EXPERIMENTS
THAT MICROBES DO NOT ORIGINATE
SPONTANEOUSLY

The problem of the origin of life was not settled by Redi's discovery, or by Vallisnieri's extension of it; indeed, as was noted in the Introduction to this part, the question of spontaneous generation was not to be settled until the mid-nineteenth century. A hundred years after Redi's publication, the controversy flared up again, this time to receive the attention of the first of the great experimental physiologists, Lazaro Spallanzani.

Educated as a lawyer, Spallanzani entered the Catholic priesthood (eventually becoming an abbot) and began teaching in Northern Italy. He was primarily a biologist, but his active investigations extended into physics and mineralogy. His experimental techniques were remarkably advanced, and he followed, deliberately or otherwise, the advice of Vallisnieri "to carry out experiments and observations again and again, and never to tire of collecting and comparing them in order to find out the truth."

Spallanzani's interests ranged over all the animal functions: the processes of reproduction, fertilization and development; the nature of the digestive process; the circulation of the blood;

and the phenomena of respiration. He used for his experiments, all kinds of animal life, and especially the creatures of the rivers and streams, so easily available to him in the rich valley of the Po.

The occasion for Spallanzani's intervention in the controversy over spontaneous generation was his study of the experiments of J. T. Needham (1713-1781), an English priest, reported in 1748. Needham was interested in testing the application of Redi's conclusions to microscopic organisms. His experiment consisted in boiling a meat broth, then sealing the flask to exclude airborne organisms. Inspecting the infusion after various periods of time, he found the broth contained "animalcules" and, assuming that by his boiling he had destroyed all earlier organisms and that his seals were adequate to exclude the air, he concluded that the new life had originated spontaneously from lifeless matter.

Spallanzani was not convinced by these demonstrations. Supposing that Needham had not boiled his infusions long enough, he repeated the experiments, varying the length of boiling time and hermetically sealing his containers. Though the procedures were simple, they were disciplined and controlled, and the results were precisely interpreted. He found that various sorts of animalcula could withstand different boiling periods, some resisting for up to forty-five minutes, but that adequate boiling would destroy them. The infusions, thus treated, could be kept indefinitely without the appearance of micro-organisms; but restored to contact with the air, the contents of his flasks soon contained microscopic life. Needham's contention that Spallanzani's boiling destroyed the "vital principle" in the infusion was thus effectively disposed of; yet Needham and his supporters refused to accept these findings and the debate continued well into the nineteenth century until Pasteur and Tyndall finally established the doctrine of biogenesis.

The selection that follows is taken from *Tracts on the Nature of Animals and Vegetables,* translated by J. G. Dalyell in 1799.

WHETHER, ACCORDING TO A NEW THEORY OF GENERATION, ANIMALCULA ARE PRODUCED BY A VEGETATIVE POWER IN MATTER

Infusions and Infused Substances Exposed to Heat

Nothing is more common with philosophers who have invented any theory, or given a new form to one already established, and universally known, than to republish it on some other occasion, corrected, improved, or illustrated, with additional information. If we would review our discoveries, if we would examine them profoundly and with impartiality, we should in general find defects unnoticed before, which arise from the want of connection in sentiment, from the want of a necessary and laudable perspicuity, or because they are discordant with more recent discoveries.

A certain vegetative power some have conceived to reside in matter, appropriated to the formation and regulation of organised existence; that by it are the numberless combinations of the animal machine effected; the operation of nutrition and perspiration, the variety of constitution, the animal appetites and dimensions of the human frame. By the same means has it been explained why a blind or a maimed person may have children vigorous and entire; because the vegetative power will restore to them the members defective in the parent.

Not only has it been supposed to be destined for the organization of matter in animated beings, but that it might change an animal to the vegetable state, and the vegetable again to an animal; that it acts on plants while living, and when dead regenerates them in new beings; these are the animalcula of infusions, which cannot strictly be called animals, but beings simply *vital*.

One proof adduced in support of this hypothesis, is derived from the origin of animalcula. We are told they must either come from specific seeds, or be produced by the vegetative power; that the first cannot take place, because they are found in close vessels subjected to the action of heat, equally as in open vessels, whereas the included germs, if there were any, ought not to survive. Therefore, they must originate from the vegetative power alone. Nothing has been omitted to obtain favourable arguments for this opinion, and to give it that clearness, elegance, and simplicity most likely to gain converts.

Nineteen vessels, containing infused substances, were hermetically sealed, and kept an hour in boiling water. Being opened at a proper time, not a single animalcula was to be seen. To this experiment of mine, it was objected that the long continuance of heat had perhaps entirely destroyed the vegetative power of the infused substances, or materially injured the elasticity of the air remaining included in the vessels; thus, it was not surprising if animalcula did not appear.

To estimate the weight of these objections, I conceived an experiment apparently decisive; which was, to make nineteen infusions, and boil some of them a short time, others longer, and the rest very long. If it was founded, the number of animalcula would be less according to the duration of boiling, if not, the number would be alike in all cases.

Vegetable seeds, being the most fit for producing animalcula, were preferred to other substances, and those that never failed to produce them though they had experienced the influence of heat. White kidney beans, vetches, buckwheat, barley, maize, the seeds of mallows and beets were infused; and, that the experiment might be the more accurate, I endeavoured as much as possible to take each species of seed from the same plant. As the yolk of an egg in maceration abounds with animalcula, one was also infused.

Experiment has demonstrated, that the heat of boiling water is not always the same, but greater, if the atmosphere is heavier; and less, if lighter: therefore, water will acquire more heat at one time than another, which will be proportioned to the state of the atmosphere. In this, and my other experiments, the seven different kinds of seeds, and the yolk, were all boiled in equal time, that they might acquire the same degree of heat. Here the experiment was diversified, by boiling a certain quantity of each infusion half an hour; another quantity, an hour; a third, an hour and a half; and a fourth, two hours. Thus, four classes of infusion, and the egg, could be formed. The same water, in which the seeds had boiled, was taken for the infusions, and what had boiled half an hour alone taken for the seeds that had boiled half an hour. The like proportions of time were preserved in the water for the other three classes of infusions; that is, an hour, one and a half, and two hours.

Each of the four classes was marked with a different number, to avoid all hazard of confusion or error: and, because an equal temperature was most essential, all were deposited in the same place. The vessels, containing the infusions, were not hermetically sealed, but loosely stopped with corks; the only object of this examination being to discover, whether long protracted ebullition would prejudice or destroy the property of infused substances in producting animalcula; if it did, there would be no difference whether the vessels were open or close.

The examination of one, or of few drops, will often induce an observer to suppose the infusion quite deserted, or very thinly inhabited, while the observation of many drops proves it to be otherwise. I was not content with one drop only, but uniformly took a considerable number from each infusion.

The surface of infusions is generally covered with a gelatinous scum, thin at first, and easily broken, which, in process of time, acquires consistence. Here, animalcula are always most numerous, as may be seen by a method I have constantly practiced, examining with a magnifier a portion placed in a strong light.

Where the animalcula are minute, or rare, the thickness of the infusion often prevents the observer from distinguishing whether any are there or not. It is then necessary to dilute the drops with water. Elsewhere it has been remarked, that distilled water was taken to make the infusions; common water might introduce some latent animalcule. In the course of these observations and experiments, distilled water has also been employed for dilution, when required; and, for greater security, examined with a magnifier before being used. In particular cases, the accidental concealment of a single animalcule might vitiate the truth of the experiment.

I conceive it my duty to mention precautions so essential, and to put it in every individual's power to judge not only of the experiments and observations themselves, but of the mode of conducting them in matters so nice and important.

On the 15 of September, I made thirty-two infusions; and on the 23 examined them for the first time. Animalcula were in all; but the number and species different in each. In the maize infusions, they were smaller, and proportionally more rare, according to the duration of boiling.

From this it may seem, that although long continued heat had not prevented the production of animalcula, it had contributed to diminish the number, or alter the kind. But with the rest of the infusions it was otherwise: the kidney beans, vetches, barley, and mallow seeds, were in a better condition, after sustaining the violent impression of heat two hours, than those that had been exposed to it less. Let us enter on that detail which the subject merits.

In the infusion of kidney beans, boiled two hours, were three species of animalcula; very large; middle sized; and very small. The figure of the first, partly umbellated and attached to long filaments dragged along in their progress; the second were cylindrical; and the third, globular. All three were incredibly numerous.

In the infusion boiled two hours, were animalcula of the largest and smallest class, but few in number; still fewer, in that boiled an hour; and fewest of all, in that boiled half an hour.

The infusion of mallows, boiled two hours, produced middle sized circular animalcula; and some very large, with the head extremity hooked. In two infusions, boiled an hour, and an hour and a half, the number and species were the same: and though they might be surpassed by those of the infusions boiled two hours, still they were much more numerous than in those boiled half an hour.

In vetches, boiled half an hour, was an immense number of semi-circular bell-shaped animalcula, all of considerable size, while in those boiled an hour and a half, they were small and rare. Some bell-shaped animalcula might be seen in an infusion boiled an hour, but it gave the eye pain to discover a few, and these most minute, when it had boiled only half an hour.

Those in a barley infusion boiled two hours were numerous beyond description, and large; part of an elliptic figure, others oblong. The infusions boiled an hour and a half had but a moderate number of animalcula very minute; and some appeared when boiled half an hour.

There was no fixed rule with the remaining infusions. In buckwheat boiled an hour and a half were many more animalcula than in any other infusions of it. This also happened in the egg and beet seed boiled an hour; but it is to be remarked, that fewer animalcula were in these two infusions boiled half an hour than in any of the rest.

Hitherto, the figure of these legions of animalcula has been cursorily alluded to. A circumstantial account is in my Dissertations, and it will be spoken of more at large in the course of the Tract.

Thus, it is clearly evident, that long boiling of seed infusions does not prevent the production of animalcula; and, notwithstanding the maize does not seem to favour it, four infusions strongly corroborate the fact.

What is the cause that infusions boiled least have fewest animalcula? I cannot think myself mistaken in assigning the following reason. That animalcula should appear, it is necessary that the macerating substances give some indication of the dissolution of their parts; and, in proportion as dissolution advances, at least for a limited time, the number of animalcula will increase. The uniformity of this has been shewn in another place, and would be confirmed, was it requisite, by further experiments and observations, in these new inquiries. Now, as seeds have boiled a shorter time, so are they less invested and penetrated by the dissolving power of heat; therefore, when set apart to macerate, they are not so soon decomposed as those longer boiled. Thus, there is no occasion for surprise if some infusions swarm with animalcula while others have very few: And this I do believe the reason why, when two infusions are made at the same time, one of unboiled, the other of boiled seeds, animalcula are frequently observed much sooner in the latter than in the former. A little boiling will not decompose vegetable seeds, for decomposition is effected by slow and gradual maceration.

Some days after these experiments, the number of animalcula always became greater; and towards the middle of October increased so much, that each of the thirty-two infusions was equally swarming. The only difference was in size, figure, and motion: I enjoyed this pleasing microscopic scene uninterrupted until the 10 of November; and it might have amused me longer had I continued to examine the infusions.

It ought not to be omitted, that experiments exactly similar were soon afterwards made with pease, lentils, beans, and hemp seed. Except in the beans, the result so far corresponded, that a great number of animalcula appeared in the infusions that had boiled most.

It is a fact established by the universal concurrence of philosophers, that, after water has come to the state of ebullition, it cannot acquire a greater degree of heat, however much the action of the fire may be augmented, provided it can evaporate. Therefore, when I say the seeds boiled longest have acquired greater heat, I mean it to be understood in *time* and not *intensity,* by supposing that the duration of boiling encreased the intensity of heat the seeds would be exposed to.

Recourse was had to another experiment to learn whether an en-crease of heat would obstruct the production of animalcula. The eleven species of seeds were slowly heated in a coffee roaster till they became pretty well roasted, and eleven infusions formed of them with water previously boiled as usual. But this heat, so much more intense, neither prevented the origin of animalcula nor lessened the number. They were rare at first; but about the middle of October, that is, twenty days after making the infusions, the fluid was so full as absolutely to appear animated.

The constancy of their appearing even here, excited my curiosity to augment the heat still more. The seeds were burnt and ground the same as we burn and grind coffee. Of the dust, which resembled soot, I made as many infusions as different kinds of seed: likewise, an infusion was made of the yolk of an egg, which by the thermometer had suffered 279° of heat. What followed? Animalcula equally appeared in these infusions, only a little more time elapsed before they became so numerous, because the weather was colder; and they uniformly inhabit infusions sooner or later according to the temperature of the atmosphere.

Vegetable seeds were exposed to trials more severe: they were exposed to the greatest heat that can be excited by common fires, or fire augmented by art. Burning coals, and the flame of the blow pipe, were the two agents exercising their power on them. And, in the first place, I kept them on an iron plate above burning coals until entirely consumed by the violence of the flames, and converted to a dry cinder, which was reduced to powder, and as many infusions formed as there were seeds. A cinder was also made by the blow pipe, which, besides excessive aridity, had acquired considerable hardness. I must acknowledge I did not in the least expect to find animalcula in this new infusion. After viewing them once and again, hardly able to credit my eyes, I repeated the experiment twice. Some suspicion arose that the animalcula might come from the water used rather than the burnt seeds; therefore, on repeating the experiment, the same as what formed the infusions was put in other vessels. Both times, however, they re-appeared in the burnt seeds, while not one was seen in the water.

These facts fully convinced me, that vegetable seeds never fail to produce animalcula, though exposed to any degree of heat; whence arises a direct conclusion, that the *vegetative power* is nothing but the work of imagination; and if no animalcula appear in vessels hermetically sealed and kept an hour in boiling water, their absence must proceed from some other cause.

* * *

We are therefore induced to believe, that those animalcula originate from germs there included, which, for a certain time, withstand the effects of heat, but at length yield under it; and, since animalcula of the higher classes only exist when the heat is less intense, we must imagine they are much sooner affected by it, than those of the lower classes. Whence, we should conclude, that this multitude of the superior animalcula, seen in the infusions of open vessels, exposed not only to the heat of boiling water, but to the flame of a blowpipe, appears there, not because their germs have withstood so great a degree of heat, but because new germs come to the infusions, after cessation of the heat.

*"We must lay it down as an incontestable axiom,
that in all the operations of art and nature, nothing is
created; and equal quantity of matter exists both before and after
the experiment . . . and nothing takes place beyond changes
and modifications in the combination of these elements.
Upon this principle, the whole art of performing
experiments depends: We must always suppose
an exact equality between the elements of
the body examined and those of
the product of its analysis."*
—Antoine Lavoisier

THE BURNING QUESTION

The dictionaries define a revolution as a reversal of conditions, a fundamental change. As applied to society, the word implies a forcible substitution by subjects of a new government or ruler for the old. The revolution in chemistry brought about a fundamental change in the conditions of that science just at the time of two major political revolutions, one in America and the other in France; and, even more significantly, in the midst of another revolution whose existence, at the time of which we write, had scarcely been realized. The Industrial Revolution, which received new acceleration from every advance in science, has, in its turn, promoted other revolutions in the political, social, and economic life of the world. Concentrated in the few years between 1755 and 1789 there were a series of activities in chemistry which at last turned man's steps in the direction of solving the problem: what is the origin and nature of matter? These activities were concerned with fire and its consequences.

From primitive times man had watched fire, sometimes in awe, often in terror, almost always in reverence, but never with understanding. By the middle of the seventeenth century, the phenomenon was receiving increasing attention from scientists. As early as 1630, Jean Rey, a Frenchman, realized that there was a similarity between ordinary combustion and what happened when lead and tin were heated in air (calcined). He noted an increase in weight in the calx, and he attributed it to the fixation of air in the metal, much as water is absorbed by sand. Rey was followed by John Mayow (1645-1679), a contemporary of Robert Boyle, who described a constituent of air which he called "spiritus nitro-aereus," found also in saltpeter, which combined with metals when calcined and which keeps fires burning and animals living. He said, "We must believe that animals and fire draw particles of the same kind from the air." In his experiments he burned combustible substances in air confined over water, an experiment familiar to students today. When a portion of the air was used up, burning ceased. A small animal confined in a similar container used up the same constituent, leaving a residue which would not support combustion or respiration.

Unfortunately no one followed up these ideas; even Boyle, who observed the increase of weight in the calx and realized that it came from the air, failed to follow his contemporaries' suggestions and explained that fire had passed through the glass into the closed container and combined with the metal within.

As we have seen above (page 208), Georg Ernst Stahl, following his teacher Johann Becher (1635-1682), announced, at the opening of the eighteenth century, that the principle of inflammability was "phlogiston." Stahl's doctrine was seized upon as a convenient framework around which to examine the consequences of combustion. For a time, the investigators were, in effect, diverted by the phlogiston doctrine from studying the "airs" themselves. When it came to be realized that common air was something different from a number of other "completely elastic fluids," the end of Stahl's theory was in sight.

The readings that follow describe some of the stages which brought about the change. They are presented, at least with respect to the first four, in an arbitrary order, since all the men whose discoveries are recorded were more or less contemporaries. All except Scheele were in active communication with one another. (Even Scheele, as we shall see, told Lavoisier, in advance of his formal publication, of his observation of an "air in which a candle will burn.") And all except Lavoisier did their work in a phlogistic context, without real detriment to the value of their discoveries. All except Lavoisier, however, reported their findings in a terminology based on phlogistic reasoning, which became more and more involved as they probed deeper into the nature of gases. Lavoisier succeeded in cutting through the confusion. It does not detract from his original contributions to remind the reader of his debt to his contemporaries. Black introduced him to the importance of precise quantitative measurement. Priestley and Scheele brought oxygen to his attention—before it was named; Cavendish's experiments provided invaluable raw material for Lavoisier's own work.

The answer to the "burning question" was found in a few years of rigorous international research. By 1789 a new approach to chemistry was available and the approach to the new field of organic chemistry became possible.

"This account of lime and alkalis
recommended itself by its simplicity, and by affording
an easy solution of many phaenomena, but appeared upon a
nearer view to be attended with consequences that
were so very new and extraordinary as to
render suspicious the principles from
which they were drawn."

Joseph Black

1728 — 1799

THE CHEMISTRY OF FIXED AIR (CARBON DIOXIDE) IS STUDIED EXPERIMENTALLY

There is no easy explanation of Joseph Black's choice of a subject for his dissertation, submitted in 1754 to the University of Edinburgh. Written in Latin and entitled *"De Humore Acido a Cibis Orto et Magnesia Alba,"* it might have been left, like many similar documents when they have served their purpose, to molder in an obscure corner of a library. Fortunately, Black's interests went beyond the mere attainment of a medical degree, and within the year he amplified his studies and presented them, in English, to the Philosophical Society of Edinburgh as *Experiments upon Magnesia Alba [Magnesium Carbonate], Quicklime and some other Alcaline Substances.* With this "brilliant model, perhaps the first successful model, of quantitative chemical investigation ... a classic exemplar of experimental science worthy of comparison with Newton's *Optiks,"*[1] Black established the British school of pneumatic chemists and contributed materially, if indirectly, to Lavoisier's achievement.

Black was a Scot born at Bordeaux, France, where his father had established himself as a successful merchant. He was sent, at the age of twelve, to a private school in Ireland and then at sixteen entered the University of Glasgow to study medicine. Here he came under the influence of Dr. William Cullen who, at that time, introduced the study of chemistry at the University. These lectures represent the turning point in Black's career. He became Cullen's assistant, served him at Glasgow, and followed him to Edinburgh, where he received the degree of Doctor of Medicine in 1754.

Black's paper of 1755 describes the chemical behavior of some common alkalis (carbonates) such as limestone, chalk, and magnesium carbonate. When such substances are calcined (burned), they give off a gas Black called "fixed air."

We now know that the gas observed by Black was carbon dioxide, but Black did not go beyond establishing by intensive and careful experimentation that the gas was a constituent of the compounds from which it was released by heating and roasting and that this gas (which he called *air*) was different from atmospheric air, resembling air which had been vitiated by combustion or by respiration.

Black, who later became Professor of Chemistry at the University of Edinburgh, went on to develop the use of accurate measuring instruments in his studies of heat. He is largely responsible for defining the concepts of specific and latent heat. He is remembered, too, in his association with James Watt, whose experiments with heat arose out of his attempts to improve the Newcomen atmospheric engine and led to the development of the first effective steam engine.

The experiments described in the following extract (from *Experiments in Magnesia Alba*) exemplify the sort of material which stimulated Black's contemporaries, in particular Priestley and Cavendish.

---

[1] Henry Guerlac, "Joseph Black and Fixed Air," *Isis*, Vol. 48, 1957, p. 125.

PART I

... By the following experiments, I proposed to know whether this substance could be reduced to a quick-lime.

An ounce of *magnesia* was exposed in a crucible for about an hour to such a heat as is sufficient to melt copper. When taken out, it weighed three drams and one scruple, or had lost 7/12 of its former weight.

I repeated, with the *magnesia* prepared in this manner, most of those experiments I had already made upon it before calcination, and the result was as follows.

It dissolves in all the acids, and with these composes salts exactly similar to those described in the first set of experiments: but what is particularly to be remarked, it is dissolved without any the least degree of effervescence.

It slowly precipitates the corrosive sublimate of mercury in the form of a black powder.

It separates the volatile alkali in a salt-ammoniac from the acid, when it is mixed with a warm solution of that salt. But it does not separate an acid from a calcarious earth, nor does it induce the least change upon lime-water.

Lastly, when a dram of it is digested with an ounce of water in a bottle for some hours, it does not make any the least change in the water. The *magnesia,* when dried, is found to have gained ten grains; but it neither effervesces with acids, nor does it sensibly affect lime-water.

Observing *magnesia* to lose such a remarkable proportion of its weight in the fire, my next attempts were directed to the investigation of this volatile part, and among other experiments, the following seemed to throw some light upon it.

Three ounces of *magnesia* were distilled in a glass retort and receiver, the fire being gradually increased until the *magnesia* was obscurely red hot. When all was cool, I found only five drams of a whitish water in the receiver, which had a faint smell of the spirit of hartshorn, gave a green colour to the juice of violets, and rendered the solutions of corrosive sublimate and of silver very slightly turbid. But it did not sensibly effervesce with acids.

The *magnesia,* when taken out of the retort, weighed an ounce, three drams, and thirty grains, or had lost more than half of its weight. It still effervesced pretty briskly with acids, tho' not so strongly as before this operation.

The fire should have been raised here to the degree requisite for the perfect calcination of *magnesia*. But even from this imperfect experiment, it is evident, that of the volatile parts contained in that powder, a small proportion only is water; the rest cannot, it seems, be retained in vessels, under a visible form. Chemists have often observed, in their distillations, that part of a body has vanished from their senses, notwithstanding the utmost care to retain it; and they have always found, upon further inquiry, that subtile part to be air, which having been imprisoned in the body, under a solid form, was set free, and rendered fluid and elastic by the fire. We may therefore safely conclude, that the volatile matter, lost in the calcination of *magnesia,* is mostly air; and hence the calcined *magnesia* does not emit air, or make an effervescence when mixed with acids.

The water, from its properties, seems to contain a small portion of volatile alkali, which was probably formed from the earth, air, and water, or from some of these combined together; and perhaps also from a small quantity of inflammable matter which adhered accidentally to the *magnesia.* Whenever Chemists meet with this salt, they are inclined to ascribe its origin to some animal, or putrid vegetable, substance; and this they have always done, when they obtained it from the calcarious earths, all of which afford a small quantity of it. There is, however, no doubt that it can sometimes be produced independently of any such mixture, since many fresh vegetables and tartar afford a considerable quantity of it. And how can it, in the present instance, be supposed, that any animal or vegetable matter adhered to the *magnesia,* while it was dissolved by an acid, separated from this by an alkali, and washed with so much water?

Two drams of *magnesia* were calcined in a crucible, in the manner described above, and thus reduced to two scruples and twelve grains. This calcined *magnesia* was dissolved in a sufficient quantity of spirit of vitriol, and then again separated from the acid by the addition of an alkali, of which a large quantity is necessary for this purpose. The *magnesia* being very well washed and dried, weighed one dram and fifty grains. It effervesced violently, or emitted a large quantity of air, when thrown into acids, formed a red powder when mixed with a solution of sublimate, separated the calcarious earths from an acid, and sweetened lime-water: and had thus recovered all those properties which it had but just now lost by calcination: Nor had it only recovered its original properties, but acquired besides an addition of weight nearly equal to what had been lost in the fire; and, as it is found to effervesce with acids, part of the addition must certainly be air.

This air seems to have been furnished by the alkali from which it was separated by the acid; for Dr. Hales has clearly proved, that alkaline salts contain a large quantity of fixed air, which they emit in great abundance when joined to a pure acid. In the present case, the alkali is really joined to an acid, but without any visible emission of air; and yet the air is not retained in it: for the neutral salt, into which it is converted, is the same in quantity, and in every other respect, as if the acid employed had not been previously saturated with *magnesia,* but offered to the alkali in its pure state, and had driven the air out of it in their conflict. It seems therefore evident, that the air was forced from the alkali by the acid, and lodged itself in the *magnesia.*

These considerations led me to try a few experiments, whereby I might know what quantity of air is expelled from an alkali, or from *magnesia,* by acids.

Two drams of a pure fixed alkaline salt, and an ounce of water, were put into a Florentine flask, which, together with its contents, weighed two ounces and two drams. Some oil of vitriol diluted with water was dropt in, until the salt was exactly saturated; which it was found to be, when two drams, two scruples, and three grains of this acid had been added. The phial with its contents now weighed two ounces, four drams, and fifteen grains. One scruple, therefore, and eight grains were lost during the ebullition, of which a trifling portion may be water, or something of the same kind. The rest is air.

The celebrated *Homberg* has attempted to estimate the quantity of solid salt contained in a determined portion of the several acids. He saturated equal quantities of an alkali with each of them; and, observing the weight which the alkali had gained, after being perfectly dryed, took this for the quantity of solid salt contained in that share of the acid which performed the saturation. But we learn from the above experiment, that his estimate was not accurate, because the alkali loses weight as well as gains it.

Two drams of *magnesia,* treated exactly as the alkali in the last experiment, were just dissolved by four drams, one scruple, and seven grains of the same acid liquor, and lost one scruple and sixteen grains by the ebullition.

Two drams of *magnesia* were reduced, by the action of a violent fire, to two scruples and twelve grains, with which the same process was repeated, as in the two last experiments; four drams, one scruple, and two grains of the same acid, were required to compleat the solution, and no weight was lost in the experiment.

As in the separation of the volatile from the fixed parts of bodies, by means of heat, a small quantity of the latter is generally raised with the former; so the air and water, originally contained in the *magnesia,* and afterwards dissipated by the fire, seem to have carried off a small part of the fixed earth of this substance. This is probably the reason, why calcined *magnesia* is saturated with a quantity of acid, somewhat less than what is required to dissolve it before calcination: and the same may be assigned as one cause which hinders us from restoring the whole of its original weight, by solution and precipitation.

I took care to dilute the vitriolic acid, in order to avoid the heat and ebullition which it would otherwise have excited in the water; and I chose a Florentine flask, on account of its lightness, capacity, and shape, which is peculiarly adapted to the experiment; for the vapours raised by the ebullition circulated for a short time, thro' the wide cavity of the phial, but were soon collected upon its sides, like dew, and none of them seemed to reach the neck, which continued perfectly dry to the end of the experiment.

We now perceive the reason why crude and calcined *magnesia,* which differ in many respects from one another, agree however in composing the same kind of salt, when dissolved in any particular acid; for the crude *magnesia* seems to differ from the calcined chiefly by containing a considerable quantity of air, which air is unavoidably dissipated and lost during the dissolution.

From our experiments, it seems probable, that the increase of weight which some metals acquire, by being first dissolved in acids, and then separated from them again by alkalis, proceeds from air furnished by the alkalis. And that in the *aurum fulminans,* which is prepared by the same means, this air adheres to the gold in such a peculiar manner, that, in a moderate degree of heat, the whole of it recovers its elasticity in the same instant of time; and thus, by the violent shock which it gives to the air around, produces the loud crack or fulmination of this powder. Those who will imagine the explosion of such a minute portion of fixed air, as can reside in the *aurum fulminans,* to be insufficient for the excessive loudness of the noise, will consider, that it is not a large quantity of motion communicated to the air, but rather a smart stroke which produces sound, and that the explosion of but a few particles of fixed air may be capable of causing a loud noise, provided they all recover their spring suddenly, and in the same instant.

The above experiments lead us also to conclude, that volatile alkalis, and the common absorbent earths, which lose their air by being joined to acids, but shew evident signs of their having recovered it, when separated from them by alkalis, received it from these alkalis which lost it in the instant of their joining with the acid.

The following are a few experiments upon three of the absorbent earths, made in order to compare them with one another, and with *magnesia.*

Suspecting that *magnesia* might possibly be no other than a common calcarious earth, which had changed its nature by having been previously combined with an acid, I saturated a small quantity of chalk with the muriatic acid, separated the acid from it again by means of a fixed alkali, and carefully washed away the whole of the salt.

The chalk when dryed was not found to have suffered any alteration; for it effervesced with the vitriolic acid, but did not dissolve in it; and when exposed to a violent fire, was converted into a quick-lime, in all respects similar to that obtained from common chalk.

In another experiment of the same kind, I used the vitriolic acid with the same event.

Any calcarious matter reduced to a fine powder, and thrown into a warm solution of alum, immediately raises a brisk effervescence. But the powder is not dissolved; it is rather increased in bulk: and if the addition be repeated until it is no longer accompanied with effervescence, the liquor loses all taste of the alum, and yields only a very light cloud upon the admixture of an alkali.

From this experiment we learn, that acids attract the calcarious earth more strongly then they do the earth of alum; and as the acid in this salt is exactly the same with the vitriolic, it composes with the calcarious earth a neutral substance, which is very difficultly soluble in water, and therefore falls down to the bottom of the vessel along with the earth of alum, which is deprived of its acid. The light cloud formed by the alkali proceeds from the minute portion of the calcarious compound which saturates the water.

The earth of animal bones, when reduced to a fine powder and thrown into a diluted vitriolic acid, gradually absorbs the acid in the same manner as the calcarious earths, but without any remarkable effervescence. When it is added to the nitrous or to the muriatic acid, it is slowly dissolved. The compound liquor thence produced is extremely acrid, and still changes the colour of the juice of violets to a red, even after it is fully saturated with the absorbent. Distilled vinegar has little or no effect upon this earth; for after a long digestion it still retains its sour taste, and gives only a light cloud upon the addition of an alkali.

By dropping a dissolved fixed alkali into a warm solution of alum, I obtained the earth of this salt, which, after being well washed and dryed, was found to have the following properties:

It is dissolved in every acid but very slowly, unless assisted by heat. The several solutions, when thoroughly saturated, are all astringent with a slight degree of an acid taste, and they also agree with a solution of alum in this, that they give a red colour to the infusion of turnsol.

Neither this earth, nor that of animal bones, can be converted into quick-lime by the strongest fire, nor do they suffer any change worth notice. Both of them seem to attract acids but weakly, and to alter their properties less when united to them than the other absorbents.

PART II

In reflecting afterwards upon these experiments, an explication of the nature of lime offered itself, which seemed to account, in an easy manner, for most of the properties of that substance.

It is sufficiently clear, that the calcarious earths in their native state, and that the alkalis and *magnesia* in their ordinary condition, contain a large quantity of fixed air, and this air certainly adheres to them with considerable force, since a strong fire is necessary to separate it from *magnesia,* and the strongest is not sufficient to expel it entirely from fixed alkalis, or take away their power of effervescing with acid salts.

These considerations led me to conclude, that the relation between fixed air and alkaline substances was somewhat similar to the relation between these and acids; that as the calcarious earths and alkalis attract acids strongly and can be saturated with them, so they also attract fixed air, and are in their ordinary state saturated with it: and when we mix an acid with an alkali or with an absorbent earth, that the air is then set at liberty, and breaks out with violence; because the alkaline body attracts it more weakly than it does the acid, and because the acid and air cannot both be joined to the same body at the same time.

I also imagined that, when the calcarious earths are exposed to the action of a violent fire, and are thereby converted into quick-lime, they suffer no other change in their composition than the loss of a small quantity of water and of their fixed air. The remarkable acrimony which we perceive in them after this process, was not supposed to proceed from any additional matter received in the fire, but seemed to be an essential property of the pure earth, depending on an attraction for those several substances which it then became capable of corroding or dissolving, which attraction had been insensible as long as the air adhered to the earth, but discovered itself upon the separation.

This supposition was founded upon an observation of the most frequent consequences of combining bodies in chemistry. Commonly when we join two bodies together, their acrimony or attraction for other substances becomes immediately either less perceivable or entirely insensible; altho' it was sufficiently strong and remarkable before their union, and may be rendered evident again by disjoining them. A neutral salt, which is composed of an acid and alkali, does not possess the acrimony of either of its constituent parts. It can easily be separated from water, has little or no effect upon metals, is incapable of being joined to inflammable bodies, and of corroding and dissolving animals and vegetables; so that the attraction both of the acid and alkali for these several substances seems to be suspended till they are again separated from one other.

Crude lime was therefore considered as a peculiar acrid earth rendered mild by its union with fixed air: and quick-lime as the same earth, in which, by having separated the air, we discover that acrimony or attraction for water, for animal, vegetable, and for inflammable substances.

That the calcarious earths really lose a large quantity of air when they are burnt to quick-lime, seems sufficiently proved by an experiment of Mr. *Margraaf,* an exceedingly accurate and judicious Chemist. He subjected eight ounces of *osteocolla* to distillation in an earthen retort, finishing his process with the most violent fire of a reverberatory, and caught in the receiver only two drams of water, which by its smell and properties shewed itself to be slightly alkaline. He does not tell us the weight of the *osteocolla* remaining in the retort, and only says, that it was converted into quick-lime; but as no calcarious earth can be converted into quick-lime, or bear the heat which he applied without losing above a third of its weight, we may safely conclude, that the loss in his experiment was proportional, and proceeded chiefly from the dissipation of fixed air.

According to our theory, the relation of the calcarious earth to air and water appeared to agree with the relation of the same earth to the vitriolic and vegetable acids. As chalk for instance has a stronger attraction for the vitriolic than for the vegetable acid, and is dissolved with more difficulty when combined with the first, than when joined to the second: so it also attracts air more strongly than water, and is dissolved with more difficulty when saturated with air than when compounded with water only.

A calcarious earth deprived of its air, or in the state of quick-lime, greedily absorbs a considerable quantity of water, becomes soluble in that fluid, and is then said to be slaked; but as soon as it meets with fixed air, it is supposed to quit the water and join itself to the air, for which it has a superior attraction, and is therefore restored to its first state of mildness and insolubility in water.

When slaked lime is mixed with water, the fixed air in the water is attracted by the lime, and saturates a small portion of it, which then becomes again incapable of dissolution, but part of the remaining slaked lime is dissolved and composes lime-water.

If this fluid be exposed to the open air, the particles of quick-lime which are nearest the surface gradually attract the particles of fixed air which float in the atmosphere. But at the same time that a particle of lime is thus saturated with air, it is also restored to its native state of mildness and insolubility; and as the whole of this change must happen at the surface, the whole of the lime is successively collected there under its original form of an insipid calcarious earth, called the cream or crusts of lime-water.

When quick-lime itself is exposed to the open air, it absorbs the particles of water and of fixed air which come within its sphere of attraction, as it meets with the first of these in greatest plenty, the greatest part of it assumes the form of slaked lime; the rest is restored to its original state; and if it be exposed for a sufficient length of time, the whole of it is gradually saturated with air, to which the water as gradually yields its place.

We have already shewn by experiment, that *magnesia alba* is a compound of a peculiar earth and fixed air. When this substance is mixed with lime-water, the lime shews a stronger attraction for fixed air than that of the earth of *magnesia;* the air leaves this powder to join itself to the lime. And as neither the lime when saturated with air, nor the *magnesia* when deprived of it, are soluble in water, the lime-water becomes perfectly pure and insipid, the lime which it contained being mixed with the *magnesia.* But if the *magnesia* be deprived of air by calcination before it is mixed with the lime-water, this fluid suffers no alteration.

If quick-lime be mixed with a dissolved alkali, it likeways shews an attraction for fixed air superior to that of the alkali. It robs this salt of its air, and thereby becomes mild itself, while the alkali is consequently rendered more corrosive, or discovers its natural degree of acrimony or strong attraction for water, and for bodies of the inflammable, and of the animal and vegetable kind; which attraction was less perceivable as long as it was saturated with air. And the volatile alkali when deprived of its air, besides this attraction for various bodies, discovers likeways its natural degree of volatility, which was formerly somewhat repressed by the air adhering to it, in the same manner as it is repressed by the addition of an acid.

This account of lime and alkalis recommended itself by its simplicity, and by affording an easy solution of many *phænomena,* but appeared upon a nearer view to be attended with consequences that were so very new and extraordinary, as to render suspicious the principles from which they were drawn.

I resolved however to examine, in a particular manner, such of these consequences as were the most unavoidable, and found the greatest number of them might be reduced to the following propositions:

I. If we only separate a quantity of air from lime and alkalis, when we render them caustic they will be found to lose part of their weight in the operation, but will saturate the same quantity of acid as before, and the saturation will be performed without effervescence.

II. If quick-lime be no other than a calcarious earth deprived of its air, and whose attraction for fixed air is stronger than that of alkalis, it follows, that, by adding to it a sufficient quantity of alkali saturated with air, the lime will recover the whole of its air, and be entirely restored to its original weight and condition: and it also follows, that the earth separated from lime-water by an alkali, is the lime which was dissolved in the water now restored to its original mild and insoluble state.

III. If it be supposed that slaked lime does not contain any parts which are more firey, active, or subtile than others, and by which chiefly it communicates its virtues to water; but that it is an uniform compound of lime and water: it follows, that, as part of it can be dissolved in water, the whole of it is also capable of being dissolved.

IV. If the acrimony of the caustic alkali does not depend on any part of the lime adhering to it, a caustic or soap-ley will consequently be found to contain no lime, unless the quantity of lime employed in making it were greater than what is just sufficient to extract the whole air of the alkali; for then as much of the superfluous quick-lime might possibly be dissolved by the ley as would be dissolved by pure water, or the ley would contain as much lime as lime-water does.

V. We have shewn in the former experiments, that absorbent earths lose their air when they are joined to an acid; but recover it, if separated again from that acid, by means of an ordinary alkali: the air passing from the alkali to the earth, at the same time that the acid passes from the earth to the alkali.

If the caustic alkali therefore be destitute of air, it will separate *magnesia* from an acid under the form of a *magnesia* free of air, or which will not effervesce with acids; and the same caustic alkali will also separate a calcarious earth from acids under the form of a calcarious earth destitute of air, but saturated with water, or under the form of slaked lime.

These were all necessary conclusions from the above suppositions. Many of them appeared too improbable to deserve any further attention; some however, I found upon reflection, were already seconded by experience. Thus *Hoffman* has observed, that quick-lime does not effervesce with spirit of vitriol; and it is well known that the caustic spirit of urine, or of salt ammoniac, does not emit air, when mixed with acids. This consideration excited my curiosity, and determined me to inquire into the truths of them all by way of experiment. I therefore engaged myself in a set of trials; the history of which is here subjoined. Some new facts are likeways occasionally mentioned; and here it will be proper to inform the reader, that I have never mentioned any, without satisfying myself of their truth by experiment, tho' I have sometimes taken the liberty to neglect describing the experiments when they seemed sufficiently obvious.

Desiring to know how much of an acid a calcarious earth will absorb, and what quantity of air is expelled during the dissolution, I saturated two drams of chalk with diluted spirit of salt, and used the Florentine flask, as related in a similar experiment upon *magnesia*. Seven drams and one grain of the acid finished the dissolution, and the chalk lost two scruples and eight grains of air.

This experiment was necessary before the following, by which I proposed to inquire into the truth of the first proposition so far as it relates to quick-lime.

Two drams of chalk were converted into a perfect quick-lime, and lost two scruples and twelve grains in the fire. This quick-lime was slaked or reduced to a milky liquor with an ounce of water, and then dissolved in the same manner, and with the same acid, as the two drams of chalk in the preceding experiment. Six drams, two scruples and fourteen grains of the acid finished the saturation without any sensible effervescence or loss of weight.

It therefore appears from these experiments, that no air is separated from quick-lime by an acid, and that chalk saturates nearly the same quantity of acid after it is converted into quick-lime as before.

With respect to the second proposition, I tried the following experiments.

A piece of perfect quick-lime made from two drams of chalk, and which weighed one dram and eight grains, was reduced to a very fine powder, and thrown into a filtrated mixture of an ounce of a fixed alkaline salt and two ounces of water. After a slight digestion, the powder being well washed and dried, weighed one dram and fifty eight grains. It was simliar in every trial to a fine powder of ordinary chalk, and was therefore saturated with air which must have been furnished by the alkali.

A dram of pure salt of tartar was dissolved in fourteen pounds of limewater, and the powder thereby precipitated, being carefully collected and dried, weighed one and fifty grains. When exposed to a violent fire, it was converted into a true quick-lime, and had every other quality of a calcarious earth.

This experiment was repeated with the volatile alkali, and also with the fossil or alkali of sea-salt, and exactly with the same event.

The third proposition had less appearance of probability than the fore-going; but, as an accurate experiment was the only test of its truth, I reduced eight grains of perfect quick-lime made of chalk, to an exceedingly subtile powder, by slaking it in two drams of distilled water boiling hot and immediately threw the mixture into eighteen ounces of distilled water in a flask. After shaking it, a light sediment, which floated thro' the liquor, was allowed to subside; and this, when collected with the greatest care, and dried, weighed, as near as I could guess, one third of a grain. The water tasted strongly of the lime, had all the qualities of lime-water and yielded twelve grains of precipitate, upon the addition of salt of tartar. In repeating this experiment, the quantity of sediment was some times less than the above, and sometimes amounted to half a grain. It consisted partly of an earth which effervesced violently with *aqua fortis,* and partly of an ochry powder, which would not dissolve in that acid. The ochry powder, as it usually appears in chalk to the eye, in the form of veins running thro' its substance, must be considered only as an accidenta or foreign admixture; and, with respect to the minute portion of alkaline earth which composed the remainder of the sediment, it cannot be supposed to have been originally different from the rest, and incapable, from its nature, of being converted into quick-lime, or of being dissolved in water; it seems rather to have consisted of a small part of the chalk in its mild state, or saturated with air, which had either remained, for want of a sufficient fire to drive it out entirely, or had been furnished by the distilled water.

I indeed expected to see a much larger quantity of sediment produced from the lime, on account of the air which water constantly contains, and with a view to know whether water retains its air when fully saturated with lime, a lime-water was made as strong as possible; four ounces of which were placed under the receiver of an air-pump, together with four ounces of common water in a phial of the same size; and, upon exhausting the receiver, without heating the phials, the air arose from each, in nearly the same quantity: from whence it is evident, that the air, which quick-lime attracts, is of a different kind from that which is mixed with water. And that it is also different from common elastic air, is sufficiently proved by daily experience; for lime-water, which soon attracts air, and forms a crust when exposed in open and shallow vessels, may be preserved, for any time, in bottles which are but slightly corked, or closed in such a manner as would allow free access to elastic air, were a vacuum formed in the bottle. Quick-lime therefore does not attract air when in its most ordinary form, but is capable of being joined to one particular species only, which is dispersed thro' the atmosphere, either in the shape of an exceedingly subtle powder, or more probably in that of an elastic fluid. To this I have given the name of fixed air, and perhaps very improperly; but I thought it better to use a word already familiar in philosophy, than to invent a new name, before we be more fully acquainted with the nature and properties of this substance, which will probably be the subject of my further inquiry.

"Upon this, as upon other occasions,
I can only repeat, that it is not my opinions, on which I would be
understood to lay any stress. Let the new facts, from which
I deduce them, be considered as my discoveries,
and let other persons draw better inferences
from them if they can."

Joseph Priestley
1733 – 1804

OXYGEN IS PREPARED BY HEATING
MERCURIC OXIDE, AND ITS ABILITY
TO SUPPORT COMBUSTION
IS DESCRIBED

Joseph Priestley typifies the revolutionary period in which he lived. He was an active participant in those movements which were the inevitable outcome of the expansion of the towns under the stimulus of the Industrial Revolution. The shift of power in Britain from the landowners to the expanding industrial communities was accompanied by the spread of Nonconformism, the revolt against the Established Church. The dissenters represented the struggle for civil, religious, and political liberty against the vested interests of those who monopolized Parliament and the right to vote.

Born near Leeds, in Yorkshire, into a Calvinist family, Priestley was trained at a Nonconformist academy and in due course became a minister. For the rest of his life, whether as minister, schoolmaster, or private tutor, Priestley's gospel was that of freedom and progress. His advocacy of these principles was helped by his facile pen, and he published many tracts in support of them. These intellectual pursuits, though dominant in his life, left him time to take up the study of the chemistry of gases. Without any scientific training in his early education, Priestley did work in the study of gases of such quality as to establish him as the real founder of that field of chemistry. His principal contributions, however, lay in the collection of observed facts. Others, such as Lavoisier, applied the theory and sometimes took the credit for discoveries already made by Priestley.

Priestley's scientific studies began in the field of electricity, and in his later researches into the nature of gases, he frequently made use of "electric explosions." He turned to the study of gases at Leeds, where he lived next door to a brewery which produced a large amount of "fixed air" (carbon dioxide), the gas so thoroughly studied by Black. Priestley's experiments on the gas showed that when it was dissolved in water a potable beverage resulted—soda water. Though this was probably not successful in helping sailors to resist scurvy, as the British Admiralty had hoped, it was the first move in the direction of the soda-fountain, so important a feature of American life.

Priestley's greatest contribution was his preparation and discovery of oxygen, which he obtained in 1774 by heating red oxide of mercury in a closed container. He solved ingeniously the problem of how to do this by using a large lens to concentrate the sun's rays on the substance in a closed glass container. He found that the "air" expelled, as he put it, from the oxide caused a candle to burn more brilliantly and was purer and better than common air for respiration. He suggested that it could be used to increase "the force of fire" and that "it might be peculiarly salutary to the lungs in certain morbid cases," practical applications which are commonplace today. Priestley did not know until 1777 that he had been anticipated by Scheele, who had observed oxygen in 1773 but did not immediately publish his findings.

Priestley's discovery was the outcome of earlier researches into the nature of respiration. He observed that burning candles or breathing animals so vitiated the air in a closed container that the air would no longer support combustion. He found, too, that this air could be restored by the action of green plants so that it would again support combustion or life.

Priestley reported on a long series of different "airs" which he had obtained in his many experiments. He extended Stephen Hales' (1677-1761) method of collecting gas over water by using mercury to collect water-soluble gases. But instead of devising his own theory as to the nature of these various gases, Priestley accepted the logic of the phlogiston theory to explain them. Oxygen was air which had been dephlogisticated. "Inflammable air" was phlogiston mixed with water. Earlier Priestley thought that "inflammable air" (hydrogen) was itself phlogiston. Atmospheric air was a combination of "dephlogisticated air" and "phlogisticated air" (nitrogen). As we have seen, Priestley was not alone in adhering to the doctrines of Stahl.

In 1791 Priestley's house, library, laboratory, and manuscript were destroyed by fire by a mob allegedly aroused by his attitude toward the French Revolution. Four years later, in 1795, he and his family came to the United States and settled at Northumberland, Pennsylvania. There he spent the rest of his life, enjoying the friendship of George Washington, Thomas Jefferson, and John Adams. Thus the revolutionary came to rest among the revolutionaries.

Some of Priestley's apparatus is preserved at the Smithsonian Institute in Washington. It provides an exciting link with this fascinating period of the history of chemistry.

The two readings are taken from the six-volume *Experiments and Observations on Different Kinds of Air* published in 1775.

SECTION III

Of Dephlogisticated Air, and the Constitution of the Atmosphere

The contents of this section will furnish a very striking illustration of the truth of a remark, which I have more than once made in my philosophical writings, and which can hardly be too often repeated, as it tends greatly to encourage philosophical investigations; viz. that more is owing to what we call *chance,* that is, philosophically speaking, to the observation of *events arising from unknown causes,* than to any proper *design,* or pre-conceived *theory* in this business. This does not appear in the works of those who write *synthetically* upon these subjects; but would, I doubt not, appear very strikingly in those who are the most celebrated for their philosophical acumen, did they write *analytically* and ingenuously.

For my own part, I will frankly acknowledge, that, at the commencement of the experiments recited in this section, I was so far from having formed any hypothesis that led to the discoveries I made in pursuing them, that they would have appeared very improbable to me had I been told of them; and when the decisive facts did at length obtrude themselves upon my notice, it was very slowly, and with great hesitation, that I yielded to the evidence of my senses. And yet, when I re-consider the matter, and compare my last discoveries relating to the constitution of the atmosphere with the first, I see the closest and the easiest connexion in the world between them, so as to wonder that I should not have been led immediately from the one to the other. That this was not the case, I attribute to the force of prejudice, which, unknown to ourselves, biasses not only our *judgments,* properly so called, but even the perceptions of our senses: for we may take a maxim so strongly for granted, that the plainest evidence of sense will not entirely change, and often hardly modify our persuasions; and the more ingenious a man is, the more effectually he is entangled in his errors; his ingenuity only helping him to deceive himself, by evading the force of truth.

There are, I believe, very few maxims in philosophy that have laid firmer hold upon the mind, than that air, meaning atmospherical air (free from various foreign matters, which were always supposed to be dissolved, and intermixed with it) is a *simple elementary substance,* indestructible, and unalterable, at least as much so as water is supposed to be. In the course of my inquiries, I was, however, soon satisfied that atmospherical air is not an unalterable thing; for that the phlogiston with which it becomes loaded from bodies burning in it, and animals breathing it, and various other chemical processes, so far alters and depraves it, as to render it altogether unfit for inflammation, respiration, and other purposes to which it is subservient; and I had discovered that agitation in water, the process of vegetation, and probably other natural processes, by taking out the superfluous phlogiston, restore it to its original purity. But I own I had no idea of the possibility of going any farther in this way, and thereby procuring air purer than the best common air. I might, indeed, have naturally imagined that such would be air that should contain less phlogiston than the air of the atmosphere; but I had no idea that such a composition was possible.

It will be seen in my last publication, that, from the experiments which I made on the marine acid air, I was led to conclude that common air consisted of some acid (and I naturally inclined to the acid that I was then operating upon) and phlogiston; because the union of this acid vapour and phlogiston made inflammable air; and inflammable air, by agitation in water, ceases to be inflammable, and becomes respirable. And though I could never make it quite so good as common air, I thought it very probable that vegetation, in more favourable circumstances than any in which I could apply it, or some other natural process, might render it more pure.

Upon this, which no person can say was an improbable supposition, was founded my conjecture, of volcanos having given birth to the atmosphere of this planet, supplying it with a permanent air, first inflammable, then deprived of its inflammability by agitation in water, and farther purified by vegetation.

Several of the known phenomena of the *nitrous acid* might have led me to think, that this was more proper for the constitution of the atmosphere than the marine acid: but my thoughts had got into a different train, and nothing but a series of observations, which I shall now distinctly relate, compelled me to adopt another hypothesis, and brought me, in a way of which I had then no idea, to the solution of the great problem, which my reader will perceive I have had in view ever since my discovery that the atmospherical air is alterable, and therefore that it is not an elementary substance, but a *composition,* viz. what this composition is, or *what is the thing that we breathe,* and how is it to be made from its constituent principles.

At the time of my former publication, I was not possessed of a *burning lens* of any considerable force; and for want of one, I could not possibly make many of the experiments that I had projected, and which, in theory, appeared very promising. I had, indeed, a *mirror* of force sufficient for my purpose. But the nature of this instrument is such, that it cannot be applied, with effect, except upon substances that are capable of being suspended, or resting on a very slender support. It cannot be directed at all upon any substance in the form of a *powder,* nor hardly upon any thing that requires to be put into a vessel of quicksilver; which appears to me to be the most accurate method of extracting air from a great variety of substances, as was explained in the Introduction to this volume. But having afterwards procured a lens of twelve inches diameter, and twenty inches focal distance, I proceeded with great alacrity to examine, by the help of it, what kind of air a great variety of substances, natural and factitious, would yield, putting them into the vessels represented fig. *a,* which I filled with quicksilver, and kept inverted in a bason of the same. Mr. Warltire, a good chymist, and lecturer in natural philosophy, hapening to be at that time in Calne, I explained my views to him, and was furnished by him with many substances, which I could not otherwise have procured.

With this apparatus, after a variety of other experiments, an account of which will be found in its proper place, on the 1st of August, 1774, I endeavoured to extract air from *mercurious calcinatus per se;* and I presently found that, by means of this lens, air was expelled from it very readily. Having got about three or four times as much as the bulk of my materials, I admitted water to it, and found that it was not imbibed by it. But what surprized me more than I can well express, was, that a candle burned in this air with a remarkably vigorous flame, very much like that enlarged flame with which a candle burns in nitrous air, exposed to iron or liver of sulphur; but as I had got nothing like this remarkable appearance from any kind of air besides this particular modification of nitrous air, and I knew no nitrous acid was used in the preparation of *mercurius calcinatus,* I was utterly at a loss how to account for it.

In this case, also, though I did not give sufficient attention to the circumstance at that time, the flame of the candle, besides being larger, burned with more splendor and heat than in that species of nitrous air; and a piece of red-hot wood sparkled in it, exactly like paper dipped in a solution of nitre, and it consumed very fast; an experiment which I had never thought of trying with nitrous air.

At the same time that I made the above mentioned experiment, I extracted a quantity of air, with the very same property, from the common *red precipitate,* which being produced by a solution of mercury in spirit of

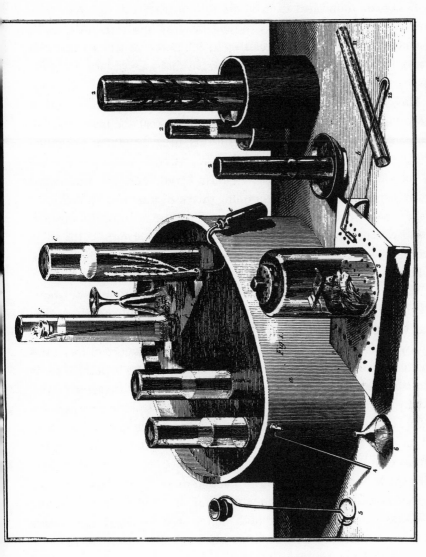

Some of Priestley's apparatus for experiments on the gases of the atmosphere. The tube on the right contains a mint plant, and the jar in the foreground contains some mice. From Joseph Priestley's *Observations on Different Kinds of Air*, London, 1772. (Courtesy of the Burndy Library.)

nitre, made me conclude that this peculiar property, being similar to that of the modification of nitrous air above mentioned, depended upon something being communicated to it by the nitrous acid; and since the *mercurius calcinatus* is produced by exposing mercury to a certain degree of heat, where common air has access to it, I likewise concluded that this substance had collected something of *nitre,* in that state of heat, from the atmosphere.

This, however, appearing to me much more extraordinary than it ought to have done, I entertained some suspicion that the mercurius calcinatus, on which I had made my experiments, being bought at a common apothecary's, might, in fact, be nothing more than red precipitate; though, had I been any thing of a practical chymist, I could not have entertained any such suspicion. However, mentioning this suspicion to Mr. Warltire, he furnished me with some that he had kept for a specimen of the preparation, and which, he told me, he could warrant to be genuine. This being treated in the same manner as the former, only by a longer continuance of heat, I extracted much more air from it than from the other.

This experiment might have satisfied any moderate sceptic: but, however, being at Paris in the October following, and knowing that there were several very eminent chymists in that place, I did not omit the opportunity, by means of my friend Mr. Magellan, to get an ounce of mercurius calcinatus prepared by Mr. Cadet, of the genuineness of which there could not possibly be any suspicion; and at the same time, I frequently mentioned my surprize at the kind of air which I had got from this preparation to Mr. Lavoisier, Mr. le Roy, and several other philosophers, who honoured me with their notice in that city; and who, I dare say, cannot fail to recollect the circumstance.

At the same time, I had no suspicion that the air which I had got from the mercurius calcinatus was even wholesome, so far was I from knowing what it was that I had really found; taking it for granted, that it was nothing more than such kind of air as I had brought nitrous air to be by the processes above mentioned; and in this air I have observed that a candle would burn sometime quite naturally, and sometimes with a beautiful enlarged flame, and yet remain perfectly noxious.

At the same time that I had got the air above mentioned from mercurius calcinatus and the red precipitate, I had got the same kind from *red lead* or *minium.* In this process, that part of the minium on which the focus of the lens had fallen, turned yellow. One third of the air, in this experiment, was readily absorbed by water, but, in the remainder, a candle burned very strongly, and with a crackling noise.

That fixed air is contained in red lead I had observed before; for I had expelled it by the heat of a candle, and had found it to be very pure. I imagine it requires more heat than I then used to expel any of the other kind of air.

This experiment with *red lead* confirmed me more in my suspicion, that the *mercurius calcinatus* must get the property of yielding this kind of air from the atmosphere, the process by which that preparation, and this of red lead is made, being similar. As I never make the least secret of any thing that I observe, I mentioned this experiment also, as well as those with the mercurius calcinatus, and the red precipitate, to all my philosophical acquaintance at Paris, and elsewhere; having no idea, at that time, to what these remarkable facts would lead.

Presently after my return from abroad, I went to work upon the *mercurius calcinatus,* which I had procured from Mr. Cadet; and, with a very moderate degree of heat, I got from about one fourth of an ounce of it, an ounce-measure of air, which I observed to be not readily imbibed, either by the substance itself from which it had been expelled (for I suffered them to continue a long time together before I transferred the air to any other place) or by water, in which I suffered this air to stand a considerable time before I made any experiment upon it.

In this air, as I had expected, a candle burned with a vivid flame; but what I observed new at this time (Nov. 19), and which surprised me no less than the fact I had discovered before, was, that, whereas a few moments agitation in water will deprive the modified nitrous air of its property of admitting a candle to burn in it; yet, after more than ten times as much agitation as would be sufficient to produce this alteration in the nitrous air, no sensible change was produced in this. A candle still burned in it with a strong flame; and it did not, in the least, diminish common air, which I have observed that nitrous air, in this state, in some measure, does.

But I was much more surprized, when, after two days, in which this air had continued in contact with water (by which it was diminished about one twentieth of its bulk) I agitated it violently in water about five minutes, and found that a candle still burned in it as well as in common air.

The same degree of agitation would have made phlogisticated nitrous air fit for respiration indeed, but it would certainly have extinguished a candle.

These facts fully convinced me, that there must be a very material difference between the constitution of the air from mercurius calcinatus, and that of phlogisticated nitrous air, notwithstanding their resemblance in some particulars. But though I did not doubt that the air from *mercurius calcinatus* was fit for respiration, after being agitated in water, as every kind of air without exception, on which I had tried the experiment, had been, I still did not suspect that it was respirable in the first instance; so far was I from having any idea of this air being, what it really was, much superior, in this respect, to the air of the atmosphere.

In this ignorance of the real nature of this kind of air, I continued from this time (November) to the 1st of March following; having, in the mean time, been intent upon my experiments on the vitriolic acid air above recited, and the various modifications of air produced by spirit of nitre, an account of which will follow. But in the course of this month, I not only ascertained the nature of this kind of air, though very gradually, but was led by it to the complete discovery of the constitution of the air we breathe.

Till this 1st of March, 1775, I had so little suspicion of the air from mercurius calcinatus, &c. being wholesome, that I had not even thought of applying to it the test of nitrous air; but thinking (as my reader must imagine I frequently must have done) on the candle burning in it after long agitation in water, it occurred to me at last to make the experiment; and putting one measure of nitrous air to two measures of this air, I found, not only that it was diminished, but that it was diminished quite as much as common air, and that the redness of the mixture was likewise equal to that of a similar mixture of nitrous and common air.

After this I had no doubt but that the air from mercurius calcinatus was fit for respiration, and that it had all the other properties of genuine common air. But I did not take notice of what I might have observed, if I had not been so fully possessed by the notion of there being no air better than common air, that the redness was really deeper, and the diminution something greater than common air would have admitted.

Moreover, this advance in the way of truth, in reality, threw me back into error, making me give up the hypothesis I had first formed, viz. that the mercurius calcinatus had extracted spirit of nitre from the air; for I now concluded, that all the constituent parts of the air were equally, and in their proper proportion, imbibed in the preparation of this substance, and also in the process of making red lead. For at the same time that I made the above-mentioned experiment on the air from mercurius calcinatus, I likewise observed that the air which I had extracted from red lead, after the fixed air was washed out of it, was of the same nature, being diminished by nitrous air like common air: but, at the same time, I was puzzled to find that air from the red precipitate was diminished in the same manner, though the process for making this substance is quite different from that of making the two others. But to this circumstance I happened not to give much attention.

I wish my reader be not quite tired with the frequent repetition of the word *surprize,* and others of similar import; but I must go on in that style a little longer. For the next day I was more surprized than ever I had been before, with finding that, after the above-mentioned mixture of nitrous air and the air from mercurius calcinatus, had stood all night, (in which time the whole diminution must have taken place; and, consequently, had it been common air, it must have been made perfectly noxious, and intirely unfit for respiration or inflammation) a candle burned in it, and even better than in common air.

I cannot, at this distance of time, recollect what it was that I had in view in making this experiment; but I know I had no expectation of the real issue of it. Having acquired a considerable degree of readiness in making experiments of this kind, a very slight and evanescent motive would be sufficient to induce me to do it. If, however, I had not happened, for some other purpose, to have had a lighted candle before me, I should probably never have made the trial; and the whole train of my future experiments relating to this kind of air might have been prevented.

Still, however, having no conception of the real cause of this phenomenon, I considered it as something very extraordinary; but as a property that was peculiar to air extracted from these substances, and *adventitious;* and I always spoke of the air to my acquaintance as being substantially the same thing with common air. I particularly remember my telling Dr. Price, that I was myself perfectly satisfied of its being common air, as it appeared to be so by the test of nitrous air; though, for the satisfaction of others, I wanted a mouse to make the proof quite complete.

On the 8th of this month I procured a mouse, and put it into a glass vessel, containing two ounce-measures of the air from mercurius calcinatus. Had it been common air, a full-grown mouse, as this was, would have lived in it about a quarter of an hour. In this air, however, my mouse lived a full half hour; and though it was taken out seemingly dead, it appeared to have been only exceedingly chilled; for, upon being held to the fire, it presently revived, and appeared not to have received any harm from the experiment.

By this I was confirmed in my conclusion, that the air extracted from mercurius calcinatus, &c. was, *at least, as good* as common air; but I did not certainly conclude that it was any *better;* because, though one mouse would live only a quarter of an hour in a given quantity of air, I knew it was not impossible but that another mouse might have lived in it half an hour; so little accuracy is there in this method of ascertaining the goodness of air: and indeed I have never had recourse to it for my own satisfaction, since the discovery of that most ready, accurate, and elegant test that nitrous air furnishes. But in this case I had a view to publishing the most generally-satisfactory account of my experiments that the nature of the thing would admit of.

This experiment with the mouse, when I had reflected upon it some time, gave me so much suspicion that the air into which I had put it was better than common air, that I was induced, the day after, to apply the test of nitrous air to a small part of that very quantity of air which the mouse had breathed so long; so that, had it been common air, I was satisfied it must have been very nearly, if not altogether, as noxious as possible, so as not to be affected by nitrous air; when, to my surprise again, I found that though it had been breathed so long, it was still better than common air. For after mixing it with nitrous air, in the usual proportion of two to one, it was diminished in the proportion of $4\frac{1}{2}$ to $3\frac{1}{2}$; that is, the nitrous air had made it two ninths less than before, and this in a very short space of time; whereas I had never found that, in the longest time, any common air was reduced more than one fifth of its bulk by any proportion of nitrous air, nor more than one fourth by any phlogistic process whatever. Thinking of this extraordinary fact upon my pillow, the next morning I put another measure of nitrous air to the same mixture, and, to my utter astonishment, found that it was farther diminished to almost one half of its original quantity. I then put a third measure to it; but this did not diminish it any farther: but, however, left it one measure less than it was even after the mouse had been taken out of it.

Being now fully satisfied that this air, even after the mouse had breathed it half an hour, was much better than common air; and having a quantity of it still left, sufficient for the experiment, viz. an ounce-measure and a half, I put the mouse into it; when I observed that it seemed to feel no shock upon being put into it, evident signs of which would have been visible, if the air had not been very wholesome; but that it remained perfectly at its ease another full half hour, when I took it out quite lively and vigorous. Measuring the air next day, I found it to be reduced from $1\frac{1}{2}$ to $\frac{2}{3}$ of an ounce-measure. And after this, if I remember well (for in my *register* of the day I only find it noted, that it was *considerably diminished* by nitrous air) it was nearly as good as common air. It was evident, indeed, from the mouse having been taken out quite vigorous, that the air could not have been rendered very noxious.

For my farther satisfaction I procured another mouse, and putting it into less than two ounce-measures of air extracted from mercurius calcinatus and air from red precipitate (which, having found them to be of the same quality, I had mixed together) it lived three quarters of an hour. But not having had the precaution to set the vessel in a warm place, I suspect that the mouse died of cold. However, as it had lived three times as long as it could probably have lived in the same quantity of common air, and I did not expect much accuracy from this kind of test, I did not think it necessary to make any more experiments with mice.

Being now fully satisfied of the superior goodness of this kind of air, I proceeded to measure that degree of purity, with as much accuracy as I could, by the test of nitrous air; and I began with putting one measure of nitrous air to two measures of this air, as if I had been examining common air; and now I observed that the diminution was evidently greater than common air would have suffered by the same treatment. A second measure of nitrous air reduced it to two thirds of its original quantity, and a third measure to one half. Suspecting that the diminution could not proceed much farther, I then added only half a measure of nitrous air, by which it was diminished still more; but not much, and another half measure made it more than half of its original quantity; so that, in this case, two measures of this air took more than two measures of nitrous air, and yet remained less than half of what it was. Five measures brought it pretty exactly to its original dimensions.

At the same time, air from *red precipitate* was diminished in the same proportion as that from *mercurius calcinatus,* five measures of nitrous air being received by two measures of this without any increase of dimensions. Now as common air takes about one half of its bulk of nitrous air, before it begins to receive any addition to its dimensions from more nitrous air, and this air took more than four half-measures before it ceased to be diminished by more nitrous air, and even five half-measures made no addition to its original dimensions, I conclude that it was between four and five times as good as common air. It will be seen that I have since procured air better than this, even between five and six times as good as the best common air that I have ever met with.

SECTION VII

Of the Purification of Air by Plants and the Influence of Light
on that Process

One of my earliest observations on the subject of air, but made casually, when, in fact, I expected a contrary result from the process, was the purification of air injured by respiration or putrefaction, by the vegetation of plants. But at that time I was altogether ignorant of the part that *light* had to act in the business. At the publication of the experiments recited in the last section, I had fully ascertained the influence of light in the production of dephlogisticated air in water by means of a *green substance,* which I at first supposed to be a plant, but not being able to discover the form of one, I contended myself with calling it simply *green matter.*

Several of my friends, however, better skilled in botany than myself, never entertained any doubt of its being a plant; and I had afterwards the fullest conviction that it must be one. Mr. Bewly has lately observed the regular form of it by a microscope. My own eyes having always been weak, I have, as much as possible, avoided the use of a microscope.

The principal reason that made me question whether this green matter was a plant, besides my not being able to discover the form of it, was its being produced, as I then thought, in a vial close stopped. But this being only with a common cork, the seeds of this plant, which must float invisibly in the air, might have insinuated themselves through some unperceived fracture in it; or the seeds might have been contained in the water previous to its being put into the phial. Both Mr. Bewly and myself found, in the course of the last summer, that when distilled water was exposed to the sun, in phials filled in part with quicksilver, and in part with distilled water, and inverted in basons of quicksilver, none of this green matter was ever produced; no seed of this plant having been able to penetrate through the mercury, to reach the water incumbent upon it, though, in several cases, it will be seen, that these seeds diffuse and insinuate themselves, in a manner that is truly wonderful.

Without light, it is well known, that no plant can thrive; and if it do grow at all in the dark, it is always white, and is, in all other respects, in a weak and sickly state. Healthy plants are probably in a state similar to that of *sleep* in the absence of light, and do not resume their proper functions, but by the influence of light, and especially the action of the rays of the sun. This was the reason why no green matter was ever produced by means of mere *warmth* in my former experiments, and that in jars standing in the same exposure, but covered so that the light had no access to them, no pure air was collected, none of the green matter being then found in them.

This I verified most completely by covering the greatest part of a glass jar with black sealing-wax, which made it thoroughly opaque; and besides answering that purpose better than brown paper, as I made the experiment before mentioned, did not imbibe any of the water, and therefore did not promote the evaporation of it. To be able to observe whether any air was collected in these jars, or not, the upper part of them was not coated with sealing-wax, but had a thick movable cap of paper, which I could easily take off, and then inspect the surface of the water.

In order to satisfy myself as fully as possible with respect to this remarkable circumstance, I also made the following experiments, the results of which are, indeed, very decisive in favour of the influence of *light* in this case.

Having a large trough of water, full of recent green matter, giving air very copiously, so that all the surface of it was covered with froth, and jars filled with it, and inverted, collected great quantities of it, and very fast; I filled a jar with it, and, inverting it in a bason of the same, I placed it in a dark room. From that instant no more air was yielded by it, and in a few days it had a very offensive smell, the green vegetable matter with which it abounded being then all dead, and putrid.

Again, having filled a receiver with fresh pump water, and having waited till it was in a state of giving air copiously, I removed it into a dark room; and from that time the production of air from it intirely ceased. When I placed it again in the sun, it gave no air till about ten days after, when it had more green matter, the former plants being probably all dead; and no air could be produced till new ones were formed. . . .

It appears from these experiments, that air combined with water is liable to be phlogisticated by respiration, and to be dephlogisticated by vegetation, as much as air in an elastic state, out of water. For fishes, as I shall observe, foul the air contained in the water in which they are confined, and water plants now appear to purify it. This is no doubt one of the great uses of weeds, and other aquatic plants, with which fresh water lakes, and even seas abound, as well as their serving for food to a great number of fishes.

"But to watch new phenomena this
is all my care, and how glad is the enquirer when discovery
rewards his diligence; then his heart rejoices."

Carl Wilhelm Scheele

1742 — 1786

OXYGEN IS DISCOVERED AND RECOGNIZED
AS AN ELEMENT

In 1774 Scheele wrote a letter of thanks to Lavoisier for a
copy of one of Lavoisier's works and suggested an experiment in
which dry silver carbonate is heated with a burning glass and
the gas given off is collected. "You will see," he wrote, "how
much air is produced in which a candle will burn and an animal
will live." This letter leaves no doubt that Scheele had prepared
oxygen and observed some of its properties before Priestley's
independent discovery. In his experiments Scheele had isolated
oxygen by the action of heat on silver carbonate, mercuric carbonate, mercuric oxide, manganese dioxide, and other substances.

The life of Scheele was a perpetual struggle against poverty
and ill health, but this failed to restrain a man possessed of unusual powers of observation. Scheele was born at Stralsund, Pom-
erania, a Swedish province at the time of his birth. His formal
schooling was brief, and at the age of fourteen he was appren-
ticed to an apothecary. In the eight years of his service, his master
encouraged him to study chemistry and pharmacy and to experiment with the many substances to be found in the stock-in-trade
of the pharmacist. Having served his apprenticeship, Scheele

worked for the next ten years for two other apothecaries and finally in 1775 he purchased his own business. His entire life was devoted to the study of chemistry, and his discoveries earned for him the title of the greatest experimental chemist of the eighteenth century.

Scheele was remote from the circles of Edinburgh, London, Paris, and Northern Italy whose members freely communicated their discoveries. The absence of regular scientific periodicals left him uninformed about the work of other scientists in the field. Like many other experimenters, he accumulated his data until he had enough material for a book; hence, although he had actually isolated what he called "fire-air," the discovery was not known, except perhaps to Lavoisier, until Scheele's great *Chemical Treatise on Air and Fire* was published in 1777. It is certain that Scheele had not seen Priestley's book and was not aware of his discoveries.

The *Chemical Treatise on Air and Fire* (translated by Leonard Dobbins in 1931) is the source of the selections chosen to illustrate Scheele's work. They reveal quite clearly the correctness of Scheele's methods. He was able to account for the phenomena he observed in phlogistic terms. In addition to the detailed study of oxygen and its chemical behavior he described his discovery of the composition of the atmosphere and a host of other new observations, in which he probably again anticipated Priestley. One of the most notable of these was his recognition of the chemical effect of light upon compounds of silver, in which, in effect, he provided a basis for the invention of photography. His other great discoveries included chlorine, arsenic, tartaric, citric, benzoic and lactic acids, glycerine, and prussic acid. He recognized manganese as a metal and studied the chemical properties of silica, magnesia, oxalic acid, and fluorspar as well as molybdic and tungstic acids.

Scheele was made a Fellow of the Swedish Royal Academy of Sciences two years before his *Treatise* was published, an honor never before or since bestowed upon a pharmacist. He poured his life's blood into his chemical experiments, exposing himself to all types of chemicals and fumes, unquestionably undermining his health in his burning zeal for science. He died in his forty-fifth year, a victim, in a sense, of his own inner fire.

CHEMICAL TREATISE ON AIR AND FIRE

1. It is the object and chief business of chemistry to skilfully separate substances into their constituents, to discover their properties, and to compound them in different ways.

How difficult it is, however, to carry out such operations with the greatest accuracy, can only be unknown to one who either has never undertaken this occupation, or at least has not done so with sufficient attention.

2. Hitherto chemical investigators are not agreed as to how many elements or fundamental materials compose all substances. In fact this is one of the most difficult problems; some indeed hold that there remains no further hope of searching out the elements of substances. Poor comfort for those who feel their greatest pleasure in the investigation of natural things! Far is he mistaken, who endeavours to confine chemistry, this noble science, within such narrow bounds! Others believe that earth and phlogiston are the things from which all material nature has derived its origin. The majority seem completely attached to the peripatetic elements.

3. I must admit that I have bestowed no little trouble upon this matter in order to obtain a clear conception of it. One may reasonably be amazed at the numerous ideas and conjectures which authors have recorded on the subject, especially when they give a decision respecting the fiery phenomenon; and this very matter was of the greatest importance to me. I perceived the necessity of a knowledge of fire, because without this it is not possible to make any experiment; and without fire and heat it is not possible to make use of the action of any solvent. I began accordingly to put aside all explanations of fire; I undertook a multitude of experiments in order to fathom this beautiful phenomenon as fully as possible. I soon found, however, that one could not form any true judgment regarding the phenomena which fire presents, without a knowledge of the air. I saw, after carrying out a series of experiments, that air really enters into the mixture of fire, and with it forms a constituent of flame and of sparks. I learned accordingly that a treatise like this, on fire, could not be drawn up with proper completeness without taking the air also into consideration.

4. Air is that fluid invisible substance which we continually breathe, which surrounds the whole surface of the earth, is very elastic, and possesses weight. It is always filled with an astonishing quantity of all kinds of exhalations, which are so finely subdivided in it that they are scarcely visible even in the sun's rays. Water vapours always have the preponderance amongst these foreign particles. The air, however, is also mixed with another elastic substance resembling air, which differs from it in numerous properties, and is, with good reason, called aerial acid by Professor Bergman. It owes its presence to organised bodies, destroyed by putrefaction or combustion.

5. Nothing has given philosophers more trouble for some years than just this delicate acid or so-called fixed air. Indeed it is now surprising that the conclusions which one draws from the properties of this elastic acid are not favourable to all who are prejudiced by previously conceived opinions. These defenders of the Paracelsian doctrine believe that the air is in itself unalterable; and, with Hales, that it really unites with substances thereby losing its elasticity; but that it regains its original nature as soon as it is driven out of these by fire or fermentation. But since they see that the air so produced is endowed with properties quite different from common air, they conclude, without experiment proofs, that this air has united with foreign materials, and that it must be purified from these admixed foreign particles by agitation and filtration with various liquids. I believe that there would be no hesitation in accepting this opinion, if one could only demonstrate clearly by experiments that a given quantity of air is capable of being completely converted into fixed or other kind of air by the admixture of foreign materials; but since this has not been done, I hope I do not err if I assume as many kinds of air as experiment reveals to me. For when I have collected an elastic fluid, and observe concerning it that its expansive power is increased by heat and diminished by cold, while it still uniformly retains its elastic fluidity, but also discover in it properties and behaviour different from those of common air, then I consider myself justified in believing that this is a peculiar kind of air. I say that air thus collected must retain its elasticity even in the greatest cold, because otherwise an innumerable multitude of varieties of air would have

to be assumed, since it is very probable that all substances can be converted by excessive heat into a vapour resembling air.

6. Substances which are subjected to putrefaction or to destruction by means of fire diminish, and at the same time consume, a part of the air; sometimes it happens that they perceptibly increase the bulk of the air, and sometimes finally that they neither increase nor diminish a given quantity of air—phenomena which are certainly remarkable. Conjectures can here determine nothing with certainty, at least they can only bring small satisfaction to a chemical philosopher, who must have his proofs in his hands. Who does not see the necessity of making experiments in this case, in order to obtain light concerning this secret of nature?

7. *General properties of ordinary air.*

(1.) Fire must burn for a certain time in a given quantity of air. (2.) If, so far as can be seen, this fire does not produce during combustion any fluid resembling air, then, after the fire has gone out of itself, the quantity of air must be diminished between a third and a fourth part. (3.) It must not unite with common water. (4.) All kinds of animals must live for a certain time in a confined quantity of air. (5.) Seeds, as for example peas, in a given quantity of similarly confined air, must strike roots and attain a certain height with the aid of some water and of a moderate heat.

Consequently, when I have a fluid resembling air in its external appearance, and find that it has not the properties mentioned, even when only one of them is wanting, I feel convinced that it is not ordinary air.

8. *Air must be composed of elastic fluids of two kinds.*

First Experiment.—I dissolved one ounce of alkaline liver of sulphur in eight ounces of water; I poured 4 ounces of this solution into an empty bottle capable of holding 24 ounces of water, and closed it most securely with a cork; I then inverted the bottle and placed the neck in a small vessel with water; in this position I allowed it to stand for 14 days. During this time the solution had lost a part of its red colour and had also deposited some sulphur: afterwards I took the bottle and held it in the same position in a larger vessel with water, so that the mouth was under and the bottom above the water-level, and withdrew the cork under the water; immediately water rose with violence into the bottle. I closed the bottle again, removed it from the water, and weighed the fluid which it contained. There were 10 ounces. After subtracting from this the 4 ounces of solution of sulphur there remain 6 ounces, consequently it is apparent from this experiment that of 20 parts of air 6 parts have been lost in 14 days.

9. Second Experiment.—(*a.*) I repeated the preceding experiment with the same quantity of liver of sulphur, but with this difference that I only allowed the bottle to stand a week, tightly closed. I then found that of 20 parts of air only 4 had been lost. (*b.*) On another occasion I allowed the very same bottle to stand 4 months; the solution still possessed a somewhat dark yellow colour. But no more air had been lost than in the first experiment, that is to say 6 parts.

10. Third Experiment.—I mixed 2 ounces of caustic ley, which was prepared from alkali of tartar and unslaked lime and did not precipitate lime water, with half an ounce of the preceding solution of sulphur which likewise did not precipitate lime water. This mixture had a yellow colour. I poured it into the same bottle, and after this had stood 14 days, well closed, I found the mixture entirely without colour and also without precipitate. I was enabled to conclude that the air in this bottle had likewise diminished, from the fact that air rushed into the bottle with a hissing sound after I had made a small hole in the cork.

11. Fourth Experiment.—(*a.*) I took 4 ounces of a solution of sulphur in lime water; I poured this solution into a bottle and closed it tightly. After 14 days the yellow colour had disappeared, and of 20 parts of air 4 parts had been lost. The solution contained no sulphur, but had allowed a precipitate to fall which was chiefly gypsum. (*b.*) Volatile liver of sulphur likewise diminishes the bulk of air. (*c.*) Sulphur, however, and volatile spirit of sulphur, undergo no alteration in it.

12. Fifth Experiment.—I hung up over burning sulphur, linen rags which were dipped in a solution of alkali of tartar. After the alkali was saturated with the volatile acid, I placed the rags in a flask, and closed the mouth most carefully with a wet bladder. After 3 weeks had elapsed I found the bladder strongly pressed down; I inverted the flask, held its mouth in water, and made a hole in the bladder; thereupon water rose with violence into the flask and filled the fourth part.

13. Sixth Experiment.—I collected in a bladder the nitrous air which arises on the dissolution of the metals in nitrous acid, and after I had tied the bladder tightly I laid it in a flask and secured the mouth very carefully with a wet bladder. The nitrous air gradually lost its elasticity, the bladder collapsed, and became yellow as if corroded by *aqua fortis*.

After 14 days I made a hole in the bladder tied over the flask, having previously held it, inverted, under water; the water rose rapidly into the flask, and it remained only ⅔ empty.

14. Seventh Experiment.—(*a.*) I immersed the mouth of a flask in a vessel with oil of turpentine. The oil rose in the flask a few lines every day. After the lapse of 14 days the fourth part of the flask was filled with it; I allowed it to stand for 3 weeks longer, but the oil did not rise higher. All those oils which dry in the air, and become converted into resinous substances, possess this property. Oil of turpentine, however, and linseed oil rise up sooner if the flask is previously rinsed out with a concentrated sharp ley. (*b.*) I poured 2 ounces of colourless and transparent animal oil of Dippel into a bottle and closed it very tightly; after the expiry of two months the oil was thick and black. I then held the bottle, inverted, under water and drew out the cork; the bottle immediately became ¼ filled with water.

15. Eighth Experiment.—(*a.*) I dissolved 2 ounces of vitriol of iron in 32 ounces of water, and precipitated this solution with a caustic ley. After the precipitate had settled, I poured away the clear fluid and put the dark green precipitate of iron so obtained, together with the remaining water, into the before-mentioned bottle (§ 8), and closed it tightly. After 14 days (during which time I shook the bottle frequently), this green calx of iron had acquired the colour of crocus of iron, and of 40 parts of air 12 had been lost. (*b.*) When iron filings are moistened with some water and preserved for a few weeks in a well closed bottle, a portion of the air is likewise lost. (*c.*) The solution of iron in vinegar has the same effect upon air. In this case the vinegar permits the dissolved iron to fall out in the form of a yellow crocus, and becomes completely deprived of this metal. (*d.*) The solution of copper prepared in closed vessels with spirit of salt likewise diminishes air. In none of the foregoing kinds of air can either a candle burn or the smallest spark glow.

16. It is seen from these experiments that phlogiston, the simple inflammable principle, is present in each of them. It is known that the air strongly attracts to itself the inflammable part of substances and deprives them of it: not only this may be seen from the experiments cited, but it is at the same time evident that on the transference of the inflammable substance to the air a considerable part of the air is lost. But that the inflammable substance alone is the cause of this action, is plain from this, that, according to the 10th paragraph, not the least trace of sulphur remains over, since, according to my experiments this colourless ley contains only some vitriolated tartar. The 11th paragraph likewise shews this. But since sulphur alone, and also the volatile spirit of sulphur, have no effect upon the air (§ 11. *c*), it is clear that the decomposition of liver of sulphur takes place according to the laws of double affinity,—that is to say, that the alkalies and lime attract the vitriolic acid, and the air attracts the phlogiston.

It may also be seen from the above experiments, that a given quantity of air can only unite with, and at the same time saturate, a certain quantity of the inflammable substance: this is evident from the 9th paragraph, *letter b.* But whether the phlogiston which was lost by the substances was still present in the air left behind in the bottle, or whether the air which was lost had united and fixed itself with the materials such as liver of sulphur, oils, &c., are questions of importance.

From the first view, it would necessarily follow that the inflammable substance possessed the property of depriving the air of part of its elasticity, and that in consequence of this it becomes more closely compressed by the external air. In order now to help myself out of these uncertainties, I formed the opinion that any such air must be specifically heavier than ordinary air, both on account of its containing phlogiston and also of its greater condensation. But how perplexed was I when I saw that a very thin flask which was filled with this air, and most accurately weighed, not only did not counterpoise an equal quantity of ordinary air, but was even somewhat lighter. I then thought that the latter view might be admissible; but in that case it would necessarily follow also that the lost air could be separated again from the materials employed. None of the experiments cited seemed to me capable of shewing this more clearly than that according to the 10th paragraph, because this residuum, as already mentioned, consists of vitriolated tartar and alkali. In order therefore to see whether the lost air had been converted into fixed air, I tried whether the latter shewed itself when some of the caustic ley was poured into lime water; but in vain—no precipitation took place. Indeed, I tried in several ways to obtain the lost air from this alkaline mixture, but as the results were similar to the foregoing, in order to avoid prolixity I shall not cite these experiments. Thus much I see from the experiments mentioned, that the air consists of two fluids, differing from each other, the one of which does not manifest in the least the property of attracting phlogiston, while the other, which composes between the third and the fourth part of the whole mass of the air, is peculiarly disposed to such attraction. But where this latter kind of air has gone to after it has united with the inflammable substance, is a question which must be decided by further experiments, and not by conjectures.

We shall now see how the air behaves towards inflammable substances when they get into fiery motion. We shall first consider that kind of fire which does not give out during the combustion any fluid resembling air.

17. First Experiment.—I placed 9 grains of phosphorus from urine in a thin flask, which was capable of holding 30 ounces of water, and closed its mouth very tightly. I then heated, with a burning candle, the part of the flask where the phosphorus lay; the phosphorus began to melt, and immediately afterwards took fire; the flask became filled with a white cloud, which attached itself to the sides like white flowers; this was the dry acid of phosphorus. After the flask had become cold again, I held it, inverted, under water and opened it; scarcely had this been done when the external air pressed water into the flask; this water amounted to 9 ounces.

18. Second Experiment.—When I placed pieces of phosphorus in the same flask and allowed it to stand, closed, for 6 weeks, or until it no longer glowed, I found that ⅓ of the air had been lost.

19. Third Experiment.—I placed 3 teaspoonfuls of iron filings in a bottle capable of holding 2 ounces of water; to this I added an ounce of water, and gradually mixed with them half an ounce of oil of vitriol. A violent heating and fermentation took place. When the froth had somewhat subsided, I fixed into the bottle an accurately fitting cork, through which I had previously fixed a glass tube A (Fig. 1). I placed this bottle in a vessel filled with hot water, B B (cold water would greatly retard the solution). I then approached a burning candle to the orifice of the tube, whereupon the inflammable air took fire and burned with a small yellowish-green flame. As soon as this had taken place, I took a small flask C, which was capable of holding 20 ounces of water, and held it so deep in the water that the little flame stood in the middle of the flask. The water at once began to rise gradually into the flask, and when the level had reached the point D the flame went out. Immediately afterwards the water began to sink again, and was entirely driven out of the flask. The space in the flask up to D contained 4 ounces, therefore the fifth part of the air had been lost. I poured a few ounces of lime water into the flask in order to see whether any ærial acid had also been produced during the combustion, but I did not find any. I made the same experiment with zinc filings, and it proceeded in every way similarly to that just mentioned. I shall demonstrate the constituents of this inflammable air further on; for, although it seems to follow from these experiments that it is only phlogiston, still other experiments are contrary to this.

We shall now see the behaviour of air towards that kind of fire which gives off, during the combustion, a fluid resembling air.

20. *Fourth Experiment.*—It is well known that the flame of a candle absorbs air; but as it is very difficult, and, indeed, scarcely possible, to light a candle in a closed flask, the following experiment was made in the first place:—I set a burning candle in a dish full of water; I then placed an inverted flask over this candle; at once there arose from the water large air bubbles, which were caused by the expansion, by heat, of the air in the flask. When the flame became somewhat smaller, the water began to rise in the flask; after it had gone out and the flask had become cold, I found the fourth part filled with water. This experiment was very undecisive to me, because I was not assured whether this fourth part of the air had not been driven out by the heat of the flame; since necessarily in that case the external air resting upon the water seeks equilibrium again after the flask has become cold, and presses the same measure of water into the flask as of air had been previously driven out by the heat. Accordingly, I made the following experiment:—

21. *Fifth Experiment.*—(*a.*) I pressed upon the bottom of the dish A (Fig. 2) a tough mass, of the thickness of two fingers, made of wax, resin, and turpentine melted together; in the middle I fastened a thick iron wire which reached to the middle of the flask B; upon the point of this wire C, I stuck a small wax candle, whose wick I had twisted together out of three slender threads. I then lighted the candle, and at the same time placed over it the inverted flask B, which I then pressed very deep into the mass. As soon as this was done, I filled the dish with water. After the flame was extinguished and everything had become quite cold, I opened the flask in the same position under the water, when 2 ounces of water entered; the flask held 160 ounces of water. Accordingly, there is wanting

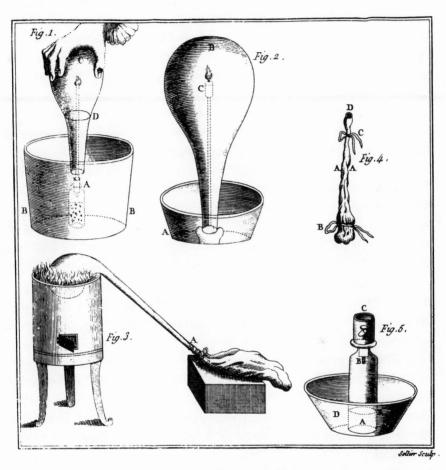

Drawings of some of the apparatus used by Carl Wilhelm Scheele in his experiments on gases. From Scheele's *Chemische Abhandlung von der Luft und dem Feuer*, Upsala and Leipzig, 1777. (Courtesy of the Burndy Library.)

here so much air as occupies the space of 2 ounces of water. Has the air been absorbed by the inflammable substance, or has the heat of the small flame driven it out even before I could press the flask into the tough mass? The latter seems to have taken place in this case, as I conclude from the following:—I took a small flask capable of holding 20 ounces of water; in this I caused a candle to burn as in the preceding; after everything had become cold, I opened this flask likewise under water, whereupon similarly nearly 2 ounces entered. Had the former 2 ounces measure of air been absorbed, then there should have been only 2 drachms measure absorbed in this experiment.

(*b*.) I repeated the preceding experiment with the large flask in exactly the same way, except that I employed spirit of wine in place of the candle. I fastened three iron wires, which were of equal length and reached up to the middle of the flask, into the tough mass which was firmly pressed on to the bottom of the dish. Upon these wires I laid a four-cornered plate of metal, and upon this I placed a small vessel into which spirit of wine was poured. I set fire to this and placed the flask over it. After cooling, I observed that 3 ounces measure of air had been driven out by the heat of the flame.

(*c*.) Upon the same stand I placed a few small glowing coals, and allowed them to go out in the same way under the flask. I found after cooling that the heat of the coals had driven out three and a half ounces measure of air.

These experiments seem to prove that the transference of phlogiston to the air does not always diminish its bulk, which, however, the experiments mentioned in §§ 8-16 shew distinctly. But the following will shew that that portion of the air which unites with the inflammable substances, and is at the same time absorbed by it, is replaced by the newly formed ærial acid.

*	*	*

24. *Experiments which prove that ordinary air, consisting of two kinds of elastic fluids, can be compounded again after these have been separated from each other by means of phlogiston.*

I have already stated in § 16 that I was not able to find again the lost air. One might indeed object, that the lost air still remains in the residual air which can no more unite with phlogiston; for, since I have found that it is lighter than ordinary air, it might be believed that the phlogiston united with this air makes it lighter, as appears to be known already from other experiments. But since phlogiston is a substance, which always presupposes some weight, I much doubt whether such hypothesis has any foundation.

* * *

42. First Experiment.—I filled a bottle which was capable of holding 16 ounces of water with pure fire-air. . . . I placed the bottle, inverted, in a glass which was filled with a solution of liver of sulphur. The solution rose a little into the bottle hour by hour, and after the lapse of 2 days the bottle was filled with it.

43. Second Experiment.—I mixed in a bottle 14 parts of that air from which the fire-air had been removed by liver of sulphur (§ 8), and which I have called vitiated air (§ 29), with 4 parts of our fire-air, and placed the bottle, inverted and open, in a vessel which was also filled with a solution of liver of sulphur. After 14 days the 4 parts of fire-air were lost, and the solution had risen into their place.

44. Third Experiment.—After I had filled a bottle with our air, I poured some colourless animal oil into it and closed it tightly. After a few hours it had already become brown, and by the next day black. It is no small inconvenience to preserve this oil white in apothecaries' shops. It is found necessary to pour this oil into small phials, and to preserve it most carefully from the access of air. When such a colourless oil is mixed with any acid, the acid, as well as the oil, becomes black even in an hour, although it has been diluted with water. Even vinegar has the same effect. There is no other reason, therefore, why the oil becomes at once black in the air, than that the fire-air present in the air deprives it of its phlogiston, and thereby develops a subtle acid, previously united with this phlogiston, which produces the blackness.

45. Fourth Experiment.—(*a.*) Into a bottle of 7 ounces, which was filled with fire-air, I put a piece of phosphorus from urine and closed it with a cork. I then heated, by means of a burning candle, the place where the phosphorus lay; the phosphorus took fire with very great brilliancy. As soon as the flame had gone out, the bottle broke into fragments.

(*b.*) As the bottle in the foregoing experiment was very thin, I repeated it with a somewhat thicker bottle, and after everything had become cold I wanted to take the cork out of the bottle under water. It was not possible for me to do this, however, so tightly did the external air press the cork into the bottle. Accordingly I forced it inside the bottle; thereupon water entered the bottle and filled it almost completely. Since the first bottle was only very thin, the reason that it was crushed must be ascribed to the external air.

(*c.*) When I mixed vitiated air with one third of fire-air, and burned a piece of phosphorus in the mixture, only ⅓ of it was absorbed.

* * *

49. I have mentioned (§ 16) that I found vitiated air lighter than ordinary air. Must it not follow from this that the fire-air is heavier than our air? As a matter of fact, I actually found, when I accurately weighed as much fire-air as occupied the space of 20 ounces of water, that this was almost 2 grains heavier than the same bulk of common air.

50. These experiments shew, therefore, that this fire-air is just that air by means of which fire burns in common air; only it is there mixed with a kind of air which seems to possess no attraction at all for the inflammable substance, and this it is which places some hindrance in the way of the otherwise rapid and violent inflammation. And in fact, if air consisted of nothing but fire-air, water would surely render small service in extinguishing outbreaks of fire. Aerial acid mixed with this fire-air, has the same effect as vitiated air. I mixed one part of fire-air with 4 parts of ærial acid; in this mixture a candle still burned moderately well. The heat which lurks in the small interstices of the inflammable substance cannot possibly make up so much heat as is felt in fire; and I think I am not mistaken when I conclude from my experiments that the heat is really brought forth and produced in the first place from fire-air and the phlogiston of the inflammable subsance. . . .

*"As this experiment seemed likely to throw
great light on the subject I had in view, I thought it
well worth examining more closely."*

Henry Cavendish

1731 – 1810

WATER IS SHOWN TO BE A COMPOUND
AND NOT AN ELEMENT

Eccentricity is often the hallmark of genius, for intense con-
centration is not always conducive to correct social behavior. In
modern scientific circles it is less easy to ignore public opinion
and even the most brilliant of our scientists manage to accom-
modate themselves to the exigencies of community life, but the
eighteenth and nineteenth centuries produced a number of men
whose escapades enliven their biographies. Among these, Henry
Cavendish is a notable example; a wealthy bachelor, consumed
with scientific curiosity, he lived in the heart of London society
but went to extreme and often absurd lengths to avoid the crowd.
Shy of women especially (his female servants were required to
keep out of his sight), he spent a lifetime in the laboratory and
the library. One of his retreats was a house built into the branches
of a tree in the square which now bears his name.

Out of this solitude came contributions to science which put
Cavendish into the same rank as his great contemporaries, Black,
Priestley, Scheele, and Lavoisier.

Cavendish was a most versatile investigator. Many of his
researches were not revealed in his lifetime. His notes on some
pioneer work in electricity, in which he anticipated Faraday, were

found and published by Clerk Maxwell only in 1879. A detailed study of the chemistry of arsenic, made available in 1921, shows his priority over Scheele. His ingenious experiment to measure the density of the earth with the use of a torsion balance achieved such a remarkably precise result that it has not been appreciably improved upon since.

Our immediate interest is in Cavendish's studies of carbon dioxide and hydrogen, which were published as researches on "factitious air." These works of first importance represented the last of the contributions to pneumatic chemistry which, begun by Black and continued by Scheele and Priestley, served as the experimental basis from which Lavoisier established the general structure of modern chemistry.

In his experiments on hydrogen, which he called "inflammable air," Cavendish found that he could produce this gas by the action of metals such as zinc, iron, and tin on dilute acids, particularly hydrochloric and sulfuric. He used precise methods for collecting the gas over water and for measuring it, and he discovered that equal weights of the same metal yielded the same amount of gas whichever acid was used. His conclusions were not always accurate. Like many of his contemporaries, Cavendish assumed that the gas came from the metal and was either phlogiston or a compound of phlogiston with water.

In the selection which we have chosen to illustrate his experimental methods, Cavendish describes a repetition of an experiment of Priestley in which an explosion of inflammable air with common air produced a dew which lined the walls of the vessel. Priestley reported that a loss of weight occurred in this chemical reaction. Cavendish's experiment showed no loss of weight; the common air lost one-fifth of its volume, whereas all the inflammable air disappeared in giving rise to the dew. By burning hydrogen in air and collecting the resulting dew, Cavendish found in it the properties of water. He had, in fact, established that water is a compound, but he, like Priestley, did not realize the significance of his observation.

Cavendish's accurate quantitative studies entitle him to share the credit for the discovery with Lavoisier, who recognized its significance. Moreover, Cavendish, by further experiments along similar lines, was able to detect the existence of an unexplained residue which, a century later, was discovered to be the element *argon.* Cavendish measured this minute unknown as constituting 0.80 percent of common air. Actually argon constitutes 0.94 percent—a remarkable tribute to Cavendish's accurate researches.

The selection that follows is taken from "Experiments on Air," published in *Philosophical Transactions,* Vol. 74 (1784).

EXPERIMENTS ON AIR

THE FOLLOWING EXPERIMENTS were made principally with a view to find out the cause of the diminution which common air is well known to suffer by all the various ways in which it is phlogisticated, and to discover what becomes of the air thus lost or condensed; and as they seem not only to determine this point, but also to throw great light on the constitution and manner of production of dephlogisticated air, I hope they may be not unworthy the acceptance of this society.

Many gentlemen have supposed that fixed air is either generated or separated from atmospheric air by phlogistication, and that the observed diminution is owing to this cause; my first experiments therefore were made in order to ascertain whether any fixed air is really produced thereby. Now, it must be observed, that as all animal and vegetable substances contain fixed air, and yield it by burning, distillation, or putrefaction, nothing can be concluded from experiments in which the air is phlogisticated by them. The only methods I know, which are not liable to objection, are by the calcination of metals, the burning of sulphur or phosphorus, the mixture of nitrous air, and the explosion of inflammable air. Perhaps it may be supposed, that I ought to add to these the electric spark; but I think it much most likely, that the phlogistication of the air, and production of fixed air, in this process, is owing to the burning of some inflammable matter in the apparatus. When the spark is taken from a solution of tournsol, the burning of the tournsol may produce this effect; when it is taken from lime-water, the burning of some foulness adhering to the tube, or perhaps of some inflammable matter contained in the lime, may have the same effect; and when quicksilver or metallic knobs are used, the calcination of them may contribute to the phlogistication of the air, though not to the production of fixed air.

There is no reason to think that any fixed air is produced by the first method of phlogistication. Dr. Priestley never found lime-water to become turbid by the calcination of metals over it: Mr. Lavoisier also found only a very slight and scarce perceptible turbid appearance, without any precipitation, to take place when lime-water was shaken in a glass vessel full of the air in which lead had been calcined; and even this small diminution of transparency in the lime-water might very likely arise, not from fixed air, but only from its being fouled by particles of the calcined metal, which we are told adhered in some places to the glass. This want of turbidity has been attributed to the fixed air uniting to the metallic calx, in preference to the lime; but there is no reason for supposing that the calx contained any fixed air; for I do not know that any one has extracted it from calces prepared in this manner; and though most metallic calces prepared over the fire, or by long exposure to the atmosphere, where they are in contact with fixed air, contain that substance, it by no means follows that they must do so when prepared by methods in which they are not in contact with it.

Dr. Priestley also observed, that quicksilver, fouled by the addition of lead or tin, deposits a powder by agitation and exposure to the air, which consists in great measure of the calx of the imperfect metal. He found too some powder of this kind to contain fixed air;[1] but it is by no means clear that this air was produced by the phlogistication of the air in which the quicksilver was shaken; as the powder was not prepared on purpose, but was procured from quicksilver fouled by having been used in various

---

[1] Though fixed air is absorbed in considerable quantity by water, as I shewed in Phil. Trans. vol. LVI. yet it is not easy to deprive common air of all the fixed air contained in it by means of water. On shaking a mixture of ten parts of common air, and one of fixed air, with more than an equal bulk of distilled water, not more than half of the fixed air was absorbed, and on transferring the air into fresh distilled water only half the remainder was absorbed, as appeared by the diminution which it still suffered on adding lime water.

experiments, and may therefore have contained other impurities besides the metallic calces.

I never heard of any fixed air being produced by the burning of sulphur or phosphorus; but it has been asserted, and commonly believed, that lime water is rendered cloudy by a mixture of common and nitrous air; which, if true, would be a convincing proof that on mixing those two substances some fixed air is either generated or separated; I therefore examined this carefully. Now it must be observed, that as common air usually contains a little fixed air, which is no essential part of it, but is easily separated by lime-water; and as nitrous air may also contain fixed air, either if the metal from which it is procured be rusty, or if the water of the vessel in which it is caught contain calcareous earth, suspended by fixed air, as most waters do, it is proper first to free both airs from it by previously washing them with lime water. Now I found, by repeated experiments, that if the lime water was clean, and the two airs were previously washed with that substance, not the least cloud was produced, either immediately on mixing them, or on suffering them to stand upwards of an hour, though it appeared by the thick clouds which were produced in the lime water, by breathing through it after the experiment was finished, that it was more than sufficient to saturate the acid formed by the decomposition of the nitrous air, and consequently that if any fixed air had been produced, it must have become visible. Once indeed I found a small cloud to be formed on the surface, after the mixture had stood a few minutes. In this experiment the lime water was not quite clean; but whether the cloud was owing to this circumstance, or to the air's having not been properly washed, I cannot pretend to say.

Neither does any fixed air seem to be produced by the explosion of the inflammable air obtained from metals, with either common or dephlogisticated air. This I tried by putting a little lime-water into a glass globe fitted with a brass cock, so as to make it air tight, and an apparatus for firing air by electricity. This globe was exhausted by an air-pump, and the two airs, which had been previously washed with lime-water, let in, and suffered to remain some time, to shew whether they would affect the limewater, and then fired by electricity. The event was, that not the least cloud was produced in the lime-water, when the inflammable air was mixed with common air, and only a very slight one, or rather diminution of transparency, when it was combined with dephlogisticated air. This, however, seemed not to be produced by fixed air; as it appeared instantly after the explosion, and did not increase on standing, and was spread uniformly through the liquor; whereas if it had been owing to fixed air, it would have taken up some short time before it appeared, and would have begun first at the surface, as was the case in the abovementioned experiment with nitrous air. What it was really owing to I cannot pretend to say; but if it did proceed from fixed air it would shew that only an excessively minute quantity was produced.[2] On the whole, though it is not improbable that fixed air may be generated in some chymical processes, yet it seems certain that it is not the general effect of phlogisticating air, and that the diminution of common air is by no means owing to the generation or separation of fixed air from it.

As there seemed great reason to think, from Dr. Priestley's experiments, that the nitrous and vitriolic acids were convertible into dephlogisticated air, I tried whether the dephlogisticated part of common air might not, by phlogistication, be changed into nitrous or vitriolic acid. For this purpose I impregnated some milk of lime with the fumes of burning sulphur, by putting a little of it into a large glass receiver, and burning sulphur therein, taking care to keep the mouth of the receiver stopt till the fumes were all absorbed; after which the air of the receiver was changed, and more sulphur burnt in it as before, and the process repeated till 122 grains of sulphur were consumed. The milk of lime was then filtered and evaporated, but it yielded no nitrous salt, nor any other substance except selenite; so that no sensible quantity of the air was changed into nitrous acid. It must be observed, that as the vitriolic acid produced by the burning sulphur is changed by its union with the lime into selenite, which is very little soluble in water, a very small quantity of nitrous salt, or any other substance which is soluble in water, would have been perceived.

In Dr. Priestley's last volume of experiments is related an experiment of Mr. Warltire's, in which it is said that, on firing a mixture of common and inflammable air by electricity in a close copper vessel holding about three pints, a loss of weight was always perceived, on an average

---

[2] Dr. Priestley also found no fixed air to be produced by the explosion of inflammable and common air. Vol. V. p. 124.

about two grains, though the vessel was stopped in such a manner that no air could escape by the explosion. It is also related, that on repeating the experiment in glass vessels, the inside of the glass, though clean and dry before, immediately became dewy; which confirmed an opinion he had long entertained, that common air deposits its moisture by phlogistication. As the latter experiment seemed likely to throw great light on the subject I had in view, I thought it well worth examining more closely. The first experiment also, if there was no mistake in it, would be very extraordinary and curious; but it did not succeed with me; for though the vessel I used held more than Mr. Warltire's, namely, 24,000 grains of water, and though the experiment was repeated several times with different proportions of common and inflammable air, I could never perceive a loss of weight of more than one-fifth of a grain, and commonly none at all. It must be observed, however, that though there were some of the experiments in which it seemed to diminish a little in weight, there were none in which it increased.[3]

In all the experiments, the inside of the glass globe became dewy, as observed by Mr. Warltire; but not the least sooty matter could be perceived. Care was taken in all of them to find how much the air was diminished by the explosion, and to observe its test. The result is as follows: the bulk of the inflammable air being expressed in decimals of the common air,

Common air.	Inflammable air.	Diminution.	Air remaining after the explosion.	Test of this air in first method.	Standard.
1	1,241	,686	1,555	,055	,0
	1,055	,642	1,413	,063	,0
	,706	,647	1,059	,066	,0
	,423	,612	,811	,097	,03
	,331	,476	,855	,339	,27
	,206	,294	,912	,648	,58

In these experiments the inflammable air was procured from zinc, as it was in all my experiments, except where otherwise expressed: but I made two more experiments, to try whether there was any difference between the air from zinc and that from iron, the quantity of inflammable air being the same in both, namely, 0,331 of the common; but I

[3] Dr. Priestley, I am informed, has since found the experiment not to succeed.

could not find any difference to be depended on between the two kinds of air, either in the diminution which they suffered by the explosion, or the test of the burnt air.

From the fourth experiment it appears, that 423 measures of inflammable air are nearly sufficient to completely phlogisticate 1000 of common air; and that the bulk of the air remaining after the explosion is then very little more than four-fifths of the common air employed; so that as common air cannot be reduced to a much less bulk than that by any method of phlogistication, we may safely conclude, that when they are mixed in this proportion, and exploded, almost all the inflammable air, and about one-fifth part of the common air, lose their elasticity, and are condensed into the dew which lines the glass.

The better to examine the nature of this dew, 500000 grain measures of inflammable air were burnt with about $2\frac{1}{2}$ times that quantity of common air, and the burnt air made to pass through a glass cylinder eight feet long and three-quarters of an inch in diameter, in order to deposit the dew. The two airs were conveyed slowly into this cylinder by separate copper pipes, passing through a brass plate which stopped up the end of the cylinder; and as neither inflammable nor common air can burn by themselves, there was no danger of the flame spreading into the magazines from which they were conveyed. Each of these magazines consisted of a large tin vessel, inverted into another vessel just big enough to receive it. The inner vessel communicated with the copper pipe, and the air was forced out of it by pouring water into the outer vessel; and in order that the quantity of common air expelled should be $2\frac{1}{2}$ times that of the inflammable, the water was let into the outer vessels by two holes in the bottom of the same tin pan, the hole which conveyed the water into that vessel in which the common air was confined being $2\frac{1}{2}$ times as big as the other.

In trying the experiment, the magazines being first filled with their respective airs, the glass cylinder was taken off, and water let, by the two holes, into the outer vessels, till the airs began to issue from the ends of the copper pipes; they were then set on fire by a candle, and the cylinder put on again in its place. By this means upwards of 135 grains of water were condensed in the cylinder, which had no taste nor smell, and which left no sensible sediment when evaporated to dryness; neither did it yield any pungent smell during the evaporation; in short, it seemed pure water.

In my first experiment, the cylinder near that part where the air was fired was a little tinged with sooty matter, but very slightly so; and that little seemed to proceed from the putty with which the apparatus was luted, and which was heated by the flame; for in another experiment, in which it was contrived so that the luting should not be much heated, scarce any sooty tinge could be perceived.

By the experiments with the globe it appeared, that when inflammable and common air are exploded in a proper proportion, almost all the inflammable air, and near one-fifth of the common air, lose their elasticity, and are condensed into dew. And by this experiment it appears, that this dew is plain water, and consequently that almost all the inflammable air, and about one-fifth of the common air, are turned into pure water.

In order to examine the nature of the matter condensed on firing a mixture of dephlogisticated and inflammable air, I took a glass globe, holding 8800 grain measures, furnished with a brass cock and an apparatus for firing air by electricity. This globe was well exhausted by an air-pump, and then filled with a mixture of inflammable and dephlogisticated air, by shutting the cock, fastening a bent glass tube to its mouth, and letting up the end of it into a glass jar inverted into water, and containing a mixture of 19500 grain measures of dephlogisticated air, and 37000 of inflammable; so that, upon opening the cock, some of this mixed air rushed through the bent tube, and filled the globe.[4] The cock was then shut, and the included air fired by electricity, by which means almost all of it lost its elasticity. The cock was then again opened, so as to let in more of the same air, to supply the place of that destroyed by the explosion, which was again fired, and the operation continued till almost the whole of the mixture was let into the globe and exploded. By this means, though the globe held not more than the sixth part of the mixture, almost the whole of it was exploded therein, without any fresh exhaustion of the globe.

As I was desirous to try the quantity and test of this burnt air, without letting any water into the globe, which would have prevented my examining the nature of the condensed matter, I took a larger globe, furnished also with a stop cock, exhausted it by an air-pump, and screwed it on upon

[4] In order to prevent any water from getting into this tube, while dipped under water to let it up into the glass jar, a bit of wax was stuck upon the end of it, which was rubbed off when raised above the surface of the water.

the cock of the former globe; upon which, by opening both cocks, the air rushed out of the smaller globe into the larger, till it became of equal density in both; then, by shutting the cock of the larger globe, unscrewing it again from the former, and opening it under water, I was enabled to find the quantity of the burnt air in it; and consequently, as the proportion which the contents of the two globes bore to each other was known, could tell the quantity of burnt air in the small globe before the communication was made between them. By this means the whole quantity of the burnt air was found to be 2950 grain measures; its standard was 1,85.

The liquor condensed in the globe, in weight about 30 grains, was sensibly acid to the taste, and by saturation with fixed alkali, and evaporation, yielded near two grans of nitre; so that it consisted of water united to a small quantity of nitrous acid. No sooty matter was deposited in the globe. The dephlogisticated air used in this expriment was procured from red precipitate, that is, from a solution of quicksilver in spirit of nitre distilled till it acquires a red colour.

*"Thoroughly convinced of these truths,
I have imposed upon myself as a law, never to
advance but from what is known to what is unknown; never to
form any conclusion which is not an immediate
consequence necessarily flowing from
observation and experiment. . . ."*

Antoine Laurent
Lavoisier
1743 – 1794

THE ROLE OF OXYGEN IN COMBUSTION
IS ESTABLISHED

With our account of the work of Lavoisier we celebrate the overthrow of the phlogiston doctrine; but, in doing so, we must not overlook the innumerable experiments—of Black, Priestley, and Cavendish (possibly also of Scheele)—which were inspired by the old concept and gave a stimulus to Lavoisier's own work. An erroneous but workable hypothesis had served a useful purpose. Lavoisier succeeded, however, in establishing order among the experiments and in deriving interpretations from them which were to place chemistry on a new footing. The quantitative studies of Black were refined and a new language evolved which still serves the chemist.

The son of a wealthy Parisian who was himself interested in science, Lavoisier showed his promise by winning a government prize at the age of twenty and getting himself elected to the Academy of Sciences at twenty-five. Then he was appointed farmer-general of taxes, paying the government a fixed sum for the privilege of organizing and collecting the state revenue. The difference provided him with an income which he devoted to his scientific pursuits, his career culminating in 1789 when he published his *Traité Elémentaire de Chimie*—and saw France plunged into the revolution which was to cost him his own head.

In 1772 Lavoisier had become interested in Boyle's experiments on the processes of combustion and calcination and began his own investigations. He found that when phosphorus and sulfur were burned, they combined with air. His balance verified this by revealing a gain in weight. In some of his experiments he kept his vessels closed and found that the burning did not continue indefinitely but ceased when the air (or some part of it) was consumed. When these containers were weighed, there was no gain in weight. On opening the container to the air, it was apparent that air rushed into the container and then the balance showed the increase in weight.

In 1774 Priestley visited Paris and described to Lavoisier his discovery of a new "air" (prepared by heating the calx of mercury), in which a candle burned much more brilliantly. The significance of this disclosure was Lavoisier's introduction to the only metal—mercury—known at the time which was amenable to the experiments he proceeded to make. Lavoisier concluded that the gain in weight he noted was due to the combination of the combustible substance with air, which he still regarded as a pure substance. By 1777 he had decided, after further experiments, that only a part of the air—the heavier part—was utilized in combustion, calcination, and respiration in animals. This part he named "highly respirable air," and he distinguished it from the other part of the air which was injurious to life and extinguished flame.

In May 1777, Lavoisier read to the Paris Academy of Sciences an account of a brilliant and critical experiment. Four ounces of mercury were heated for twelve days in a retort which was connected with another vessel closed over water. He observed that about one-fifth of the air in the connecting vessel was used up. The mercury was converted to the red calx (mercuric oxide), and the residual air extinguished lighted candles and asphyxiated animals. Lavoisier then took the calx of mercury formed by the calcination and heated it strongly in a vessel similar to the first one he used. He collected the "air" given off and recovered metallic mercury from the calx. The "air" given off was respirable and, when mixed with the residual air (nitrogen), resumed the nature of the common air with which he had begun his experiment. Later he called this new "air" oxygen. It should be noted that there is some evidence that Priestley had given Lavoisier a useful lead in a work published during the latter's experiments and before the publication of the Academy's report.

In 1783 Lavoisier utilized some of Cavendish's experiments on "factitious airs," which Cavendish had interpreted incompletely. He showed that the "inflammable air" of Cavendish was not phlogiston but that it combined with oxygen to produce water. He named the light gas *hydrogen,* meaning "water-former." About this time he also concluded that respiration in animals was a kind of slow combustion.

Lavoisier played an important role in reforming the language of chemistry, which he felt was cumbersome, awkward, and inconsistent. He helped to draw up the first table of nomenclature for chemical substances which would correspond with their chemical composition. Modern chemistry unquestionably began with the publication of the *Traité Elémentaire de Chimie,* which was translated into English in 1790 by Robert Kerr. The reading below is from that English translation.

Lavoisier had many interests outside his experiments and his tax-gathering. As director of the government factories, he improved the manufacture of saltpeter and gunpowder and thus helped in the military development of France. He assisted in drawing up the first geological maps of France and devised a system for lighting the streets of cities and towns at night. He took a great deal of interest in the social problems of France, especially in prison reform and in the education of the young. As an early scientific farmer, he greatly increased the yield of his own estates.

Lavoisier's wife became a partner in his scientific activities, learning Latin and English in order to translate scientific works for his use. In the process she learned much chemistry so that her assistance was more than amateur. An accomplished artist, she made the plates and engravings for his books. Their quality can be seen in the illustration on page 491, which shows the apparatus used in the experiment described in the reading. Eleven years after Lavoisier's death, she married the scientist Benjamin Thompson, better known as Count Rumford (1753-1814), an important investigator of the problems of heat.

Ironically, the scientist-humanist Lavoisier was put to death by the guillotine in 1794 because, as the president of the tribunal which tried him put it: "The Republic has no need of savants." Lavoisier was much more than a savant; he was a man of restless intellect, an innovator in agriculture, technology, and physiology as well as in finance, economics, social reform, and government. Joseph Lagrange, the mathematician, observed on the day following Lavoisier's death, "It required only a moment to sever that head, and perhaps a century will not be sufficient to produce another like it."

CHAPTER III

*Analysis of Atmospheric Air, and its Division into
two Elastic Fluids; the one fit for Respiration,
the other incapable of being respired.*

FROM WHAT HAS BEEN PREMISED, it follows, that our atmosphere is composed of a mixture of every substance capable of retaining the gasseous or aëriform state in the common temperature, and under the usual pressure which it experiences. These fluids constitute a mass, in some measure homogeneous, extending from the surface of the earth to the greatest height hitherto attained, of which the density continually decreases in the inverse ratio of the superincumbent weight. But, as I have before observed, it is possible that this first stratum is surmounted by several others consisting of very different fluids.

Our business, in this place, is to endeavour to determine, by experiments, the nature of the elastic fluids which compose the inferior stratum of air which we inhabit. Modern chemistry has made great advances in this research, and it will appear by the following details that the analysis of atmospherical air has been more rigorously determined than that of any other substance of the class. Chemistry affords two general methods of determining the constituent principles of bodies, the method of analysis, and that of synthesis. When, for instance, by combining water with alkohol, we form the species of liquor called, in commercial language, brandy or spirit of wine, we certainly have a right to conclude, that brandy, or spirit of wine, is composed of alkohol combined with water. We can produce the same result by the analytical method; and in general it ought to be considered as a principle in chemical science, never to rest satisfied without both these species of proofs.

We have this advantage in the analysis of atmospherical air, being able both to decompound it, and to form it a new in the most satisfactory manner. I shall, however, at present confine myself to recount such experiments as are most conclusive upon this head; and I may consider most of these as my own, having either first invented them, or having repeated those of others, with the intention of analysing atmospherical air, in perfectly new points of view.

I took a matrass (A, fig. 14. plate II.) of about 36 cubical inches capacity, having a long neck B C D E, of fix or seven lines internal diameter, and having bent the neck as in Plate IV. Fig. 2 so as to allow of its being placed in the furnace M M N N, in such a manner that the extremity of its neck E might be inserted under a bell-glass F G, placed in a trough of quicksilver R R S S; I introduced four ounces of pure mercury into the matrass, and, by means of a syphon, exhausted the air in the receiver F G, so as to raise the quicksilver to L L, and I carefully marked the height at which it stood by pasting on a slip of paper. Having accurately noted the height of the thermometer and barometer, I lighted a fire in the furnace M M N N, which I kept up almost continually during twelve days, so as to keep the quicksilver always almost at its boiling point. Nothing remarkable took place during the first day: The Mercury, though not boiling, was continually evaporating, and covered the interior surface of the vessels with small drops, at first very minute, which gradually augmenting to a sufficient size, fell back into the mass at the bottom of the vessel. On the second day, small red particles began to appear on the surface of the mercury, which, during the four or five following days, gradually increased in size and number; after which they ceased to increase in either respect. At the end of twelve days, seeing that the calcination of the mercury did not at all increase, I extinguished the fire, and allowed the vessels to cool. The bulk of air in the body and neck of the matrass, and in the bell-glass, reduced to a medium of 28 inches of the barometer and 10° (54.5°) of the thermometer, at the commencement of the experiment was about 50 cubical inches. At the end of the experiment the remaining air, reduced to the same medium pressure and temperature, was only between 42 and 43 cubical inches; consequently it had lost about ⅙ of its bulk. Afterwards, having collected all the red particles, formed during the experiment, from the running mercury in which they floated, I found these to amount to 45 grains.

I was obliged to repeat this experiment several times, as it is difficult in one experiment both to preserve the whole air upon which we operate, and to collect the whole of the red particles, or clax of mercury, which is formed during the calcination. It will often happen in the sequel, that I shall, in this manner, give in one detail the results of two or three experiments of the same nature.

The air which remained after the calcination of the mercury in this experiment, and which was reduced to ⅚ of its former bulk, was no longer fit either for respiration or for combustion; animals being introduced into it were suffocated in a few seconds, and when a taper was plunged into it, it was extinguished as if it had been immersed into water.

In the next place, I took the 45 grains of red matter formed during this experiment, which I put into a small glass retort, having a proper apparatus for receiving such liquid, or gasseous product, as might be extracted: Having applied a fire to the retort in a furnace, I observed that, in proportion as the red matter became heated, the intensity of its colour augmented. When the retort was almost red hot, the red matter began gradually to decrease in bulk, and in a few minutes after it disappeared altogether; at the same time 41½ grains of running mercury were collected in the recipient, and 7 or 8 cubical inches of elastic fluid, greatly more capable of supporting both respiration and combustion than atmospherical air, were collected in the bellglass.

A part of this air being put into a glass tube of about an inch diameter, showed the following properties: A taper burned in it with a dazzling splendour, and charcoal, instead of consuming quietly as it does in com-

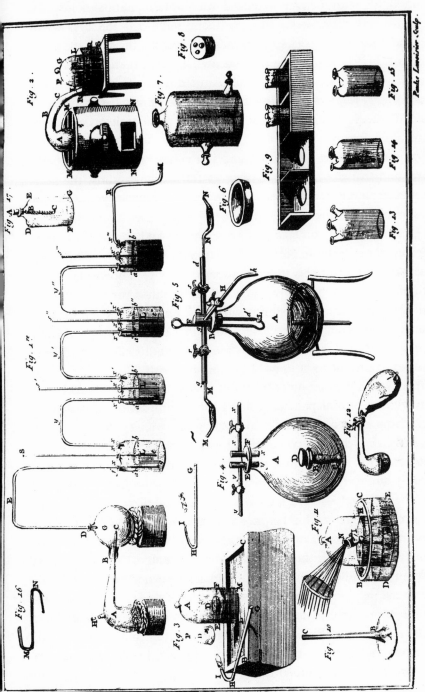

Illustrations of apparatus used by Lavoisier in his experiments. Figure 2 in this drawing is the set-up he used in preparing oxygen and to which he refers in the accompanying selection. His wife did most of the drawings for his writings. From Antoine-Laurent Lavoisier's *Traité Elémentaire de Chimie*, Paris 1789. (Courtesy of the Burndy Library.)

mon air, burnt with a flame, attended with a decrepitating noise, like phosphorus, and threw out such a brilliant light that the eyes could hardly endure it. This species of air was discovered almost at the same time by Mr. Priestley, Mr. Scheele, and myself. Mr. Priestley gave it the name of *dephlogisticated air,* Mr. Scheele called it *empyreal air.* At first I named it *highly respirable* air, to which has since substituted the term of *vital air.* We shall presently see what we ought to think of these denominations.

In reflecting upon the circumstances of this experiment, we readily perceive, and that the mercury, during its calcination, absorbs the salubrious and respirable part of the air, or, to speak more strictly, the base of this respirable part; that the remaining air is a species of mephitis, incapable of supporting combustion or respiration; and consequently that atmospheric air is composed of two elastic fluids of different and opposite qualities. As a proof of this important truth, if we recombine these two elastic fluids, which we have separately obtained in the above experiment, viz, the 42 cubical inches of mephitis, with the 8 cubical inches of respirable air, we reproduce an air precisely similar to that of the atmosphere, and possessing nearly the same power of supporting combustion and respiration, and of contributing to the calcination of metals.

Although this experiment furnishes us with a very simple means of obtaining the two principal elastic fluids which compose our atmosphere, separate from each other, yet it does not give us an exact idea of the proportion in which these two enter into its composition: For the attraction of mercury to the respirable part of the air, or rather to its base, is not sufficiently strong to overcome all the circumstances which oppose this union. These obstacles are the mutual adhesion of the two constituent parts of the atmosphere for each other, and the elective attraction which unites the base of vital air with caloric; in consequence of these, when the calcination ends, or is at least carried as far as is possible, in a determinate quantity of atmospheric air, there still remains a portion of respirable air united to the mephitis, which the mercury cannot separate. I shall afterwards show, that, at least in our climate, the atmospheric air is composed of respirable and mephitic airs, in the proportion of 27 and 73; and I shall then discuss the causes of the uncertainty which still exists with respect to the exactness of that proportion.

Since, during the calcination of mercury, air is decomposed, and the base of its respirable part is fixed and combined with the mercury, it follows, from the principles already established, that caloric and light must be disengaged during the process: But the two following causes prevent us from being sensible of this taking place: As the calcination lasts during several days, the disengagement of caloric and light, spread out in a considerable space of time, becomes extremely small for each particular moment of that time, so as not to be perceptible; and, in the next place, the operation being carried on by means of fire in a furnace, the heat produced by the calcination itself becomes confounded with that proceeding from the furnace. I might add the respirable part of the air, or rather its base, in entering into combination with the mercury, does not part with all the caloric which it contained, but still retains a part of it after forming the new compound; but the discussion of this point, and its proofs from experiment, do not belong to this part of our subject.

It is, however, easy to render this disengagement of caloric and light evident to the senses, by causing the decomposition of air to take place in a more rapid manner. And for this purpose, iron is excellently adapted, as it possesses a much stronger affinity for the base of respirable air than mercury. The elegant experiment of Mr. Ingenhouz, upon the combustion of iron, is well known. Take a piece of fine iron wire, twisted into a spiral, (BC, Plate IV. Fig. 17.) fix one of its extremities B into the cork A, adapted to the neck of the bottle DEFG, and fix to the other extremity of the wire C, a small morsel of tinder. Matters being thus prepared, fill the bottle DEFG with air deprived of its mephitic part; then light the tinder, and introduce it quickly with the wire upon which it is fixed, into the bottle which you stop up with the cork A, as is shown in the figure (17 Plate IV.) The instant the tinder comes into contact with the vital air it begins to burn with great intensity; and, communicating the inflammation to the ironwire, it too takes fire, and burns rapidly, throwing out brilliant sparks, which fall to the bottom of the vessel in rounded globules, which become black in cooling, but retain a degree of metallic splendour. The iron thus burnt is more brittle even than glass, and is easily reduced into powder, and is still attractable by the magnet, though not so powerfully as it was before combustion. As Mr. Ingenhouz has neither examined the change produced on iron, nor upon the air by this operation, I have repeated the experiment under different circumstances, in an apparatus adapted to answer my particular views, as follows.

Having filled a bell glass (A, Plate IV. Fig. 3.) of about six pints measure, with pure air, or the highly respirable part of air, I transported this jar by means of a very flat vessel, into a quicksilver bath in the bason, BC, and I took care to render the surface of the mercury perfectly dry both within and without the jar with blotting paper. I then provided a small capsule of china-ware D, very flat and open, in which I placed some small pieces of iron, turned spirally, and arranged in such a way as seemed most favourable for the combustion being communicated to every part. To the end of one of these pieces of iron was fixed a small morsel of tinder, to which was added about the sixteenth part of a grain of phosphorus, and, by raising the bell-glass a little, the china capsule, with its contents, were introduced into the pure air. I know that, by this means, some common air must mix with the pure air in the glass; but this, when it is done dexterously, is so very trifling, as not to injure the success of the experiment. This being done, a part of the air is sucked out from the bell-glass, by means of a syphon GHI, so as to raise the mercury within the glass to EF; and, to prevent the mercury from getting into the syphon, a small piece of paper is twisted round its extremity. In sucking out the air, if the motion of the lungs only be used, we cannot make the mercury rise above an inch or an inch and a half; but, by properly using the muscles of the mouth, we can, without difficulty, cause it to rise six or seven inches.

I next took an iron wire, properly bent for the purpose, and making it red hot in the fire, passed it through the mercury into the receiver, and brought it in contact with the small piece of phosphorus attached to the tinder. The phosphorus instantly takes fire, which communicates to the tinder, and from that to the iron. When the pieces have been properly arranged, the whole iron burns, even to the last particle, throwing out a white brilliant light similar to that of Chinese fireworks. The great heat produced by this combustion melts the iron into round globules of different sizes, most of which fall into the China cup; but some are thrown out of it, and swim upon the surface of the mercury. At the beginning of the combustion, there is a slight augmentation in the volume of the air in the bell-glass, from the dilatation caused by the heat; but, presently afterwards, a rapid diminution of the air takes place, and the mercury rises in the glass; insomuch that, when the quantity of iron is sufficient, and the air operated upon is very pure, almost the whole air employed is absorbed.

It is proper to remark in this place, that, unless in making experiments for the purpose of discovery, it is better to be contented with burning a moderate quantity of iron; for, when this experiment is pushed too far, so as to absorb much of the air, the cup D, which floats upon the quicksilver, approaches too near the bottom of the bell-glass; and the great heat produced, which is followed by a very sudden cooling, occasioned by the contact of the cold mercury, is apt to break the glass. In which case, the sudden fall of the column of mercury, which happens the moment the least flaw is produced in the glass, causes such a wave, as throws a great part of the quicksilver from the bason. To avoid this inconvenience, and to ensure success to the experiments, one gross and a half of iron is sufficient to burn in a bell-glass, which holds about eight pints of air. The glass ought likewise to be strong, that it may be able to bear the weight of the column of mercury which it has to support.

By this experiment, it is not possible to determine, at one time, both the additional weight acquired by the iron, and the changes which have taken place in the air. If it is wished to ascertain what additional weight has been gained by the iron, and the proportion between that and the air absorbed, we must carefully mark upon the bell-glass, with a diamond, the height of the mercury, both before and after the experiment.[1] After this, the syphon (GH, Pl. IV. fig. 3.) guarded, as before, with a bit of paper, to prevent its filling with mercury, is to be introduced under the bell-glass, having the thumb placed upon the extremity, G, of the syphon, to regulate the passage of the air; and by this means the air is gradually admitted, so as to let the mercury fall to its level. This being done, the bell-glass is to be carefully removed, the globules of melted iron contained in the cup, and those which have been scattered about, and swim upon the mercury, are to be accurately collected, and the whole is to be weighed. The iron will be found in that state called *martial ethiops* by the old chemists, possessing a degree of metallic brilliancy, very friable, and readily reducible into powder, under the hammer, or with a pestle and mortar. If the experiment has succeeded well, from 100 grains of

---

[1] It will likewise be necessary to take care that the air contained in the glass, both before and after the experiment, be reduced to a common temperature and pressure, otherwise the results of the following calculations will be fallacious. [Trans. note.]

iron will be obtained 135 or 136 grains of ethiops, which is an augmentation of 35 per cent.

If all the attention has been paid to this experiment which it deserves, the air will be found diminished in weight exactly equal to what the iron has gained. Having therefore burnt 100 grains of iron, which has acquired an additional weight of 35 grains, the diminution of air will be found exactly 70 cubical inches; and it will be found, in the sequel, that the weight of vital air is pretty nearly half a grain for each cubical inch; so that, in effect, the augmentation of weight in the one exactly coincides with the loss of it in the other.

I shall observe here, once for all, that, in every experiment of this kind, the pressure and temperature of the air, both before and after the expriment, must be reduced, by calculation, to a common standard of $10°$ ($54.5°$) of the thermometer, and 28 inches of the barometer. . . .

If it be required to examine the nature of the air which remains after this experiment, we must operate in a somewhat different manner. After the combustion is finished, and the vessels have cooled, we first take out the cup, and the burnt iron, by introducing the hand through the quicksilver, under the bell-glass; we next introduce some solution of potash, or caustic alkali, or of the sulphuret of potash, or such other substance as is judged proper for examining their action upon the residuum of air. I shall, in the sequel, give an account of these methods of analysing air, when I have explained the nature of these different substances, which are only here in a manner accidentally mentioned. After this examination, so much water must be let into the glass as will displace the quicksilver, and then, by means of a shallow dish placed below the bell-glass, it is to be removed into the common water, pneumato-chemical apparatus, where the air remaining may be examined at large, and with great facility.

When very soft and very pure iron has been employed in this experiment, and, if the combustion has been performed in the purest respirable or vital air, free from all admixture of the noxious or mephitic part, the air which remains after the combustion will be found as pure as it was before; but it is difficult to find iron entirely free from a small portion of charry matter, which is chiefly abundant in steel. It is likewise exceedingly difficult to procure the pure air perfectly free from some admixture of mephitis, with which it is almost always contaminated; but this species of noxious air does not, in the smallest degree, disturb the result of the experiment, as it is always found at the end exactly in the same proportion as at the beginning.

I mentioned before, that we have two ways of determining the constituent parts of atmospheric air, the method of analysis, and that by synthesis. The calcination of mercury has furnished us with an example of each of these methods, since, after having robbed the respirable part of its base, by means of the mercury, we have restored it, so as to recompose an air precisely similar to that of the atmosphere. But we can equally accomplish this synthetic composition of atmospheric air, by borrowing the materials of which it is composed from different kingdoms of nature. We shall see hereafter that, when animal substances are dissolved in the nitric acid, a great quantity of gas is disengaged, which extinguishes light, and is unfit for animal respiration, being exactly similar to the noxious or mephitic part of atmospheric air. And, if we take 73 parts, by weight, of this elastic fluid, and mix it with 27 parts of highly respirable air, procured from calcined mercury, we will form an elastic fluid precisely similar to atmospheric air in all its properties.

There are many other methods of separating the respirable from the noxious part of the atmospheric air, which cannot be taken notice of in this part, without anticipating information, which properly belongs to the subsequent chapters. The experiments already adduced may suffice for an elementary treatise; and, in matters of this nature, the choice of our evidences is of far greater consequence than their number.

I shall close this article, by pointing out the property which atmospheric air, and all the known gasses, possess of dissolving water, which is of great consequence to be attended to in all experiments of this nature. Mr. Saussure found, by experiment, that a cubical foot of atmospheric air is capable of holding 12 grains of water in solution: Other gasses, as the carbonic acid, appear capable of dissolving a greater quantity; but experiments are still wanting by which to determine their several proportions. This water, held in solution by gasses, gives rise to particular phenomena in many experiments, which require great attention, and which has frequently proved the source of great errors to chemists in determining the results of their experiments.

THE INDEX TO THIS COMPLETE WORK WILL
BE FOUND AT THE END OF VOLUME TWO